CU00651452

WAGTAIL TALE
Gypsy Life of Bygone Days

by

PETER INGRAM

Limes End Yard Publishing

First published in Great Britain in 2014 by
Limes End Yard Publishing
High Street, Selborne, Hampshire. GU34 3LD
Tel: 01420 511486
E-mail: limesendyard@outlook.com

A CIP catalogue record for this book is available from the British Library.

ISBN 978-0-9928719-0-1

Printed and bound in Great Britain by
Orphans Press Limited
Leominster, Herefordshire. HR6 0LD
www.orphans.co.uk

Typeset in Garamond on 120 gsm Olin Cream

WAGTAIL TALE

'When you see the wagtail you will see Gypsies'
(old Welsh Gypsy saying)

The 1961 summer of Welsh Border Gypsies
Jimmy and Katie Lock

*In rural Shropshire a little-used narrow lane, with grass
growing in the centre, winds its way through unspoilt country
… where history meets mystery … then leads on to the rest of
the world.*

Illustrated by
K. B. Morgan

'… *that little mush, with them great big 'ands, 'e plays that old bosh've 'is
like me an' me faarthur 'ad never a-'eard afore.'* (p.204)

CONTENTS

ACKNOWLEDGEMENTS

First and foremost I would like to thank Yvonne Cheal for her patience in deciphering my handwritten manuscript and preparing the typescript. She is no stranger to the 'affairs of Little Egypt' or of 'Teulu Abram Wood', having quietly worked with Gypsy lore and people for many decades. Without Yvonne's dedication, advice and script preparation this book would not have reached fruition.

A big thank you to Katie Morgan, the artist, who has painstakingly illustrated the book, and for her sufferance when asked, 'can you just alter this drawing a little bit?'

For stimulation and advice my thanks go to Mervyn and Anne Jones of north Wales, friends of almost fifty years. They have a lifetime's knowledge and conception of Welsh and Border Romanychals, and I am delighted that Mervyn, who is a past member of the 'old' Gypsy Lore Society, has consented to write the Foreword.

My thanks also go to another friend of many years' standing: Dominic Reeve (alias Jesse), *crème de la crème* of the 'Muck Hawkers' and author of five outstanding books chronicling the travelling lifestyle from the mid-1950s. His encouraging words, after reading the manuscript, of 'I found the book addictive and full of rightness,' pleased me very much … for he is not a man to eagerly offer praise!

A big thank you goes to Reg and Charlotte Marshall of Hereford for overnight accommodation and 'good grub' when on my research trips 'up the Borders' and into Wales.

To the many 'old timers' who wish to remain anonymous, and to those whose names I have changed, I offer my thanks for their reminiscences and heart-warming friendliness – in particular R____ of Montgomeryshire, 'Queen of the meatloaf makers'.

And finally (for their patience) to the hero and heroine of the book, 'Jim' and 'Katie'. I know you thought I'd never finish it, but here it is. *Mandi's kered the lil for tutti … it's tutti's lil* (I have done the book for you, it is your book).

by Mervyn Jones

It is a privilege to be asked to write a foreword to this, the second book by Peter Ingram (co-author of *Romany Relics – The Wagon Album*, published by J. Barker, 2010). Its title, *Wagtail Tale*, relates to an old Gypsy legend concerning the flight of the Virgin Mary with the Christ child and Saint Joseph into Egypt in Biblical times. Every chapter of this book is headed with an exquisite vignette of this bird, the pied wagtail, each in a different pose, which depicts the restless character of this *chiriklo* (bird) that is always on the move. No wonder it is regarded as a lucky omen by the Gypsies.

It is somewhat of a coincidence that this book concerns the everyday activities of a family in the early 1960s, for in 1967 Fred Archer, the popular chronicler of Rural Life was writing his first book, *The Distant Scene*, which was about life in his native Worcestershire village; he (like the author of this book) set out to preserve the memories of family life and rural customs which were rapidly vanishing. In Archer's own words: 'I felt it would be such a pity if when these characters died their sayings, customs, ways of life, how they dressed, etc. should vanish with them.'

And that, too, is the reason why Peter has written *Wagtail Tale*. This book is about the Romany Gypsy Locks – a very talented and distinguished West Country people. They are mentioned in some of the best books ever written about Gypsy life which followed on from George Borrow's 19th-century semi-autobiographical novels,

Lavengro and *The Romany Rye*. My favourite of these was 'edited' by one F. W. Carew (incidentally a pseudonym for A. E. G. Way) when he wrote *No.747 – Being the Autobiography of a Gypsy*. Such has been the lasting impact of this book that the British Library has recently reissued it in its Historical Collection Series at a modest £16.99, whereas an original edition is now costing about £200. The hero, prisoner 747, and the purported author of this book, is one Sampson Loveridge. Gypsy scholars, when the book came out in 1891, were of the opinion that *No.747* was one of the Locks; in fact, A. E. G. Way admitted in a letter to a member of the Gypsy Lore Society: 'The West Country gypsies described are not Loveridges but principally Coopers and Locks.'

In 1880 a book entitled *In Gypsy Tents* by Francis Hindes Groome, the scholarly son of an East Anglican clergyman, had preceded Way's *No.747*, and in this too the author gave all his Gypsy characters pseudonyms. In reality they were, in the main, Locks, and close relatives of the Gypsy girl that he married – Esmeralda, daughter of Noah and Delaira. Esmeralda (or Izzie) was a close friend of Dora Yates who gave a brief but affectionate account of this vivacious lady in her book *My Gypsy Days*. Esmeralda is, to this day, the pride of her north-Walian Lock relatives, and deservedly so: the University of Liverpool's Scott Macfie Gypsy Collection houses over thirty newspaper cuttings concerning her!

The Locks are still, mainly, a West Country people who moved north from Devon, Somerset and Gloucestershire. In recent years tracing one's ancestors has become a popular hobby and various family history societies have sprung up on the Internet world-wide. Gypsy genealogy, prior to this, had been the province of a few members of the Gypsy Lore Society who gathered information verbally from the Gypsies around their camp fires. This was more reliable than it might sound because Gypsies belong to close family units and living in a house does not exclude one from the Travelling Fraternity. Yet, as far as Authority is concerned – a Gypsy is only a Gypsy whilst he is of no fixed abode. The law to this day does not recognise Gypsies as a separate race.

Many of the Locks have lived in houses (some for short periods, often just for the winter months) for generations now. If these people follow a settled occupation, for example that of a gamekeeper (a surprising number did just that), the ten-yearly National Census gives no indication that they are Romanies. At the present time there is a Lock Internet site, based in the USA, which is collecting DNA to trace blood relatives. It needs to be said, however, that Lock (or Locke) is a ubiquitous name and is by no means confined to Romany Gypsies. Thanks to the members of the Gypsy Lore Society – especially the Reverend George Hall – there is a basic family tree of the Locks which goes back to Matthew Lock's union with Memberensi Boswell. It can be accessed in the Liverpool University Gypsy Collection.

Now what can I say about Peter Ingram? I have known him for almost half a century and have never ceased to admire his dedication, craftsmanship and knowledge. Since the passing of Denis Harvey (co-author of *The English Gypsy Caravan* and author of *The Gypsies: Waggontime and After*) he is acknowledged as THE authority on the Gypsy caravan.

He is a world traveller and tremendously popular amongst Romany Gypsies and Travellers the world over. His Dog Star has led him to pay respects to his personal heroes: with pilgrimages to the Canadian wilderness to visit Grey Owl's cabin and grave; to British Columbia in the steps of Robert Service, whose most popular poems he can recite by heart; as far as Australia to pay his homage to Banjo Patterson's and Henry Lawson's poetry. In return he has gained the respect not only of the Travelling people, some Canadian Indians, and the Patagonian descendants of the old Welsh settlers who he has met, but also of some of the Old Timers of these places, who, with life's hard-learnt lessons behind them, do not award it lightly.

What secret does this man have? I think it is that he has RESPECT for the people he looks up to (and who, in the 'old country' way, he would call his 'Betters'). These do not have to be on the top of the ladder of success; they can be striving to climb onto the first rung. This respect goes back to his childhood love of his grandfather, at whose knee he heard the tales of his part in the last British Cavalry Charge in the First World War. He is no longer the young lad who, many years ago, set out from his home county of Worcestershire on life's great adventure – whistling as he went, yet he still whistles a good tune and can sing an old song!

We need to get back to fundamentals, so we are told. The pre-Waggon Time Welsh Gypsy Woods (kinsmen of the Locks mentioned in this book and well known in rural Wales) gained the sobriquet 'Teulu Abram Wood'. This translated from the Welsh simply means 'Abraham Wood's Family'.

Peter Ingram's book is a story about a family, but more than that it is an attempt to show the meaning of love.

Peter is an individual in the sense that John Stuart Mill used the term. Like Cobbett, like John Seymour (the Guru of modern-day self-sufficiency, whom he knew), he defies the powers of Society to quash the individual's right to free speech and opinions. He has no interest in politics or organised religion and when occasion demands it can show a vitriolic contempt for 'political correctness'.

He does not fail (even now with three score and ten coming up on his digital clock!) to attract the ladies and many a chauvinistic acquaintance is jealous of this charisma. Possibly the attraction is his ardent admiration of their patient subjugation!

So what of the chief characters in this book? He presents Old John, warts and all, for you to make your own decision … and Genty, what would she have said about 'her man' had you asked her?

Lastly, there is one thing I'd say in detriment regarding my old pal Peter Stretton Ingram. He smokes 'roll-your-owns'. Mind, he's courteous enough to go outside your home to do so.

This is a book worthy of any bookshelf for it carries a powerful, sweet and gentle message drifting down that little-used, grassy Shropshire lane.

Mervyn Jones, North Wales (2012)

Early one Sunday morning in June 2006 I started the 2½-hour journey to a little village on the outskirts of Cardiff. I had been asked to look at an old Gypsy caravan that a middle-aged couple had in their garden. The caravan had been there when they bought the house and they were keen to know all about it, and possibly have it restored. As soon as I saw it I knew what it was.

'It's a George Cox of Hereford Square-Bow, built in the 1940s,' I said with enthusiasm.

'Well, that's amazing,' said the husband. 'Mr Lock said the same but didn't know when it was made, his grandfather had one very similar.'

Bells started to ring.

'Wouldn't be Jimmy Lock,' I said, 'whose grandfather was John?'

Both parties looked surprised and said, 'Yes, we call him Jim and he talks very fondly of his grandfather and grandmother. He says the caravan was burnt when his grandfather died.'

'Indeed it was,' I replied. 'I was at the funeral. Little Jimmy would have been about eleven years old then,' I said. 'Does he live locally?'

'Just down the lane,' came the reply. 'He and his wife have a bungalow, you can't miss it – it's rather smart.'

After examining the caravan – which really was in a sad state but still retained some original dark blue and red painted chamfers that Cox vans were renowned for – I was ushered into the house for coffee. This couple 'loved' Gypsies – Little Jimmy had 'worked the spell', selling them a large picture of a colourful encampment scene and several plates with horses and vans painted on. Like so many others, these people only saw the romance – not the reality of the old horse-drawn wagon days. I remarked how lovely they were.

Taking my leave I drove down the lane to visit Jimmy. I had moved to the south of England almost fifty years ago and had not seen him since he was a boy. The 'rather smart' bungalow was a picture: immaculate, paintwork glistening, lacy curtains to the windows, urns of flowers either side of the doorway. The black iron gates were open, concrete horses' heads on their posts, so I drove in on the well-laid tarmac drive with manicured lawns either side. To the right of the bungalow was a tarmacked yard with a large building. I gave a couple of toots on the horn and parked up. A man appeared from the building and started to walk towards me. 'Is this Jimmy?' I thought. I'd not seen him since he was eleven years old – tall, dark, and carrying himself well – yes, it must be.

'Can I help you?' he said, and I smiled. We both looked at each other for a few seconds and then he said, 'Lordy, Lordy, Lord, it's Pete, isn't it?' shaking my hand vigorously. 'Brother, you've gone all blondy-headed – like an old badger.'

My big mop of black hair had indeed changed colour!

'Where you been all these years? Come on in, the Missus'll put the kettle on!'

Jimmy's wife Janet was charming, coming from an old south Wales travelling family. They had two children, both married, and they now had five grandchildren. We talked and talked, Janet made lunch, more tea and still we talked, conversation coming round time and again to Old John and Genty. Jimmy's grandparents had had more of an effect on him than I realised; he'd prospered in his business and was well respected in the area.

'As my old Granfer used to say – takes you a long time to get a good name, and you can lose it just like that,' and he snapped his fingers. 'I loved me old Granfer and Granny, as you know, *mush* (man),' he said. 'Taught me and me sister Katie a lot, they did … and we wasn't with them long, was we? Them old days is long gone now, *chavvies* (children) don't know much about them now, do they? We got it much better now, haven't we? Look at me place here, *kushti* (good), eh? But a lot of hard work has been done for it and really, *mush*, it was me Granfer and Granny who I owe it all to.'

And Jimmy went back again to the summer of 1961 he and his sister spent with their grandparents in Shropshire.

'*Dordi!* could he make a wooden flower! Wonderful to watch – big, curly-headed they was.'

Yes, John's wooden flowers did indeed look like real chrysanthemums.

'*Dordi!* could he make a peg! *Dordi!* could he catch a rabbit! *Dordi!* could he play that fiddle … and me Granny's meat puddings, oh *dordi!* to die for!'

Janet gave him a quick glance and he said, 'Mind you, my Jani's takes some beating!'

Late in the afternoon I took my leave, after exchanging telephone numbers, and made my way homeward. What a lovely day, I mused, conversations of the old days strongly on my mind.

'*Chavvies* don't know much about them now, do they?' Jimmy had said. And this is where the idea of this book started.

A few days later I phoned Jimmy and put the idea to him. He was enthusiastic, but said, 'You'd better have a *rokker* (talk) to our Katie as well.'

He gave me her phone number and a few days later I was on the road heading for north Wales to meet her and her husband, who had settled in a small village not far from Wrexham. Katie had married a north-Walian Gypsy boy from a settled family and they too were in 'bricks'. A warm welcome was given and I was ushered into a pretty kitchen with the words, 'Oh my dear Blessed Lord, my Pete, you 'ent changed a bit.'

With a smile I replied, 'So I've always looked like this?'

They laughed, and tea was made. A cloth was taken off a huge pile of sandwiches.

'Get stuck in,' said Katie. She had inherited her grandmother's and mother's hospitality, still retaining the old ways of putting the kettle on and providing some food for visitors, a worldwide courtesy amongst nomadic people.

'Little Jimmy phoned and said about the book, and we think it's a *kushti* idea, but our Jimmy said he didn't want nothing put in the book about us when we were in Wolverhampton, or the hidings he got when we was first with our Granfer and Granny. *Dordi!* we was only little *chavvies* then, warn't we? – but me brother had got in some bad ways an' all – God love him. Me Granny and Granfer was the last of their kind, wasn't they, Pete, and they showed us the way to go on – eh, *dordi!* could they *rokker* (talk – in this case meaning *Romanes*), so could our mam, God rest her soul, but not as *kushti* as they.'

It was good to hear *Romanes* still being used by Jimmy and Katie, even stringing a few sentences together – I wondered if their children and grandchildren could. I put the question to Katie.

'They knows a few words, my Pete, but they 'ent really interested now.'

'This book would be good for them, don't you think?' I said.

'Aye man,' came the reply, 'but me and Jimmy was thinking, and we wondered if you could do it, but not about us?'

'How do you mean?' I said.

'Well, you knows what Travellers is like, don't you, and *gauji foki* (non-Gypsy people) tries to get their noses into our business – so could you use different names and that?'

I agreed straight away. So 'Jimmy' and 'Katie' are fictitious names, and so are the names of other members of their family. Some other names and places have also been changed – but not all.

Over the last six years this book has come together. I've travelled to south and north Wales to see 'Jimmy' and 'Katie' so many times I now forget how many. We and a small number know who the people in the pages of this book are, and we know where the places depicted are, but to others they must remain – as the 'old people' called it –'a secret of Little Egypt'.

This book is dedicated to the memory of 'Old John' and 'Genty'.
THE LAST OF THEIR KIND

The Old-fashioned Ways

As I sit on the steps of me wagon
dreaming of days long ago,
the *chavvies* have grown up and left me
to a life full of hardship and woe.

The roads are not free as they once were
no place for the horses to graze,
with the lorries and motors and trailers
there's no time for the old-fashioned ways.

We could stop on the old open heathland
for a week, maybe two, three or more;
they've built houses all over that heath now
and forgotten the old ancient lore.

Me daughters are married to *gaujos,*
me sons are out after the scrap,
I don't know why ever they do it
for I love me old pony and trap.

The men no longer wear *dicklos,*
the women have cut off their hair;
I'm clinging to me old-fashioned life
but they give it all up and don't care.

But I'll end me days on the road, though,
With me dogs and me *vardo* and *grai,*
and I hope they'll remember tradition
and burn it all up when I die.

Peter Ingram (1967)

CHAPTER 1

A BIT OF HEAVEN

Thursday: – market day in the little Welsh border town of Church
Stretton in the county of Shropshire. Thursday has always been
market day for as long as local people can remember; some things
never change, but one market day in April in the year of 1961 things
were about to change for Old John and Genty Lock.

Old John and Genty were Romanies; most people called them
Gypsies. In 1949 they and their 19-year-old daughter Adaline had
pulled onto a farm not so many miles from Church Stretton, and
never put their horses into the shafts of their living-wagons again.
The farmer had allowed them to pull their wagons onto a piece of
land that he never used; a small grassy strip between a large wood
and a small brook.
'Tis our own bit've 'eaven, baint it?' Genty would say to Old John,
and he would reply 'Owli (yes), the dear kind genlemun, 'is faarthur
komed (liked) us people an' all, dinna 'e, the dear blessed man, God
rest 'is soul.'

Both he and Genty spoke in this strange rural manner, combining
country dialects from the border counties through which they had
travelled, as had their forefathers. Frequently they would add to the
conversation words of the 'border' dialect of *Romanes* (the Romani
language). When the occasion arose more Romani words – (Old

John pronounced it Rumuny) – would be added, making it impossible for *gauji foki* (non-Gypsies) to understand.

And so, this fine mid-April day in the year of 1961 saw Old John and Genty waiting for the early morning bus to take them on their weekly shopping excursion to Church Stretton. They waited at the bus stop in the little village street with several villagers who also did the once-a-week shopping trip. Conversation flowed freely between them, as Old John and Genty were now well known in the small village and surrounding area, and were looked upon, by most, as decent and respectable people. Of course there were a few who maintained that they didn't like 'dirty Gyppos' and never would, but they were in the minority.

'Dirty Gyppos' is something that Old John and Genty were not, and never had been; but like all old fashioned Gypsy people, whose home hearth was a stick fire, they did have the 'sweet smell of woodsmoke' about them.

Old John was 73 years of age, tall and wiry as all of his people were – they were known amongst border folk as the Lanky or Gentleman Locks. Dark of complexion, his face was now heavily lined and his once black hair had now turned grey, bordering on white. His large grey moustache was heavily nicotine stained from habitually smoking his pipe.

'Fur a-gooin' t'town' he was dressed in a heavy serge navy blue suit, a nosegay of wild violets in the lapel button-hole on the jacket, which he had picked from the hedgerow of the little lane with grass growing in the middle, that they had walked down on their way to the village bus stop.

From the top left pocket of his waistcoat, from the third button down, hung a large silver watch chain with several silver coins dangling as a fob. He wore boots – brown boots, heavy soled and high leg laced – and on his head his best black velour Trilby hat. Knotted around his neck was a navy blue and white spotted silk kerchief, the ends of which were wound around his braces, a traditional method of keeping the ends out of the way. He walked straight-backed, and carried himself with dignity and pride.

Genty was aged 71, but looked much older, as most Romany women of her generation did. The outdoor lifestyle had taken its toll. Unlike her husband she was short of stature and rather plump. Her small round face, covered in a mass of wrinkles and lines, was darker than Old John's, but her hair, which she wore in a bun, was still the colour of jet black. Hooped gold earrings hung from her pierced ear lobes. Her hands, like Old John's, were hard and strong from a lifetime of manual work. On the left hand third finger she wore a wide gold band; on the right hand third finger an 'old style' sovereign ring (the coin bent round to fit the finger, the band forked at each side and fitted to the edge of the coin) – the emblem of St George and the dragon now almost indistinguishable, worn away by years of hard work.

'Fur a-gooin' t'town' she wore her best black 'cross-over pinner', baskets of flowers embroidered on the two large horseshoe-shaped pockets. Like many Romany women she ordered these handmade 'pinners' – which had a full yard of material pleated at the back – from a Mrs Green in Birmingham, with the instructions 'to be delivered to such-and-such Post Office and marked To Be Called For'. Around her neck she wore a colourful silk Paisley scarf pinned together at the throat by a brooch made from a five shilling piece, St George and the dragon picked out in coloured enamel.

Old John always wore brown footwear, Genty preferred black; on her feet she wore black brogue lace-up shoes. On her right arm she carried a large oval wicker basket with rounded willow loops inserted into the plaited border forming a cross-over pattern. Attached to the handle was a long leather strap, used to put around her shoulders, to ease the weight on her arm when the basket was full and heavy.

Passengers on the bus took no notice of the pungent smell of woodsmoke as Old John and Genty made their way down the aisle and seated themselves, Genty handing over their fare wrapped in brown paper. The conductor put it in his leather money bag without checking it, knowing it was always the correct amount. Several of the passengers spoke to the old couple.

'Morning, Mrs Lock, how's you today?'

'Fair t'middlin',' came the reply, 'an' thank yu dear lady fur askin'.'

Another passenger calling out, 'Mornin' Mr Lock, how's your chest now?'

'Much better,' came the reply, 'it's a-gettin' better on its own accord – my old 'ummon's stuff never a-done me no good like,' and he winked his eye and threw Genty a sly smile.

'Now thur's a thing t'say,' she retaliated, 'you knows 'twere my stuff that a-eased that old chest a-yourn.'

Genty was pretty good with the 'medication', having learnt a lot from her mother Old Adaline who, up and down the Borders, had been well respected for her herbal knowledge. She had dried some mullein leaves and made Old John smoke them in his pipe, and this had indeed helped his chest complaint.

Sitting towards the rear of the bus was a white-faced young man, smartly dressed, bearing the stamp of an office worker. Turning to an elderly gentleman dressed in a tweed suit, who was seated next to him, he casually said, 'I don't like them stinky Gyppos, do you?' The elderly gentleman looked at the young man with a surprised expression, replying, 'Do you like a pint of beer, young fellow?' With a puzzled frown he replied, 'Sure I do.'

The elderly gentleman smiled and said, 'Who do you think helps to pick the hops for your beer, eh? My wife and I have recently moved to these parts, I'm a retired doctor, used to have a surgery near Worcester, and I used to have many of these "Gyppos" as you call them come to see me in sprout picking time, their fingers split open from the frost on the sprouts. I've seen them in the fields with rolls of newspaper pushed down their trouser legs to try and keep some of the wet and cold out, and women with hessian sacks tied round their waists with bits of rag tied round their fingers – all of them cold and soaked to the bone. And, may I add, working long hours as well. "Gyppos" is a very disrespectful word, young man, that old couple there aren't "Gyppos", they are Romany people. Did you notice how they behaved when they got on this bus? Maybe you did not, but I did. They got on this bus with dignity and acted in a respectful and charming manner. And just look what colour they bring, sitting amongst this dull array of passengers. I like them, you do not, and that is your prerogative, but I ask you this: Are not these people a benefit to the community?'

The white-faced young man made no reply. He turned his head and gazed out of the window.

Within a few minutes the bus turned off the main road and made its way over the bridge into the little town of Church Stretton, where it came to a halt and passengers alighted.

CHAPTER 2

THE LETTER

As usual Old John and Genty made their way first to the Post Office to draw their small pension that Farmer Hughes's wife had secured for them last year. She had taken them to the pensions office in Shrewsbury and revelled in the experience of it. On her return to the farm she was quizzed by her husband. 'How did it go?' he had asked.

'Oh! Brian, it was wonderful!' she replied. 'John and Genty are so old-fashioned, aren't they? And so charming with it. The nice young woman in the office had never met anyone like them, and John had her eating out of the palm of his hand.'

'Well what happened?' Farmer Hughes had said rather impatiently.

'Well, she asked John when he was born, and he replied "1888, somewhere in those hills the other side of Clun, that's what my dear old mother told me, but my dear old father said it was 1887, the old Queen's Golden Jubilee year, like. I saw a picture of her once, and wouldn't you say my little woman and her was like two peas in a pod, lady? Any old 'ow, I like aitin-atey-ate, it rolls off the tongue better, don't it?"

Then she asked him what day of what month, "Well," he said, "you've got me there, lady all I can tell you is that my dear old mother told me I was born at whinberry picking time, so that would be August, wouldn't it? Yes, I was born at the back end of the year."

Then she asked Genty what year she was born, and John answered for her. "My little woman is two years younger than me, so in my reckoning that would be 1890, lady." Then the nice young woman asked what day of what month? And John looked at Genty and said "You were born in the springtime, your old mother told you the primroses were out when you were born, didn't she Genty?" And she replied, "That she did, my John," and those were the only words she spoke all the time we were in the office.'

'But then, now listen to this Brian, she asked for their marriage certificate.' Smiling at his wife, Farmer Hughes had said, 'I bet they never had one, did they? How did John get over that?'

'Well, he looked at the young woman straight in the eye and said, "I was about twenty years of age and my little woman there was about eighteen when we first got together, and we haven't been apart one day in all those years, so in my reckoning we've been together more than fifty years, lady, day and night, night and day, as you might say. So I reckons that's our marriage 'tificate, don't you?" Then he added, "and we haven't ever looked at nobody else, have we Genty?" And she did say a few more words, "No we haven't, my John," and she smiled graciously at the young woman and gave her a little bow of her head. And did you know Brian, Genty's name is shortened from Gentilla – isn't that pretty?'

'Yes, it is, I've known them all these years and never known that, but the question is, did you get them a pension?'

'Yes I did! Only a small one, though, but that will help them a lot, won't it, now that John no longer does the hedging and ditching for us, and Genty only goes round the houses occasionally with her basket? Honestly, Brian, I really don't know how they manage – although their needs are very small compared to ours, I suppose.'

The Postmaster gave them a smile as they made their way to the counter. 'Letter for you today,' he said.

'A letter fer us?' replied a surprised Genty. 'Are yu sure, Postmaster?'

The Postmaster smiled again and read the envelope to them: Mr and Mrs J. Lock, c/o the Post Office, Church Stretton, Shropshire. In big letters at the top it said, TO BE CALLED FOR'.

'Now that's you, isn't it?' he said and handed Genty the envelope.

'Oh! my dear blessed Lord, my John, whosoever can this be from?' Genty said, staring at the envelope.

Knowing that neither of them could read or write, the kindly Postmaster said, 'Postmark is from Wolverhampton.' They both looked at each other, then Old John, in a discernful voice said, 'Oh! my Lord, it must be from 'er-what-baint-with-us-no-more. Now thur's a surprise arter all on these yers 'as a-gone by.'

They had only one child and named her Adaline after Genty's mother. The child had been the apple of their eyes, and was brought up in a good Romany way, as was befitting for a child with the surname Lock. She had gained a little education at village schools, a few days at one school, maybe a week at another, whenever the occasion arose that they were encamped near enough to some small village school for Genty to take her daughter to learn what she and her husband didn't know, and that was to read and write.

All heads turned to look at Addy, for she was strikingly beautiful. Of medium height, she carried her lithe body with grace and composure, her complexion was dark and she held a look in her eyes that she knew some secret that others didn't. Her hair, black as the tip of a raven's wing, hung in one long plait right down her back, long enough to sit on.

From an early age Addy had accompanied her mother in 'calling' the cottages of the Borders, with their baskets of wares, but although perceptive, had never told people's fortunes, as her mother did. 'I doesn't want to see nothin' bad in the dear people's 'ands,' she had said.

It was a great asset to the little family for Addy to be able to read and write. No more did Genty have to get some kind person to order her 'lace bits' from a business in Ilkeston in Derbyshire. Addy took charge of that, obtaining a postal order for fifteen shillings and writing a letter to say which post office the parcel should be delivered to, adding in big letters TO BE CALLED FOR.

On receiving the parcel they would wind the 'end-of-roll lace bits' onto pieces of cardboard and arrange them in their calling baskets together with the articles Old John made, ready to sell to the ladies of the Borders.

When Addy was twenty years old she accompanied her cousin Maurice and his wife Sylvie to the May Stow-on-the-Wold horse fair. She found it all so exciting and so different from the quiet country life existence she was used to. There she met Jimmy, who with his family lived in a yard in Wolverhampton. He was so unlike anyone she had ever met before. Jimmy was a 'Jack-the-lad' – a spiv – full of bravado, and was also very good looking. Addy didn't return home to her parents with cousin Maurice and Sylvie that day. 'I couldn't do nuthin', honest to God I couldn't,' Sylvie had said to Maurice on their way home. 'Uncle John and Aunt Genty will go mad when you tells 'um, man – that they will.'

Late in the evening of that fateful May day, Maurice and Sylvie crossed the little plank bridge over the brook and made their way to the fireside of Uncle John and Aunt Genty.

'Whur's our gal to?' Old John had asked with a puzzled look.

Sylvie took a few paces back as Maurice related the story, trying to help her husband by saying, 'There was too many of his family there, Uncle John, too many of 'um for us to do anything about it, honest to God there was.'

Slowly rising from his milk bottle crate seat by the fireside Old John stood erect. Then gazing into the distance he said, 'I take an oath, never again will our gal sit round my fire; low-life mumply people, that's what they is – I knows of 'um, that *mush* warn't borned a man child, 'e wuz borned a low crawlin' snake – like all on 'is breed.'

Then, pulling the kettle-iron from the ground he slowly walked over to Addy's little bowtop wagon and with the kettle-iron held firmly in his hands, proceeded to knock the top of it to pieces.

'Don't, my John, don't my John,' Genty had pleaded in wails and tears.

Taking no notice of Genty's pleas, he had called to Maurice, 'Give us a 'and.'

'I can't, Uncle John, I can't do it,' he had replied.

'Then clear off 'ome an' let me be, goo on, clear off 'ome – may the dear Lord strike me dead, I never raised that gal t'run off with such a *wafity* (bad) low-life as 'e.'

It was not that Old John objected to his daughter 'running off'. After all, he and Genty had done the same. It was who she had 'runned off' with. And since that day, now over ten years ago, he had not spoken his daughter's name – referring to her as 'er-what-baint-with-us-no-more.

Now, in the Post Office, he looked at a letter in Genty's hand, from his daughter.
'Oh! my dear blessed Lord, my John. I wonder whatsoever it sez?' breathed Genty.
'Mrs Davies will read it t'us on our way 'ome,' replied Old John. 'Put it in yer basket 'ummon an' let's get pension an' shoppin' done.'
On entering the grocery shop Genty quietly said to Old John, 'My blessed Lord, my John, I canna a-think what I wants now, that letter from our dear gal 'as a-shook me mind t'pieces.'

Old John loved his food and quickly came to the rescue. 'Yu wants flour an' suet fur the pudden, tea, sugar, tinned milk, cheese an' bread. An' from the butcher yu wants cheap beef an' bacon. Oh! an' I wants me baccer from the little shop on the corner.'
They bought vegetables only occasionally. Living on the edge of a little country village, and being accepted and liked by most of its inhabitants, they were always being given vegetables that were surplus to requirements by the villagers who had a garden and grew their own.

Both Old John and Genty, always respectful, would say, 'Thank you my dear lady,' or 'thank you my dear sir, God bless you and your dear house and garden.'
A little servility goes a long way Genty had told Addy when she was young. Yes, always respectful, one culture respectful of the other – it had always been like that along the Borders.

The bus stopped in the village street and Old John and Genty, nodding at the remaining passengers, got off. Genty put the basket on her arm and the leather strap, attached to the handle, over her shoulder to ease the weight.

'I do hope Mrs Davies is in,' she said as they walked the short distance to her little cottage. A couple of knocks on the door brought Mrs Davies to answer it. She cheerfully beckoned them in. 'Kettle's almost boiling, me dears,' she said as she led the way into the kitchen. 'Sit yourselves down me dears and I'll make us all a nice cup of tea. Oh, I am so pleased to see you both.'

Old John could never understand why house-dwelling people always said a 'nice' cup of tea. A cup of tea was a cup of tea to him, but he often reflected that it was 'nice'. In the course of a day he consumed a large amount of it. Genty couldn't wait for the tea to be brewed. 'My dear Mrs Davies, we 'ave a letter which we'd like yu t'read t'us, iffn yu'd a-be so kind,' she blurted out.

'Of course, me dear,' replied Mrs Davies.

Genty, with a little trembling of the hand, held the letter for Mrs Davies to take, open and read. Slitting the envelope open with a kitchen knife she took out the letter and read the following to them:

Dear Mammy and Daddy, Just a few lines hoping this finds you better than it does me. Cousin Maurice and Sylvie said they would tell you and ask you what I'm going to write but I want to ask you myself. Jimmy has gone inside again, this time for a long spell. I have stuck to him all these years but he has always knocked me about and since Katie was born he's beat me up more often. Mammy and Daddy, the doctor says I've got to go and be looked after for a bit, and I don't want Jimmy's folks to look after Little Jimmy and Katie, they'll only teach them more

bad ways. I have never got on with any of them and they don't like me,
none of them ever have. What I want to ask you is, will you have them
both for a bit while I get myself sorted out? I've told them all about you
and you would really like them, they are not bad kids really. I could get
Cousin Maurice to pick them up and bring them to you. Please say you
will help me.
Love from Addy xxxx

A big silence fell, and Mrs Davies said, 'I'll pour the tea, me dears – four sugars for you, Mr Lock, and two for you, Genty dear?'

Old John cleared his throat and looked hard at Mrs Davies. 'Do yu mind if I light my pipe, dear lady?'
'Smoke by all means. I do like the smell of pipe tobacco,' replied Mrs Davies standing awkwardly and looking at the letter that she had put down on the kitchen table.
'Thank yu fur a-readin' the letter t'us,' Genty said in a quiet voice. Then, looking at Old John, she said, 'Oh my dear blessed Lord, whatsoever is we t'do, man?'
Without hesitation he replied, ' 'Ave 'um, a-course, what ages is they, 'ummon?'
'Boy'll be ten, comin' on eleven an' gal'll be eight I'm a-thinkin'. Well that's what Sylvie a-worked out earlier this year.'
'Aar, I guessed 'er an' Maurice 'ad a-kept in touch with 'um all, like. I've a-sin 'um a-whisperin' t'yu over the years,' and he puffed heavily on his pipe.
'Do you think Farmer Hughes will be alright about us 'avin' the children, an' whur shall we sleep 'um, my John?' Genty's voice sounding worried.

14

Old John puffed his pipe and let out a thin stream of smoke. 'Farmer 'ud be alright, I'd think, we'm outa the way've the farm, baint we, an' we'll keep 'um under control, like. I'll a-talk t'im a-course. An' a-beddin' down baint no trouble, I'll put a top on the dray fur the gal t'sleep in, an' boy can sleep in the tent.'

Old John spoke enthusingly; he loved children and like other Gypsy men of his age, had never really grown up. He'd always played tricks on Genty and other people as well. Like the time a lady in the village was cooing about her beautiful lawn. Old John had crept in under the cover of darkness and made 'humpty tumps' (mole hills) all over it. The following morning the poor lady was devastated and didn't find out that they were not real until she kicked one in a fit of rage. She never knew it was Old John, but she had her suspicions when she met him in the village street and he had said, with a smile, 'I 'ear yu 'ave moles in yer lawn, dear lady, 'ud yu like me t'get rid've 'um fur yu?'

'No thank you, Mr Lock,' she had replied, 'some prankster made mole hills all over my beautiful lawn under the cover of darkness, and I think it was a terrible rascally thing to do.'

'Never in this world!' Old John had said, with a twinkle in his eye. 'What a shameful trick t'play on such a dear lady as yerself. I canna a-think who'd a-do such a nasty thing,' the smile broadening on his face.

Yes, Old John was an old-fashioned country Gypsy man, and still a child at heart.

Mrs Davies had sat quietly listening, not wanting to interfere, then in a quiet voice said, 'Here now, let me pour you more tea.'

Overcome with worry about the health of her daughter and looking after her grandchildren, Genty, with tears in her eyes, looking at Mrs Davies said, 'This 'as all a-come as a shock t'us, like, d'yu think we is a-doin' the right thing?'

'Well now,' came the reply, 'this is none of my business, but I've known you both for a good many years now, so I feel I can say what I like to you both, with no offence taken.'

'No offence will be taken, dear lady,' spoke Old John in his slow deep voice.

'Do you not think you are too old to look after two young children?'

'Too old, too old!' replied Old John, sounding rather hurt. 'Why dear lady, I'm only jest over 70 year old an' could still run up them beautiful 'ills thur, if I'd a-put me mind t'it.' And he pointed a finger to her window that framed a view of outstanding Shropshire beauty. He was, of course, exaggerating. The last time he'd been up 'those beautiful Shropshire hills' was years ago, and then he'd had to keep stopping every few yards to get his breath – or, as he had said to an old pal who was accompanying him, 'we must keep stoppin' t'look at the view'.

'No, dear lady, I dunna a-think we is too old, my Genty 'ere 'as a-never bin ill in 'er life, she's as fit as me old fiddle, that she is, all've them years a-walkin' round the villages a-sellin' 'er wares 'as a-kept 'er in gud fettle. We could manage 'um, cuddna we my Genty?'

'Indeed we could, my John,' came the reply.

She had always agreed with 'her' John. In over fifty years of being together she could not think of a time when she had not. He was 'her' man, and he'd always done his best for her. They'd worked together – never been apart – she respected his judgment and they were happy. The only times they had been unhappy were when she lost her babies at birth; that had happened five times, and that is why Adaline had been so precious to them. Genty had been forty when she gave birth to Adaline who, by some miracle, had survived and grown into a strong black-haired girl that befitted a Lock and Boswell union.

'Well indeed,' said Mrs Davies, 'but what about schooling? They will have to go to school, won't they now?'

Old John smiled. 'We'll cross that bridge when we 'as to, dear lady. No doubt my 'ummon 'ere knows iffn they've a-bin schooled or not, an' can read an' write.'

'They can read an' write, my John.'

'That's gud 'nough fur me,' he said with a wry smile. 'I'll a-goo an' see farmer when we gits back, an' iffn 'e dunna mind we'll 'ave 'um as soon as I've a-got a top on the dray fur the gal t'sleep in. 'Uddnt a-tek me many days t'do it. Now dear lady, 'ud yu be so kind as t' write us a letter back? I'm assumin' the person in question 'as a-put an address t'write back to?'

'Indeed she has, Mr Lock,' and Mrs Davies opened a drawer in the sideboard and took out paper and envelopes. 'Now then, what would you like me to say?'

Old John cleared his throat, then thoughtfully said' Best iffn yu does it, my Genty.'

As with all Gypsy letters the start and end are always the same, and so Genty dictated to Mrs Davies:

My dear daughter,

Just a few lines hoping this finds you as it does us. Your daddy has agreed to have the two children, he says he'll put a top on the dray for Katie, and Little Jimmy can sleep in the kitchen

tent. He says it won't take him long. We will send word to
Maurice when we are ready. We are worried about you, please
to tell Maurice and Sylvie how you are.
Love to you and the children from Mammy xxxxx

'Does yu want me t'put yu on an' all, my John?'
'Dunna bother,' came the reply.

Mrs Davies addressed the envelope and from a little booklet tore
out a stamp and stuck it on. Genty took money from her purse to
pay, but Mrs Davies pushed her hand away saying, 'Put that away,
me dear, it's always a pleasure to do these little things for you. I'll
drop it in the post box later this afternoon when I go and see Mrs
Lloyd. Something's been bothering me, Genty, and I'd appreciate it
if you would come up the garden with me and give me a bit of
advice.'

Thinking that Mrs Davies wanted Genty to read her hand, Old John
stood up from the comfy chair and offered his sincere 'thank yous'.
'Cud yu do with some more clothes pegs, dear lady?'
'Well now, thank you Mr Lock,' she replied.
'I'll drop a couple've dozen on yer doorstep in a few days, an' thank
yu agin dear lady, yer kindness t'us is much 'ppreciated, that it is,
an' thank yu fur the tea an' all. While yu two women is a-chattin' I'll
tek meself offn into the street, like, an' a-wait fur yu, my Genty.'
(Old John not wanting to be left alone in the house in case anything
went missing and he got the blame.)

The garden of Mrs Davies was a picture, one of the old style English country gardens. She led Genty over the well kept lawn to a small bench upon which they both seated themselves.

'Whatsoever is the matter, Mrs Davies?' Genty said in her soft fortune-telling voice.

'Nothing's the matter with me, Genty, it's you that I'm worried about. I know John doesn't like your daughter's name mentioned or talk about her for that matter, but I could see that you are worried about her, as I would be if it was my daughter. Now, to put your mind at ease, what I deduce from her letter is that she is probably suffering with her nerves very badly and is going into a home for a little while to have a rest, and make herself well again. And for her to ask you both to have the children is a genuine cry for help.'

'Oh, my dear Mrs Davies,' replied Genty with more tears in her eyes. 'My blessed gal a-sufferin' with 'er nerves, whatsoever can this mean, dear lady?'

'It means that all those years of abuse, or as your daughter says 'beatings', has damaged her health; why she has stayed with him is a mystery to me. But you did tell me that John would never let her come home again, didn't you Genty dear?'

'All've them years agoo 'e took an oath, an' when 'e doos that 'e alus sticks t'it, like – 'e's an hobstunt (obstinate) man, that 'e is,' Genty said, wiping the tears from her eyes. 'It's a-that wicked low-life man wot's a-done this t'my gal, baint it? I knowed in me 'eart that she warn't 'appy, but I cuddna a-do nought about it, nor cud some of our menfolk – my John 'uddent a-let 'um, like, an' iffn they 'ad a-done thur 'ud a-bin bad trouble, thur's more've that wicked family than owern, an' my John said they'm the sort've people who'd a-come in the night an' a-burn our wagins.'

Mrs Davies looked horrified; putting her arm around Genty's shoulder, she said, 'Now wipe those tears away, me dear, and don't worry about your daughter, she is in good hands and will be well looked after, as will your two grandchildren now – you'll love having them to stay with you, won't you? And let's look on the bright side; this man is in prison for a long time, so when your daughter is better maybe she'll be able to get away and come over to this bit of country. After all, the children will be already here waiting for her, won't they? Now come on, Genty, cheer up, John will be wondering where we've got to. He'll be thinking I've got a really big problem to discuss with you,' and she gave a little laugh, and so did Genty who then looked Mrs Davies fully in the face with deep feeling and said, 'Thank yu fur yer kindness t'us dear lady, the words yu've a-spoke is true I'm sure, me old 'eart feels 'appier now.'

As they walked slowly down the village street, Old John made no comment as to the time Genty had spent with Mrs Davies, or what the discussion was about. To Old John this was women's business and of no concern to him, although he did have his suspicions that maybe they had talked about his daughter who, all those years ago, he had disowned.

Coming to a right hand bend on the outskirts of the village, they turned left up a little-used lane with grass growing in the middle of it. A short walk brought them to a small shallow ford and just before it, between high hedges, a five-barred gate. Old John opened it by slipping a binder-twine loop off the gate post and they both entered a grassy field; to their right a small brook flowed lazily, and by the edge of its bank a well worn narrow path led 'to our own little bit of heaven', as Genty called it. They walked in file along the narrow path, Old John leading the way, muttering of all the things he was going to show, and teach, the lad. Genty was now feeling reassured and much happier. Old John had always wanted a son, and she could tell by the tone of his voice that he was excited about the future.

The barking of their terrier dog, Nell, who was chained under their wagon, greeted them as they walked over the heavy plank bridge that Farmer Hughes had put there for them all those years ago. A little whisp of woodsmoke rose from the banked-up wood ash Old John had put over a half burnt log before leaving that morning. Genty made her way over to the green canvas-covered square-frame tent that they used as a kitchen when they had wet weather.

'I'll a-put these groceries away, my John, 'she called to him, 'is yu a-gooin' t'see t'Nell?'

'I will in a minute, 'ummon,' he called back as he walked over to the fire and gave the piled up wood ash a gentle kick with the toe of his boot, which then revealed lots of black embers partly with a red glow. Taking a few thin dry sticks he placed them on the embers, then flapped an old tin tray over them a few times and flames rose from the fire again. Carefully he put a few bigger pieces of wood on, then reached for the old black kettle and put it on the kettle-iron over the flames.

The little dog was now yelping with excitement, and he walked over to let her off the chain, then went up the steps of their wagon and opened the two top windows over the door.

'Kettle wanabe long,' he called to Genty as he walked back over to the fire.

'Uddent like t'put this *mass* (meat) in the safe fur me, John,' she replied.

Handing him the meat he walked over to a large shady oak tree behind the tent. Nailed to the trunk, about chest height, was a tin meat safe with a perforated zinc door and side panes. Covering it was a wet hessian sack, a bucket of water on the ground below to dip the sack into from time to time, which helped to keep the meat safe cool. Old John took the sack off, opened the door and put the meat inside; on the bottom of the safe stood a small bowl of water which also helped to keep the safe cool. Dipping the sack into the bucket he placed it back over, thinking to himself of the meat pudding Genty would make tomorrow.

By the time he got back to the fire Genty had cut bread and a big chunk of cheese for them both, and she was now busy pouring the boiling water into their old red enamel teapot, which she then placed on the edge of the fire to keep warm. The old teapot had served them well over the years; the spout was chipped, and the knob on the lid also chipped. A thin chain was wired to the knob and to the handle – the old black kettle had the same; Old John had done this when they were first bought to ensure the lids were not lost.

Many of their old stopping places in the past were up rough rutted tracks or on some out-of-the-way common land, and were bumpy places to get to. Their wagon would lurch from side to side like some small ship on a rough sea, as their old mare pulled the wagon to where they were to *atch* (stop) for a while. When on the move the kettle and cast iron hoop-handled frying pan were hung on two hooks under the cratch at the rear of the wagon and of course would swing and jiggle about when the wagon swayed from side to side, so lids sometimes came off – and got lost forever.

'We ought t'get a new *piri* (teapot), my Genty,' Old John had remarked several weeks ago.

'Indeed not, my John,' had been the reply, 'that old *piri* 'as a-served us well all on these yers, an' I'm attached t'it, that I is.'

After putting the groceries away, and before making their meal, Genty had changed into her 'work apron', folding her 'best dress black pinner' and putting it away in the wagon. She always made her own work aprons, and this one was red with white spots, four rows of pin tucks around the bottom edge, two large horse-shoe shaped pockets, a 'saddle' front with two long ties coming from it. The sides practically met at the back, the whole thing keeping her long red plaid skirt clean.

'Are yu gooin' t'get changed, my John?' Genty asked.

'*Kekka* (no), 'ummon, I'll a-goo up an' see farmer presently,' he replied, taking a brand from the fire and lighting his pipe.

Little Nell gnawed on a bone that Genty had been given by the butcher contentedly under the wagon, as Genty washed the plates and dishes in the two enamel bowls that were kept specifically for this job on the table, which stood on the left hand side of the entrance to the tent. Resuming her position by the fire, she looked steadily into it.

'I knows what's on yer mind, gal, and I baint a-gooin' t'change me mind. I took an oath all on them years agoo an' I sticks t'it. Me old faarthur 'ud a-done the same, yes 'e 'ud.'

Old John paused and re-lit his pipe. ''Er's a-med 'er bed an' must a-lie on it; an' she's a-med a mess an' a-got t'clean it up 'erself – that's my reckonin'. We brought 'er up proper, didna we, an' amongst decent people … what 'ud I say t'er iffn we found 'er a-mixin' with bad *chavvies*?'

'Anyone can stoop down an' pick up nothin',' Genty replied.

'That's right, that's right, that's wot me dear old faarthur alus a-said an' me granfer too, an' I said it t'er many a time now, didna I? But look what 'er up an' did – runned away with some low-life mumply *mush* who'd a-*chor* the *morro* outa yer *mui* (steal the bread out of your mouth). My dear blessed Lord, my Genty, what shame she've a-brought on us, we'll 'elp 'er out with the *chavvies* – but nothin' else, so 'elp me.'

Genty looked at him with tearful eyes, 'My John, cuddna yu find it in yer 'eart t'forgive an' forget?'

'No,' came the reply, as Old John raised himself up from his milk bottle crate seat. 'Better goo an' see farmer now, I'll tek the churn an' bring some *pani* (water) back,' and he walked over to the tent and emptied the water from the half-size milk churn into the 3-gallon water jack.

The churn was too heavy for Old John to carry, holding six gallons, so he had fashioned a child's pushchair to convey it. It was a nice walk to the farm, the track was level and the pushchair was easily pushed. Old John always stopped half way to enjoy the beautiful view and muse to himself how lucky he and Genty were to live in such pretty country, and be allowed to live with no trouble from anyone. Aye, he thought, we are indeed fortunate people.

Filling and lighting his pipe, his mind turned to the yard near Shrewsbury where his nephew Maurice and his wife Sylvie lived. We didna like it thur, no we didna, he thought. One day last year

Maurice had picked them up in his A-type Bedford lorry and taken them over to Shrewsbury to see his new 18-foot Siddal trailer with its pink Formica kitchen and oak veneered living area, in which were proudly displayed silver punch bowls, Royal Crown Derby china and a wonderful pair of Royal Dux figurines.

Both he and Genty had of course said how lovely it all was, but did not feel at ease as they sat in the splendour of the trailer, drinking tea from dainty fine bone china cups. As they had walked out of the trailer Genty had remarked on the gleaming stainless steel bowls and pair of water jacks (cans) that sat on a Formica-covered table by the side of the door.

'Do they tek long t'polish, gal?' she had enquired of Sylvie.

'I put some stuff on them and wipe them off, and they are done,' came the reply.

'Eh *dordi*! I 'as t'polish me old 'un with Brasso, but it dunna a-come up as shiny as they, but I meks the brass bands a-shine like gold, that I doos,' and Genty had given Sylvie a knowing nod and a little smile. (Unlike Sylvie's modern stainless steel water containers, Genty's was galvanised with brass bands fitted top and bottom, known as 'Mellors' cans, made by the firm of 'Mellor of Oldham'.)

Here on the track, Old John stood peacefully smoking his pipe, admiring the blue Shropshire hills; yes, times keep changing, he thought and his mind went back to the days of his grandfather who had travelled these hills with pack donkeys and rod tents as he himself had done with his mother and father until he was of about Little Jimmy's age. 'Me old faarthur wuz the fust of owern breed t'ave a wagin – an' now I'm the last, an' that's fur sure. Eh *dordi*, me an' me old 'ummon 'uddent a-like one of they trailers, no we 'uddent. Our gal a-wanted us t'change, I knows that, kept on about us bein' old fashioned an' everyone was a-gettin' a trailer – maybe that's why she runned off.'

His gaze turned to the pushchair and churn. 'Important t'see farmer afore 'e 'as 'is tea,' he said aloud, and walked on towards the farm.

The old sheepdog barked and wagged its tail as Old John entered the yard. 'Goo an' lay down,' he shouted to it and the dog ceased its barking. Leaving the pushchair and churn by the outside water tap in the wall of the stable, he slowly walked to the farmhouse, and made his way to the back door. Mrs Hughes had seen him through her kitchen window and before he could knock the door she opened it. With a big smile she said, 'Hello, John, do come in. Genty alright?'

'Yes thank yu, dear lady,' came the reply from Old John.

'You alright?'

And again he replied, 'Yes thank yu, dear lady.'

'Cup of tea, John?'

'I won't just now, thank yu kindly, dear lady.'

Old John always declined tea; he had seen Mrs Hughes's cat on the work surface where food was prepared and classed that as *mochadi* (unclean) – he was fastidious like that, as were all of his people.

'Is farmer about, dear lady? I'd like t'ave a word with 'im of the hutmost himportance.'

'Really! John,' she said with a smile, 'well you're in luck, here he comes now,' as she saw him pass by the window.

The door flew open and Farmer Hughes entered the kitchen, pulling his Wellingtons off in the doorway.

'Hello, John, how's you? What's up?'

'A little concerned, Sir – I'm a-wonderin' iffn I might a-tek up yer time an' 'ave a few words, like?' Old John speaking very humbly in his quiet country manner.

'Of course, John,' the farmer said with a smile, 'come on through to the parlour.'

Old John followed as Farmer Hughes led the way into the darkish cool room and beckoned him to take a seat.

'Now then, John, what's bothering you? You don't seem quite yourself – what's up?' and he stared hard into Old John's worried weatherworn face. My God, he thought, he's dark, just like his father, there aren't many like him now.

Old John had put his hat on his knee and was turning it round and round; suddenly he looked up and cleared his throat, 'You remembers our gal, Sir, dunna yu?' he said quietly.

'Indeed I do, John,' the farmer replied, 'the prettiest girl I've ever seen, must be over ten years since we've seen her – how is she?'

'Well it's just that yu see, dear Sir – she enna.'

'What do you mean "she isn't"? Do you mean that she isn't well, John?'

'Well sort've, Sir,' and Old John took a long pause. 'Yu knows on 'ow she runned offn with a bad 'un, dunna yu?'

'Yes, I remember, John, please go on.'

'Well 'e've a-gone an' a-got 'isself a-locked up agin – up t'no gud yu understands, a bad 'un through an' through. Our gal's in Wolverhampton with two children an' it seems that she baint too good with 'er 'ealth, like, an' she've a-sent us a letter askin' iffn we 'ud 'ave the two children fur a bit until 'er gits 'erself a-sorted out, like.'

Unlike Old John's usual slow speech the words came out quickly and without a pause.

'But what's all that to do with me, John?' said the farmer, looking puzzled.

Old John's head was again lowered, looking at the hat on his knee. Then raising his head slightly, he asked the question that had been bothering him.

'My dear kind Sir, I wuz a-wonderin' iffn yu'd a-mind us 'avin' the two children fur a while like. We'll mek sure as they dunna git up t'no mischief.'

Farmer Hughes gave a little laugh. 'John, how many years have you been on my land?'

'A fair few, Sir,' came the answer.

'How many years have I known you and your family?' and he answered the question himself. 'All my life, John. Why, I look upon you as family – all my family does. Why, my wife would be lost without having your wife Genty to talk to and confide in. Of course you have the children, there was no need to ask, but thank you for having the courtesy to do so.' He paused, and then said, 'You're not thinking about a modern caravan for them to sleep in, are you?'

'Indeed not, Sir!' replied Old John, 'I canna abide them tin cans – thought I'd a-top the old dray fur the gal, and young lad can a-sleep in the tent, like.'

Under his breath the farmer heaved a little sigh of relief. 'Silly of me to say such a thing, John, the Council – don't like them as you know – they do know you are on my land of course, but there have never been any complaints, and they have turned their eyes elsewhere.'

'Pays t'ave a gud name, don't it now Sir?' said Old John with a relaxed smile.

'I've told you before, John, to use that bit of land as your own, we have no use for it; I have always valued the work that you did for us here on the farm – and your father before you – finest hedge layers in Shropshire … that's what I told people.' Then with a smile he looked at Old John, 'Wolverhampton, you say? Oh my! town kids, they'll love it!'

And with that the farmer got up from his chair and walked over to the dresser. 'Now then, John, what say you to a drop of spirit – whisky?'

Old John nodded, rather overwhelmed.

'Tip it back, John, we'll have another, shall we?'

Never known to say no to a drink, Old John replied, 'Thank yu kindly, Sir, I dussn't a-mind if I do, like.'

With glasses refilled, he held his up high, and now with a twinkle in his eye, proposed a toast. '*Kushti bockt* my *rai*, an' *mi Duvel parik tutti*,' came eloquently from his lips.

'What does that mean, John?' asked the farmer.

'Why Sir, in owern speech it means "good luck my gentleman, an' God bless yu".'

Raising his glass to Old John the kindly farmer replied 'I'm proud to know you, John, and good luck having the children to stay – what ages are they?'

'Boy's ten an' gal is eight, I'm believin'.'

'Good luck to you and Genty – you'll need it,' and Farmer Hughes emptied his glass.

Leaving with many gracious 'thank yous', Old John made his way back to the yard to fill up the water churn. The old sheepdog barked and wagged his tail as usual, and Old John shouted out the customary 'lay down'.

With the filled water churn he started for home. The dear, kind people, he said to himself as he walked slowly along pushing the pushchair, and smiled to himself. Then the smile left his face. We've a-never a-sin owern grandchildren, will they tek t'us? It'll all be s' different t'em. And Farmer Hughes' words echoed in his ears – 'good luck to you and Genty – you'll need it!'

The smell of fried potatoes and onions caught his nostrils as he neared home; my Genty's a gud 'ummon an' a gud cook, he thought. Little Nell ran out to greet him and Genty called 'wash yerself up, my John, *hobben* (food) is almost ready. Yu looks alright so farmer must've a-said yes.'
'Everything's *kushti* (good) my gal, *mandy'll pooker tutti* arter we've a-*holled* the *hobben* (I'll tell you after we've eaten the food). I'm as hungry as a starvin' man can be.'
'You've a-bin a-drinkin', baint yer my John? I *jins* (know) yu 'as … yu alus *rokkers* more *Romanes* (speak more Romani) when yu've a-had a drop, an' you'm *posh motto* (half drunk), baint yer?'
'Now thur's a thing t'say 'ummon,' he replied, ''tis jest the blood of me forefathers a-comin' out've me.'

Genty had cooked pork belly rashers (done well, as Old John liked them), fried potatoes and onions and she was filling the dish plates as he came over to the fire.

' 'Ere yu is, my John,' and she handed him his dish plate topped with a thick slice of bread and butter. The two sat there by the fireside, in silence as the meal was eaten. Genty finished hers first, Old John being a very slow eater, savouring every mouthful – he loved his food. Reaching over to the kettle-iron, on which the kettle was suspended, she pulled it over the flames, and soon it was boiling and she made tea. Old John had now finished his meal and she took his dish plate from him and handed him his tea in a two-handled tea dish. They had always used these dishes for drinking their tea, Genty having bought half a dozen years ago, but now they were down to three, the others having been accidentally broken over the years.

'Now then, my John, what did farmer say?'

Old John was lighting his pipe, and taking his time about it.

'Come on, man, git that old *swiggler* (pipe) a-gooin' an' a-tell me,' Genty now said impatiently. Old John gave a little laugh and then related the whole story to her.

'I knowed the dear man 'ud a-be alright, but yu did right in a-askin' 'im, my John.'

'Aar, I feels better now, gal, an' t'morrer I starts on that old dray of owern,' and he looked across at the canvas-covered four-wheeled vehicle.

'Pour us some more *meski* (tea), gal, then I'll sort out the *kosht* (wood) fer mornin', an' then I reckons I'll a-get me old *bosh* (fiddle) an' a-tune up, like.'

The wood was sorted for the morning fire, with an old canvas sheet thrown over it; then Old John went over to the wagon and brought down his fiddle case. His father, grandfather, and great-grandfather had been good fiddle players and of course played by ear. They played traditional tunes and a few that they picked up on their travels, changing the tune a little every time it was played, according to the mood of the moment. They were often asked to play at private functions, for which they were paid, or in village inns where they offered to play 'a little tune' in return for beer, or for vegetables – or anything edible brought to their tents. The Kangaroo Inn at Aston-on-Clun was one of Old John's father's favourites, but Pembridge Fair in Herefordshire was one place that he and his son attended each year, playing their tunes hour after hour and collecting money for doing so, returning home with pockets bulging.

Old John seated himself on his milk bottle crate seat and tuned up the old fiddle. 'What's it t'be, my Genty?'

'We'm both 'appy now, my John, so play *Three Jolly Sheepskins* – 'tis a gud 'un, we dunna a-want nuthin' sad now, doos we?'

He played the old tune twice over as Genty gazed into the dying embers of the fire, then raising herself up she said, 'I think I'll *jall t'woodrus* (go to bed) – bin a 'eavy sorta day, baint it my John?'

'Aar, yu do that, my Genty,' he replied as he returned the fiddle and bow to its case. 'I'll jest sit 'ere a while an' a-think about a-toppin' the dray.'

He stirred the embers of the fire with a stick, and felt the warmth on his hands, then puffed heavily on his pipe and thought, 'My dear Lord, I baint a-topped a dray since my Genty an' me got t'gether. I reckon Old Fred 'ud give me a 'and, aye, an' 'e'll 'ave the mekins in them old sheds've 'is – all I'll 'ave t'buy is the cloth (canvas cover).'

He raised himself stiffly from his seat and walked over to the tent, poured water into the washing bowl, washed his face and hands, then called out, 'You in *woodrus* (bed), gal?'

'*Owli* (yes),' came the reply, and Old John climbed up the steps of the wagon to his bed. 'Aar,' he thought, 'it's a-bin a 'eavy sorta day, that it 'as.'

CHAPTER 3

'TOPPING' THE DRAY

Six a.m., a fine dry morning, and Old John, as usual, was up and was busy re-kindling the fire and putting the kettle on for tea, which was soon brewing in the enamel teapot on the edge of the fire. Then he re-filled the kettle and put it back over the flames to boil for Genty's washing water. Every day of their life together he had had the same routine. He poured Genty her tea and took it up to her in the wagon. 'I'm just a-*jallin'* (going) in the *vesh* (wood) with Nell,' he said, 'thought I'd a-cut the rods fur the 'top' afore I goos an' sees Fred Lloyd – I'll be back in a couple've 'ours.'

Nell bounded ahead as he made his way through the wood at the rear of their little encampment, then he followed the hedge on the side of the grassy field until he came to a gateway that opened out onto the little lane with grass growing in the centre. On the other side of the little lane was a copse, and this is where Old John was to cut the hazel rods. 'I'll want twenty-two but I'll cut twenty-four,' he thought to himself.

On entering the copse his little dark eyes scoured the clumps of hazel that grew in abundance; he was looking for straight clean rods, a little thicker than his thumb at the bottom and about eight feet long. 'That'll do,' he said aloud, as he pulled a nice straight rod down from a clump.

With his hook blade knife he cut the top thin end off in one cut, then bending the rod over towards him turned the knife round so the sharp edge faced him, then he put the blade on the rod, about a foot from the ground, and with one swift pull upwards cleanly cut it off. He scoured deeply into the copse, cutting here and cutting there, until at last he'd cut the twenty-four nice straight clean rods.

Sitting down to rest he lit his pipe, and as he sat quietly smoking in the peace of the copse, his mind went back over fifty years to the early days when he and Genty had 'runned off' together. He had had a four-wheeled dray and an old mare called Betty to pull it. For a while they had slept in a rod tent covered with a few old blankets and a scrap of canvas. They were down Bromyard way and Genty was out calling the cottages with her basket of clothes pegs and hearth brushes that Old John had made. He had been mooching round the lanes in search of 'something for the pot' when he spotted, in an out-of-the-way stack yard, a smashed to pieces carrier's cart. 'Musta bin a dodgy 'oss that a-did that, unless it was frit (frightened) by summat,' he had thought. But what had taken his eye was the canvas cover stretched over the framework.
'It dunna look in bad nick, I've a-got t'ave it,' he thought, then I can top me dray an' get me 'ummon offn the ground. (Genty at that time was suffering with a chest complaint.)
That night he and Genty cut the ropes that secured the cover to the framework, folded the sheet up carefully and carried it back to their *atchin tan* (stopping place) where they hid it in a thick hedge.

Before dawn the next day the tent was down, and the stolen sheet placed on the dray covered over with the blankets and old canvas sheet, all their possessions were piled on top, Betty was harnessed and backed in the shafts, and they were off, putting as many miles between them and the stack yard as possible.

At Crabby Apple Common they pulled in and plugged out (tethered on a long chain) poor old Betty, lit a small fire, had tea and something to eat, then yoked up and were off again. By evening time they had pulled into a little lane not far from Presteigne, a favourite old stopping place which had a brook close by. 'They'll not a-find us now, my Genty, we'll stop 'ere t'night, an' t'morrer we'll *jall* (go) on t'Bucknell an' a-git ourselves a-hid up that little track that goos through that dear little wood. And then 'ummon I'll a-mek yu somewhur nice t'lay yer 'ead.'

'It only seems like yesterday,' he thought, 'my blessed Lord, them years 'as a-gone quickly, an' 'ere I am agin goin' t'top a dray – only thing that's different is this time I 'enna got t'*chor* (steal) a sheet, I've a-got the money t'buy one. Aye, me and me old 'ummon's not done too bad, she's done well 'olding onto the money.'

He had now finished smoking his pipe, and getting up from the ground took a twist of baler twine from his jacket pocket. The rods were collected and placed all thick ends together, then Old John tied them top and bottom with the baler twine. Giving a low whistle, Nell came bounding to him, 'Come on, Nell,' he said, 'Let's get 'ome an' 'ave some breakfast.' And with that he picked the pile of rods up from the ground – thick ends down – then hoisted them onto his right shoulder, jumping them along a bit until they were well balanced. Then his right arm went up and his hand held them in place. They were heavy, and halfway back he slid them off his shoulder and had a little rest.

' 'Ow many times 'ave I done this before?' he thought, for when he'd been making clothes pegs he had cut hazel rods if willow was not available. 'I must've carried tons've these rods on me shoulder in me time,' he said to Nell who sat patiently looking at him.

Genty heard Old John's *joter* (Gypsy signal whistle) and brewed the tea, then, taking the cast iron hoop-handled frying pan, she placed it on the kettle-iron over the fire, in readiness for cooking the breakfast.

'Let me git these offn me shoulder, gal,' he said, as he came round the side of the kitchen tent, letting the rods slide forward and fall to the ground. 'Eh *dordi*! they'm 'eavy, wish I'd a-put me *huffa* (cap) on me shoulder fust, 'udda eased the pain, like.'

Old John wore his *stadi* (Trilby) only when he went out; today he was dressed in his everyday clothes, brown corduroy trousers, old tweed jacket and his big flat tweed cap. As was customary, he always wore a colourful silk scarf around his neck. Many younger Gypsy men had now given up wearing them – bad for business a few said, shows what you is.

As he was washing his hands, Genty was busy cooking the breakfast. He loved the smell of bacon frying; he was hungry and the smell made him more so.

'Doos yu want *dui youries* (two eggs), my John?' and he answered, '*Owli* (yes),' as he made his way over to the fire. Genty handed him a dish plate with two large slices of bread filled with bacon and eggs, followed by a dish of tea. The meal was finished and Old John sauntered off to see his pal Fred Lloyd who had premises in the village street. Fred had been the local carpenter and wheelwright, and had many years ago (for he'd been retired for over ten years) re-fellied the wheels on Old John and Genty's wagon. He still had the workshops out back, and did the occasional job when he felt like it – which wasn't very often.

Fred put down his newspaper on the kitchen table as he heard a loud knock on the back door, and looked at the clock on the wall. It was just after 9.30 a.m. 'Wonder who that can be?' he thought.

Opening the door he found the figure of Old John standing a few paces back, with a smile on his face. 'Mornin', Fred,' he said.

'Come on in old mate, cup of tea? It's ready made.'

'Aar, that 'ud be gud, Fred, whur's yer missus?'

'Upstairs tidying up,' came the reply, 'she's always tidying up. I put something down and next time I look for it, it's gone – and she can't remember where she's put it.'

'My old 'ummon's a tidy 'un an' all, but she dunna 'ave much t'tidy away from me, I 'enna got much, jest me old knife and me catty (catapult) in me pocket,' and he patted his jacket pocket which held his catapult. Sitting on a chair by the table he put his cap on his knee, and Fred poured the tea from a brown crock teapot and handed Old John a cup.

'I know what's going on, John, Mrs Davies come down to see my missus yesterday afternoon and told her – anything I can do to help?'

Looking a bit disconcerted he replied, 'It dunna tek long fur news t'git about in this village, do it? I'd a-never a-thought've 'er as a-bein' a gossipy sorta 'ummon, yu never knows 'um, doos yer?'

'T'be 'onest with yu, Fred, I could do with a bit've 'elp, like. I'm a-wonderin' iffn I can buy a bit've wood offn yu? I want t'put a top on me old dray t'mek somewhur fur the little gal t'sleep, like.'

Fred looked at him and gave him a big frown. 'I wouldn't sell you nothing, John Lock,' he said in a serious tone.

'Why? I've a-got the money t'pay yer, Fred.'

'I don't want your money old mate, I'm only joking, I've got sheds full of timber out back and you can have what you want for nothing. Drink your tea and we'll go and sort some out. Do you want a hand to do the job? It's bound to be a two-handed 'un.'

At eighty years of age this is just what Fred needed, something a bit different to get his teeth into. He worked in his garden most days, and hid in his workshop where he had a big comfy chair when his wife's women friends came round for a chat. He was full of enthusiasm and his eyes sparkled as they both walked up to the sheds.

'What do we need, John?' he said as he opened the big door and they walked inside, the smell of timber and paint hanging strongly in the air. Timber was in abundance, sawdust and cobwebs everywhere, old machinery now going rusty, bits of old wheels piled up, and in a corner a large tortoise slow-combustion stove and by its side Fred's comfy chair.

'Well fust Fred, we could do with a piece fur the ridge, fur the thin ends've the rods t'goo in, like.'

'What size?' Fred shouted out.

'Dray's a nine-foot 'un, we wants a dear little over'ang front an' back – so ten foot 'ud do, Fred.'

'How thick?'

Old John held his thumb and index finger apart and Fred looked at it.

'One inch,' he said, 'how wide?'

Again Old John held his thumb and index finger apart.

'Five inches?'

'Aar Fred, we wants it wider than fur a tent ridge pole, it'll mek a better shape, like.'

Moving a load of timber planks, Fred pulled one out and put his rule on it.

'Twelve foot long, John, five inches wide and a good inch thick – that'll do?'

'Aar, but it's too long,' Old John replied.

Putting his rule again on the plank, Fred measured ten feet, put a square on the mark and drew a pencil line across, then taking his saw cut the two-foot end off. 'That'll do you,' he said, 'next.'

'We could do with two uprights fur the front 'n' back,' and again Old John held his thumb and index finger apart.

'Three by two – what length?'

Old John put his hand under his chin, 'About like this, Fred.'

'Hang on,' Fred shouted as he took a thin batten, put it in front of Old John and put a pencil mark where his hand was. Then he put it on the bench and measured it with his rule. 'Five foot three inches precisely, John old mate,' and with that he pulled a length of 3" x 2" down from the rack and cut off the two lengths at precisely five feet 3 inches long.

'Next,' shouted Fred.

'Could do with four brackets.'

'What sort of brackets, John?'

'Like them,' and Old John pointed to metal brackets that held a shelf up over the work bench. Fred mooched about in boxes under the bench and at last held up four shelf brackets, saying, 'These do?'

'Aye man, they'm perfect fur the job,' came Old John's reply, 'could do with some screws t'fix 'um, like.'

Fred had by now worked out exactly how 'the top' was to be made. 'A bracket holds the three by two to the ridge piece, and a bracket holds the bottom of the three by two to the floor – am I right, John?'

'Aar, that yu is, Fred.'

'Right, so we'll want some three-quarter-inch screws and some one-inch 'uns as well. What else, old mate?'

'Could do with a brace 'n' bits t'drill 'oles in the ridge piece an' the chock rails, Fred.'

'What size bits?'

'Well Fred, I've a-cut the nut sticks t'mek the bows, like – got t'shave the ends've 'um a bit, thick end's a bit thicker than me thumb, an' thin end's like me little finger 'ere.'

With a chuckle, Fred pulled out from a canvas roll a ⅝" bit and a ⅞" bit and put them in the old frail (toolbag) together with the brace, screws, nails, screwdriver, hammer, saw, chisels, a square and a smoothing plane. 'Do we want a draw-knife, John?' Fred asked, picking one up from the bench.

'Nay, man,' replied Old John, I'll shave ends an' cut a few chamfers on the front pole with me peg knife.'

'Anything else?' Fred asked.

'Almost forgot, Fred, could do with two thin 'uns t'nail rods t'each side, about 'alfway up, like.'

'How big, how long?'

'Well, they only wants t'be thin, like,' and again Old John opened his thumb and index finger.

'Two by one,' shouted Fred, 'I'll cut them ten foot long, we can cut the end bit off later on when we've nailed 'um. Anything else, old mate?'

'I think that's about it, brother, an' I thanks yer kindly,' and Old John shook Fred's hand. He really did look upon Fred as a 'brother' … he wasn't a Gypsy man, but he was a good man just the same. And Fred was happy; he liked Old John and Genty, had many a cup of tea with them around their fire, listening to Old John playing his fiddle; and winter time he'd sat in the cosy tent with the Queenie stove throwing out heat, and the smell of the paraffin lamp which gave out just enough light in its glow to catch the colours of the rose pattern material that lined the walls. He'd sat there eating Genty's *marikli* (frypan currant cake), with thick butter on, drinking tea from a two-handled 'weeping willy' (willow patterned) dish, listening in wonderment to Old John's tales from all parts of the 'borders' and some parts of Wales. Like many people in the village he'd only ever been as far as Hereford or Shrewsbury in his life, so he loved these tales – and he loved Old John and Genty too.

'When do we start?' Fred shouted.

'Whenever yu like,' came the reply from Old John.

'How's about after dinner? I'll get me boy (Fred's son was almost sixty, but still known as 'the boy') to bring the 'makings' up to you in the van as soon as we've had the 'nosebag' on. Come on in and have another cup of tea,' he shouted. Fred was a little deaf and always shouted.

'I'll not 'ave tea, thank yu, I'll get back an' start t'shave up ends've rods, time'll be a-pushin' on,' answered Old John, and he bade his 'thank yous' again as he closed the garden gate behind him and made for home.

Nell ran out to greet him as he made his way over the plank bridge and he bent down and gave her a pat on the head. Genty was busy at the cupboard table, her hands covered in flour. 'Everythin' alright, my John?' she called to him.

'*Owli*, my Genty, everythin's *kushti*, Fred's a-sorted all the 'mekings' fur the top an' 'e an' 'is lad is a-bringin' it all up arter dinner in the van, an' Fred's a-gooin' t'give me a 'and a-dooin' it, like. Is yu dooin' a bacon pudden?' (Also known as a rasher pudding, made with flour and suet pastry rolled out thinnish, then covered in bacon rashers and sliced onions, seasoned with pepper and mixed herbs, then rolled up like a Swiss roll, wrapped loosely in a cloth with ends tied, and put into boiling water, boiled and then simmered for a good two hours.)

'I is, my John, but I shanna a-put it in the pot till later on 'sarternoon, yu an' Fred'll be a-wantin' t'git on with the job I'm expectin'.'

Old John looked at his pocket watch and exclaimed, 'Eh *dordi*! jest a-look at the time, seems t'goo quicker an' quicker as each day a-passes, that it does. I'll-a-not get them
rods a-done afore Fred an' 'is lad comes, but I'll mek a start on 'um any road, dunna do me any *hobben* (food) now, gal – I'll wait until later on.'

Walking over to the tent, he reached under the inside table and dragged out an old bag that he kept his peg making tools in, and a few other bits and bobs as well. Carrying it out onto the grass he took out his well worn ground block (also known as a molly block), his beater, chopping-off knife, and his 'osses-'ead-'andled peg-knife. These he carried over to the pile of rods that lay by the side of the tent. Taking the beater in his right hand he banged the ground block into the earth, then he proceeded to lay each thick angle-cut end of the rod on the block, put the chopping-off knife blade onto it and with a deft blow or two with the beater hit the back of the knife blade and chopped them off cleanly and square. Next he stood up and held a rod vertically in front of him, then reaching about a foot above his head he pushed his thumbnail into the bark of the thin end, so it would leave a mark. 'That should mek 'um 'bout seven foot long, like,' he said to himself. With the same procedure as before he chopped the thin ends off – using the first rod as a measure. Then, sitting on the ground by the side of the rods, he raised his right knee, and holding the peg-knife against it took a rod with his left hand and pulled the end against the sharp blade, which shaved the bark off.

He had only about half a dozen to 'shave up' and finish the job, when Nell started to bark. Looking up from his labour he saw Fred and his boy coming down the little pathway on the edge of the brook, carrying on their shoulders the 'mekins' of the job in hand. As usual Fred's boy was in a hurry and only had time to say *hello, Mr Lock*, give Genty a wave of his hand – and he was gone.

'That boy of mine always makes me feel tired, he's always rushing about,' remarked Fred, and Old John nodded his head and gave a smile.

'Right-ho! Let the dog see the rabbit,' Fred shouted out as he picked up his toolbag and put it on the four-wheeled dray, adding, 'it's a tidy dray this, John, it's a Pinvin one out of Evesham, isn't it?'

'That it is, Fred, all on these yers an' yu baint ever a-looked at it proper, 'as yer?'

To which Fred replied, 'You always had it covered over with a canvas sheet, and you know I'm never one to poke about other people's property,' and he gave a little chuckle. 'Where shall we start, John? I think I've got in mind what's to be done, but just talk me through it.'

Old John put his hand on the side chock rail and said, ''Ere's nine foot long, Fred, an' I wants 'oles a-bored in these rails every foot, like – but ends wants t'ave double 'oles, one next t'other 'un, so as t'ave eleven rods either side, like. The 'oles wants t'be bored on a slant, so's when the rods goos in they sticks out'uds an' then when they'm bent over t'fit in the ridge piece they'll mek a nice bow shape. Same as when we used t'mek the 'oles in the ground fur the tent rods, alus a-put the kettle-iron on the slant, an' then the rods 'ud mek a nice bow shape.'

'I've got it, John, and the ridge piece is to be bored to match the holes in the chock rails.'

'Yu got it, Fred, 'cept ridge piece is ten foot long so end 'oles'll be out six inches, like, so's t'give front an' back a bit've an angle.'

'A rake front and back,' said Fred.

'Aar, that's it! yu got it, Fred, an' ridge piece is 'eld up both ends with them two pieces thur, an' they'm 'eld in place with them brackets you've a-got.'

'Leave it to me, old mate,' shouted Fred, as he took his rule from a side pocket of his brown bib and brace overalls. Then he took a pencil from behind his right ear (that's where he always kept it, and a half-smoked cigarette behind the left ear), and started to measure and mark the side chock rails ready for boring the holes.

I'll a-finish a-shavin' up these rods, Fred, while you'm a-dooin' that, an' give us a shout iffn yu wants a 'and, like.'

No answer came from Fred, his mind was on the job. He felt happy and started to whistle a tuneless tune. Within a short while he had bored the holes, put the 5" x 1" ridge piece against the one chock rail and marked it to match, then he put his square on the marks and drew a pencil line across, so as to have the holes exactly opposite each other. Changing the ⅞" bit for the ⅝" bit in the brace, he called Old John to give him a hand. He had placed the ridge piece on the grass beside the dray and knelt down holding it between his knees, ready to start boring the holes.

'Get a hold of the end of this and hold it tight while I bore the holes, old mate – do you want them right through?'

'No Fred, nearly 'alf way in'll be jest right, then one end wunna push t'other out, will it?'

The ⅝" holes were bored on both sides; Fred then placed the ridge piece on the dray and marked on it the inside of the front and back rails, then he nailed it to the two pieces of 3" x 2" and screwed the brackets on top and bottom.

'Right-o, John, up she goes, have you got something I can stand on to get up on the dray? Not as nimble as I used to be,' Fred shouted, now fully charged with enthusiasm. Old John walked over to the kitchen tent and returned with the half-size milk churn, while Fred marked the centre of the front and back rails.

'Perfect,' shouted Fred, 'come on up here with me on the dray and hold the ridge piece in the middle while I screws the brackets to the floor, and I'll screw the 3" x 2" to the front and backs, rails an' all. That'll steady it up.'

All was secure and the two old men got down off the dray, Fred with difficulty, and admired their handiwork.

'Time for a little smoke,' said Fred, taking the half-smoked cigarette from behind his left ear. Genty had been watching all this going on and had smiled and thought to herself, 'They two's jest like children, that they is, jest a-look at 'um thur, 'appy as larks, they is. That Fred is enjoyin' 'isself, an' my John is like a new man, that 'e is.'

'We can put the nut sticks in next then John, can't we?'

'That we can, Fred,' answered John.

'I've just thought,' said Fred, 'that little granddaughter of yours might get a splinter in her little hands off the edges of that timber. I'm going back up on the dray to plane the arras (edges) off. You're going to chamfer the outside of the front upright, aren't you?'

'Aar, I'll do that with me peg-knife in mornin', Fred.'

With difficulty, Fred got a foot on the milk churn and heaved himself up onto the dray. Plane in hand, he soon had all the inner edges of the timber arrased off, then again with difficulty descended to the ground once more, saying, 'I feel better now. If that little girl got a splinter in her little hand I'd never forgive meself. If a job's worth doing old mate, it's worth doing proper, I've said that many a time to me boy over the years.'

Walking over to the pile of seven-foot-long rods, Old John picked them up and carried them over to the dray.

'Thur's a special knack in a-bendin' 'um Fred, so I reckons yu'll 'ave t'get back up on the dray an' a-tek the thin ends an' a-push 'um in the 'oles of the ridge piece, like.'

Fred let out a little moan, as once more with difficulty he got up on the dray uttering, 'What's this special knack then?'

'Watch an' I'll a-show yer.' replied Old John as he picked up a rod, placed the thick end against the inner centre of his left boot, then pushed his left knee around it, and with his right hand bent it slightly, turning the rod with his left hand until he found the position where it bent perfectly. Then, keeping the rod in that position, he put it in the chock rail hole and Fred, taking the thin end, pushed it into the ⅝" hole in the ridge piece. Soon all the rods were fitted, and Fred shouted out, 'I can't get down, John, these sticks has blocked me exit, will you move the churn to the front for me?'

'Yu'll 'ave t'bide whur you'm to, man, yu looks like a lion in a cage … I'm off t'ave a cup've tea now,' and he rolled about laughing before moving the churn to the front for Fred to make his escape.

'It looks good, John,' Fred said smiling, 'but now you'll have to get inside 'cause I'm going to nail the battens on from the outside while you hold them up inside. Up you go, mate!'

Old John got up on the dray and held the ten-foot thin batten on one side, roughly in the middle of the rods, while Fred stood on the milk churn and nailed through the rod into the batten, then moved to the other side and did the same. Then taking his saw, sawed the end few inches off them. And the job was completed.

'How are you going to cover the back and front, John?' asked Fred.

'Canvas t'cover the back, an' canvas flaps on front,' came the reply. 'I'll cut up the old sheet I used t'cover the dray with.'

Fred wasn't keen on the idea of a canvas back. 'I've got a couple of sheets of hardboard in the shed that's doing nothing, how about me fitting them to the back for you … and a little window for the girl to look out of? Missus would machine some pretty curtains up as well if I asked her nicely, and I might even get her to make pretty ones for the front as well – like that 'rosy' pattern that you've got the inside of your tent lined with – what do you think?'

Old John was overwhelmed with Fred's enthusiasm, and was now worried about asking him for some timber to make a bed across the back. He heaved a sigh of relief when Fred said, 'Are we going to make a bed for the little girl, like in your wagon, we don't want her sleeping on the floor, do we?'

Looking a little sheepish Old John replied, 'I 'adna a-got round t'askin' yu about that, Fred.' Fred let out a loud laugh and said, 'Give us a leg-up onto the dray and I'll have a measure up.'

Over at the fireside Genty had made a pot of tea and gave a call to the two old men.

'She's timed that well, John, that's all we can do today,' he said with a groan, as he got unsteadily down from the dray. 'I'm gasping for a cup of tea and me old back's killing me.'

'You'll a-stop an' 'ave summat t'eat, Fred? Thur's a nice pudden almost ready in the pot, an' I'm jest about ready t'put the taters an' cabbage on.'

Fred had sampled Genty's puddings before, and they had given him indigestion. 'I'd like to Genty, and thank you for asking, but I'd better get back, the old woman will be wondering what's happened to me.'

He raised himself up from his seat, shook Old John's hand and said, 'I'll get boy to bring stuff up first thing in the morning and we'll have the job finished by dinner time.' Then with back slightly bent he slowly made his way homeward.

After they had eaten, Old John decided to go up to the farm and ask Mrs Hughes if she would order him a canvas sheet to cover the 'accommodation' with.

'I'm gooin' t'ask Fred's lad if 'e'll 'ave a look in that second-'and shop in Hur-e-furd (Hereford) fur a big carpet t'put over roof when 'e comes up t'morrer,' he said to Genty, as he walked away from the fire in the direction of the farm.

Mrs Hughes was her usual welcoming self as she opened the door and bade Old John to come in.

'Not a-wanting t'be a newssance dear lady, but I was a-wonderin' iffn you'm a-gooin' t'Shrewsbury any time soon?'

'I'm going tomorrow, John, is there something you need?'

'Aar, I wants a canvas sheet ordered from the tarpaulin makers, an' I wuz a-wonderin' iffn yu'd be so kind as t'order it, like?'

'No trouble at all, John, what size do you want?' and she took a pencil and paper from the table.

'Twelve foot by fifteen foot, seams t'run fifteen foot way, raw edges, fifteen ounce green proofed.'

Old John spoke authoritatively – he knew about these things. Taking a roll of notes from his pocket he said, 'Not sure 'ow much they'll be now,' and he started to peel some pound notes off the roll.

'Don't give me any money now, John, wait until I've collected it and you can pay me then,' and she gave him a big smile and a pat on the shoulder.

Very early the following morning Fred was busy in his workshop. He had sorted out the two sheets of hardboard, all the timber for the 'mekings' of the bed, and had made a wooden frame for the window in which he had inserted a piece of perspex, thinking it would be better than a sheet of glass. 'Little girl can't bust that and cut herself,' he'd thought.

Last night he had 'spoken nicely' to his wife and she had agreed to machine up some little curtains. She had rummaged through the chest of drawers in the spare bedroom and found curtains (with a flowery pattern) that she no longer used. Before Fred left with his boy in the van with the 'mekings' for the bed, the hardboard and the window, he had given his wife the size the little curtains should be.

'You might as well take all these other curtains up with you,' she had said, 'Genty will find a use for them I'm sure.'

Little Nell started to bark and Old John looked up from his seat by the fire. 'Fred an' 'is lad's 'ere, Genty.'

'They'm early birds, baint they my John?' she replied.

It was eight o'clock and Fred's lad – always busy – wanted to deliver the 'mekings' and get off to a job he was busy with.

'Mournin', Mr Lock,' he said as he walked over to the little wagon with the two sheets of hardboard. 'You and me dad's making a good job of this, 'ent you? That's clever how you've used them nut sticks for the bows – well I never!' And then, most unusually, he stopped his rushing about, sat down on the milk churn, and enquired of his father where the bed was to be made. Fred described where and how it was to be, and then thoughtfully said, 'Have you still got them bunk beds in your garage?'

'I have dad, I've been meaning to chuck them out for months now.' With a shout Fred exclaimed, 'There you are, John old mate, we've got us a mattress for the bed!'

Seizing the opportunity of Fred's lad being in a cordial mood, Old John tentatively asked, 'You baint be a-gooin' t'Hur-e-furd soon, like, is yer?'

'I'll be there tomorrow, Mr Lock. Why, do you want something?'

'Well,' started Old John in his best quiet spoken manner, 'yu knows that second-'and shop, dunna yu? Well, what we (and he emphasised WE) wants is a big carpet, like, t'goo over roof, an' we wuz a-thinkin' that that's the very place t'git one, a nice coloured 'un, like.'

'Yes, I reckon that would be the place, Mr Lock, and you'd like me to have a look and get you one, would you?'

'Aar, lad, iffn yu'd a-be so kind as to.'

'How big?'

'Sorta ten foot by fifteen foot, or thurabouts,' Old John replied.

'Leave it to me, Mr Lock, I'll see what I can do, and if I do get one I'll drop it in with the mattress for you, how will that do?'

'I'd be much hubliged, lad, it's of the hutmost himportance.'

With that, Fred's 'boy' leapt from his seat on the churn and resumed his 'busy-busy' distinctive habit.

Old John heard in the distance the church tower clock strike midday. Fred had fitted the hardboard back, cut a hole in it, and fitted the window which appeared to be two, as the 3" x 2" upright was in the middle, and was now nailing battens on a framework fixed at the back of the little wagon for the bed, on which the mattress would lie.

'I'm done, old mate,' he shouted to Old John, 'give us a hand down, will you? Me back's a-killing me.'

'Smell that, Fred? Genty's a-fryin' slices've bacon pudden, come on over t'the fire, man, 'er'll be offended iffn yu dunna a-'ave some.'

He ate it, he liked it, but knew he would suffer later! Stiffly he got up from his seat by the fireside, 'I'll get meself off home now, could do with a little lie down. I was up at 5.30 this morning, you know

– give us a shout when the canvas comes and I'll come up and give a hand to put it on. I've got loads of tintacks in the workshop,' and saying that he made to leave.

Old John stood up too. 'Fred my brother, I dunna a-know what I'd a-do without yu – I thanks yu kindly fur all on yer 'elp,' and he put out his hand and Fred shook it, saying, 'Nay trouble, old mate.'

And Genty said, 'Will yu thank yer missus fur the curtains, they'm lovely Fred, thur's enough t'cover the back wall've the little wagin, and a-mek drapes over the little bed place. *Dordi*! it'll be a picture in thur fur the gal … honest t'God, Fred, I too thanks yer with all on me 'eart, I doos.'

Two days later, Fred's 'boy' arrived with a huge roll of colourful carpet and one of the bunk bed mattresses, carpet on his right shoulder and mattress under his left arm. He slid the carpet off his shoulder and gave a little groan, 'Heavy, that,' he said.

'I cud a-carried that in one 'and when I wuz yer age, lad,' Old John said, looking at him and laughing. And Fred's boy, on this rare occasion, laughed too. Pulling his roll of money from his pocket Old John paid for the carpet, then asked, 'How much fur the mattress an' yer bit've time, lad?'

'Buy us a pint in the pub when I see you in there,' he replied.

Old John gave a smile; he knew that Fred's lad didn't drink, and neither of them had ever been in the local pub. Putting his hand in his pocket he brought out a load of small coinage. ' 'Ere lad, I'm indebted t'yer, at least 'ave a packet've fags on me,' he said and shook Fred's lad's hand.

'You and me dad 'ent going to lift that carpet over that wagon on your own, Mr Lock, when you're ready tell me dad and I'll come up and give you both a heave-ho. Listen now, I must dash, I'm in the middle of a job,' – and he was gone.

Early the following week, Mrs Hughes drove down the track from the farm to the little encampment in her Landrover, to deliver the awaited canvas sheet. Old John settled up the amount owed, then with many 'thank you dear ladys' rushed off to see Fred, leaving Mrs Hughes and Genty alone to discuss womanly matters. Mrs Hughes, ever the romantic, 'oohed and aahed' over the little wagon that was to be Katie's sleeping quarters, then asked, 'But where is the young boy going to sleep?'

'In the kitchen tent,' answered Genty.

'What will he sleep on?' asked Mrs Hughes.

'Why, on the floor, I've a-got plenty've blankets.'

'Come, come, Genty, we cannot have that, I've got a camp bed at home – would you like that for him? Be more comfortable, wouldn't it?'

Genty agreed and gave her more 'thank you my dear ladys'.

'I'll bring it down tomorrow for you,' she said as she drove away.

'It 'ent took them many days to do that cover, John , 'as it?' Fred remarked when Old John informed him that he had the canvas ready to be put on the little wagon.

'I told the dear lady t'a-tell 'um it was hurgent, like,' he said.

'Me and the boy will be up first thing in the morning, John, and I've made something for the inside of the wagon as well, and I'll bring it up with me.'

'What is it?' asked Old John.

'Wait and see,' came the reply from Fred.

Eight o'clock on the dot, Fred and his boy walked over the plank bridge calling out, 'Mournin', let's get at it.'

Fred's boy was carrying two nine-foot-long thin battens, and Fred, with his toolbag over his shoulder, was carrying under his left arm the prettiest little wooden stool imaginable. Old John and Genty's eyes focused straight on it, Genty declaring, 'Oh Fred, that little stool is 'andsome, that it is.'

'Made it for the little girl to have in her wagon, Genty ... look,' and with that he pulled out a little secret drawer. 'She'll like that, won't she? She'll be able to keep her bits of treasures in there, eh?'

Old John was rubbing his rough old hand over it in an admiring fashion. 'You'm a gud 'un, Fred, thank yu, thank yu both fur all on yer 'elp.'

'Come on, let's get this job sorted out, I've got a lot to do today,' Fred's boy said a bit impatiently.

Within a couple of hours they had completed the job. The carpet had been put over the bows, tacked here and there on the two side chock rails and trimmed off. The canvas was put over next, and with big strong Fred's boy tugging on one side and Old John and Fred tugging on the other, they stretched the canvas tight and Fred tacked it along the edge of the chock rails. Then Fred's boy, standing on the churn, wrapped the canvas on the front and back round the rods and tacked it in place, finally cutting the remaining surplus canvas off. Fred picked up the two nine-foot-long thin battens saying, 'We'll nail one of these each side to cover the edge and the tintacks. If a job's worth doing, it's worth doing proper.'

'Me dad always says that, Mr Lock,' Fred's boy said with a laugh, which stunned Old John as Fred's boy was not known to laugh very frequently.

'Hang on, Fred, let me goo an' get a candle,' and Old John rushed over to the kitchen tent. Returning with the candle in his hand he proceeded to rub it all along the bottom edge of the two sides – covering the tintacks and the canvas edge with it; then declared, 'Nail them strips on, Fred, an' the job's a-finished.'

The strips were nailed on but Fred wasn't finished yet. Walking over to the pile of cut off rod ends, he picked one up, then from his toolbag he took a sheet of sandpaper and wrapped it around the rod end.

'What's yer up t'now, Fred?' Old John asked, looking rather puzzled. 'Them chamfers you've cut on the front 3" by 2" upright needs tidying up!' he shouted out. 'If a job's worth doing, it's worth doing proper!'

Old John shook the two men's hands. 'Honest t'God I thanks yu two with all a-me 'eart, I doos, my blessed Lord, yu two is proper genlemuns, an' I's proud t'call yu both dear friends, that I is. Come on over t'the fire an' 'ave a cup've tea.'

'I haven't got time, dad, we must go, I've got to get on with the job I'm doing,' Fred's boy said in his busy-busy manner, 'another time, Mr Lock I'm sure.'

'Yu is as welcome as the flowers in May, lad, thur's alus a welcome t'yer round me fireside any old time've the day or night.'

Fred's boy again laughed; they called out goodbye to Genty and were gone.

That afternoon Genty put the finishing touches to the inside of the little wagon. She pinned some of the pretty curtain material to the back wall, fitted the curtains either side of the window, and made curtain drapes either side of the bed place and tied them back with string. Then she pinned two curtains to hang in the open front and tied those back with string. Meanwhile Old John had cut two pieces of canvas from the old dray cover and fitted them to the front rods to keep any rain out.

' 'Ere yu is, Genty,' he said as he pushed the bunk bed mattress into the little wagon.

'Oh my John, it fits perfectly, that Fred's gud with a bit've wood, that 'e is. Pass us up that dear little stool, man, that's 'e's so kindly med fur the gal.'

Old John handed it up.

'Oh my blessed Lord, my John, 'tis andsome in 'ere,' came from the little interior, 'all we wants now is a bit've carpet fur the floor.'

Katie's little 'accommodation' awaited her. Mrs Hughes had delivered the foldaway camp bed, which was now set up against the back wall of the tent for Little Jimmy to sleep on. Old John lit his pipe, coughed and spat, 'I'll git word t'Maurice t'morrer,' he said.

Chapter 4

Arrival of the Children

'It's a gud job we got that cloth (canvas sheet) on yesterday, my Genty.'

It was a misty rain morning, and Old John and Genty were sitting in the kitchen tent having their breakfast. 'By the looks on it, it'll clear up later on,' Old John again remarked as he finished drinking his third dish of tea.

'Is yu a-gooin' t'see Fred an' ask 'im t'phone Maurice fur yu?' asked Genty.

'Aar, I will later on gal, I dunna a-want t'bother 'im too early, like. 'As yer got that bit've paper with the number on?'

Genty reached in her pinner pocket and produced the paper and handed it to him. Contacting people who had no telephone was a complicated matter amongst Gypsy people. Maurice and Sylvie could contact Addy by telephoning a public phone box that was situated just down the street from the yard in Wolverhampton. Six o'clock on a Sunday evening would be the allocated time for Addy to be waiting in the phone box for their call. She would first contact them by phoning Sylvie's mother and father, who lived in a bungalow on the outskirts of Shrewsbury, and who had a telephone, and ask them to pass the message on for them to phone her at 6.00 p.m. And Old John was now ready to ask Fred if he would kindly telephone Sylvie's mother and father and ask them if they would get a message to Maurice and ask him to come over and see them. It was not that complicated, but it did need working out first, and of course it all took time to organise.

'Come on in, John, I was expecting you,' Fred said, smiling broadly as he opened the back door to Old John's knock. 'You want me to phone up that couple in Shrewsbury and get them to ask your nephew to come over, don't you?'

'My dear blessed Lord, Fred, yu's as sharp as a razor, that yu is!' and Old John returned an even broader smile to his old friend.

'Well you said yesterday as how you'd have to get a message over to them, and the only way I know is for me to phone them. I've done it before for you, haven't I?'

Fred made the call, repeating the words that Old John had told him. 'Mr John Lock asks you kindly if you would be so good as to ask Maurice to come over and see him as soon as is possible, because it's very urgent.'

Shortly before nine o'clock the following morning Nell gave her customary bark and Old John and Genty looked up to see Maurice and Sylvie approaching. Over Maurice's shoulder hung a long coil of thick rope, Sylvie carrying two frilly-edged colourful pillows.

'We knows everything and we are ready to go at the drop of a hat, Uncle John,' Maurice said as he took a seat by the fire. 'Looks as though everything's ready here, then,' he remarked as he threw a glance at the little wagon.

'Aar lad, everything's ready 'ere, me an' Fred's a-done the gal's sleepin' arrangements, an' farmer's wife a-brought a dear little bed fur the lad, like, an' I reckons them pillers (pillows) is fur the *chavvies'*

59

dear little *sherros* (heads), baint they? Yer Aunt Genty looked pleased with 'um,' and he looked over to see the two women disappearing into the tent.

'Is yer tekin' anyone with yer when yu *jalls* over t'Wolverhampton?'

'Me and Sylvie's going, Uncle John, but I'll ask Sylvie's brother-in-law if he'll come as well, I think it might be advisable.'

Old John gave a chuckle, coughed and spat in the fire, declaring, 'What, Black Bonzo?'

Black Bonzo was the nickname of Sylvie's elder sister's husband, who had been christened 'Fusilier', his father having been a sergeant who spent many years serving in the Royal Welsh Fusiliers, but 'Black Bonzo' was the name he had answered to from a small child. He was a big dark-complexioned powerful man, of immense strength, the sort of man you wanted as a friend, not an enemy! But underneath his rugged appearance there was a gentle giant, quiet and well mannered, except on the rare occasion when someone upset him.

Standing up from his seat by the fireside Maurice picked up the large coil of thick rope, saying, 'Where we going to fix this, Uncle John?'

'What's it fur, lad?' Old John enquired, rather puzzled.

'A swing for the *chavvies*, Uncle John, which tree's best?'

Maurice followed Old John to the rear of the tent and they both stood looking at the branches on the trees. Over to the right, a good distance from the 'washing fire', stood a sturdy ash tree with a good sized branch coming out almost horizontally.

'That 'un, lad. Think yu can shin up t'that branch?'

'No bother, Uncle John,' came the reply.

Maurice securely tied the rope to the branch, then like an acrobat descended the rope to the ground.

'Cut us a piece for a handle, Uncle John.'

Doing as Maurice had asked, Old John took his bow saw and disappeared into the wood, a few minutes later returning with a clean branch about two feet long, which Maurice fixed to the rope about five feet from the ground. The end of the rope he made into a loop so the children could put a foot into it.

'They'll love that,' he said, and Old John nodded and gave him a smile, adding, 'Come on over an' 'ave a *dik* (look) at the little "accommodation".'

Maurice was impressed, as had been Sylvie. 'You and the old *mush* 'as made a good job of it, 'ent you Uncle John? And Aunt Genty has made it as pretty as a picture inside, I declare she has, it only wants a nice rug on the floor – and we've got just the one for it at home. I'll chuck it in the motor when we get back, then I shan't forget about it.'

Genty and Sylvie had made tea and they called the two men over to the fire.

' 'Ow soon can yu collect the *chavvies*, then?' asked Old John amidst the day-to-day talk. A silence fell and Maurice, looking into the fire, said rather shyly – for in all the years Addy had been gone he had never once mentioned her to his Uncle John, or that he and Sylvie had always kept in contact with her – 'Well, Uncle John, in a few days' time it will be Sunday and Sylvie here will phone Wolverhampton … so I reckon we'll go over and collect them Monday or Tuesday. That be alright for you two?'

Old John's little black eyes narrowed, then with a smile he said, 'Aar, that'll do lad, that'll do jest fine.'

It was the following Tuesday that Maurice and Sylvie set off early in the morning to collect Little Jimmy and Katie. Although Maurice was inwardly worried as to the outcome of their arrival in Wolverhampton, he jokingly remarked to Sylvie's brother-in-law Black Bonzo, who was sitting in the front seat of the motor car, 'It's a good job I've got you riding shotgun!'

Addy had sworn the two children to secrecy over their departure – no one in the yard knew. She had packed two small bags with clothes in readiness, and these stood in the doorway of the caravan. Maurice pulled up in the street opposite the entrance to the yard, and Sylvie got out, the two men remaining in the car, ready to leap out if trouble did occur.

On the telephone Addy has described the caravan and where in the yard it was situated. With confidence Sylvie strode into the yard and heaved a sigh of relief; no one was about and no dog barked. Her quick eyes focused on the caravan and she made straight for it. The door was open and she saw the two small bags – it was the right one. She walked straight in without knocking, and there stood Addy, who she had not seen for so many years. 'Oh my dear blessed Lord, gal, what's happened to you?' she thought, but did not say. Instead she threw her arms round her, giving her a big hug and whispered, 'It'll be alright now, gal, I'll phone you tonight at six o'clock.' Then, picking up the two little bags, said to the children, 'Come on quick, with me.'

Addy, in floods of tears, quickly hugged and kissed them then sat down on the sofa bench with head bowed, not wanting to see them go.

'Come on, quick,' repeated Sylvie, and Little Jimmy and Katie, with wet eyes, obediently followed her out of the yard to the waiting car, where the three of them squeezed into the back seat. Maurice hit the accelerator pedal and they were off.

No further mention will be made, observing the wishes of Jim (Little Jimmy) and Katie, of the yard in Wolverhampton, where life was not always a bed of roses.

As was to be expected, the children remained more or less silent on the return journey. Sylvie gave them lots of reassurances as to their mother's welfare. 'Your mammy is going to see the doctor tomorrow, and she's going to a lovely place to have a rest, and the doctors will make her better, and when she is, your Uncle Maurice here is going to get a nice trailer for you all in the same yard as us, and we'll all be happy together, won't we?'
Maurice and Black Bonzo were telling them how lovely their grandparents were, and how they'll love to stay with them, and Maurice proudly adding, 'I've made you a swing off a big tree!'

The other side of Bridgnorth Maurice pulled in to a small roadside café. 'I bet you two's hungry, 'ent you?' he said, as he turned round and gave the children a big grin.
'I is,' said Black Bonzo.
'He's always hungry, kids, he can eat for England, and Wales an' all, that he can. That's why he's the size he is.'
Katie gave a little giggle, but Little Jimmy remained silent.

The arrival at the encampment of their elderly grandparents and meeting them for the first time was a great culture shock for Little

Jimmy and Katie, as though they had been transported to a different period of time – which in fact they had been. Their mother had taught them certain aspects of her Romany upbringing, but they were certainly not prepared for what greeted them. They were, after all, town kids; they had never before seen food cooked on a stick fire, never seen a square-framed kitchen tent or a horse-drawn wagon.

And it was Old John and Genty's Square-Bow wagon that they first enquired about, after Genty had taken their little bags and shown them where they were to sleep.

'Do you and Granfer live in there?' Katie had asked, as she pointed a finger at the colourful vehicle.

'That's where we sleeps, gal, yu could say it's our 'ome, but I looks upon that as a-bein' me 'ome,' and she pointed a finger at the stick fire, around which Old John, Maurice and Sylvie and Black Bonzo were sitting. They of course wanted to see inside. Genty led the way up the steps and opened the door, entered the wagon and sat down on the seat on the right hand side opposite the stove. Little Jimmy and Katie entered, eyes wide open in amazement at the comfortable and pretty interior, with the smell of lavender polish in the air.

Light came in from a small window at the back and one small window either side, from which hung frilly lace curtains. The whole of the rear was taken up by the old couple's bed, which stood about two and a half feet from the floor and looked really comfortable; a silk eiderdown covered it and folded each side were Welsh blankets topped with a pillow with frilly edges. Below the bedrail were two thin drawers and below them two cut glass mirrored cupboard doors depicting vases of flowers. Genty pointed out that the big cupboard was known as the *chavvies' woodrus* (children's bed) – 'but you'm t'big t'sleep in thur now.'

On the right hand side under the window was a chest of drawers, then a seat (where Genty was sitting) and in the corner next to the doorway a curved corner cupboard with a large glass door in which Genty displayed her best china. The children sat down on the bench seat in between the black polished range stove and the bedplace, and looked towards the doorway. Built next to it was a long thin cupboard with a cut glass mirror door, again depicting an elongated vase of flowers, which was used as a wardrobe. Everything in the wagon twinkled. On top of the stove were two highly polished copper kettles with acorn knob lids; even the galvanised stove pipe that went straight up and through the roof was polished and shone like silver. Around the top of the pipe hung a frilly rose pattern valance of the same material that, behind the slats, lined the roof. The chest of drawers was covered in a white lace-edged cloth on which was displayed a large silver bowl; either side of it stood two old fashioned vases depicting hunting scenes. Linoleum covered the floor, with a good quality Kidderminster rug on top.

Katie was the first to speak. 'I loves it in here, Granny, it's *kushti*, 'ent it? And them plates is so pretty, 'ent they?' and she pointed a finger to the spindle-fronted shelf that went across the back of the wagon, over the window, where Genty had a row of colourful plates displayed.

'And these is nice and all,' and she put her little hand on one of the plates that were pushed between the bed and the bedrail. 'Don't they get bust when you and Granfer gets into bed?' she asked.

Genty, with a laugh, replied, 'I teks 'um out afore we gets in thur, gal, otherwise they'd a-get bust, that they 'ud.'

Little Jimmy, at ten years of age, was 'the little man', and had no interest in this talk of pretty plates. 'I wants to see what the outside of this wagon is all about, Granny,' he said, as he got up from his seat next to the stove and went out of the wagon. Black Bonzo's eyes were on him as he came down the steps and started to 'poke around' the outside of the wagon.

'Hey up! Uncle John, what's the *chavvi* up to? You'll have to keep your *yoks* (eyes) on him I'm betting.'

Old John sauntered over to the wagon and little Jimmy crawled out from underneath it.

'Yu baint a-never sin a wagin afore, 'as yer lad?'

'No I 'ent, Granfer,' Little Jimmy replied, 'I likes it though. What's that little brass wheel on the front for?'

'Pull them old sacks offn them two back wheels an' I'll a-show yer, lad,' Old John said with a smile.

'Why's these sacks on here anyway, Granfer?' Little Jimmy asked as he pulled the sacks off.

'I keeps 'um on the wheels, lad, an' chucks a bucket've water over 'um every so often in the summer, an' that keeps 'um from a-dryin' out, like. Now come 'ere an' I'll a-show yer what that dear little wheel doos.'

Old John spun the small brass wheel that was fitted to the nearside of the footboard, and told Little Jimmy to watch the brake blocks that moved up and down either side onto the back wheels. 'That's the brake on the wagin,' he said, 'and iffn yu looks 'ere – (and he walked round to the middle of the nearside) – this iron trough ahangin' 'ere on this chain is what we calls a drag-shoe, an' this is used as 'nother sort've brake, see 'ere?' And Old John took the heavy iron shoe off its hook and put it in front of the nearside back wheel. 'Now, when yu's about t'goo down a steep 'ill yu puts it thur, an' then the wheel goos inter the shoe, an' the chain wunt a-let it goo no further, an' the wheel a-skids all the way down the 'ill, like. Now yu put it back on the 'ook, lad, an' mind yu dunna a-burn yer fingers.' And Old John gave a little chuckle, 'Yu see, lad, iffn that drag-shoe 'ad a-bin skidded all the way down a 'ill it 'ud be very 'ot, 'uddent it? An' when yer pick it up yer 'as t'be careful, like, otherwise yu'd a-burn yer fingers.'

Little Jimmy was happy with the 'man's talk'. 'What's this box for, Granfer?' he asked as they walked to the back of the wagon. Fitted underneath was a box with two doors, with scrolls painted on the panels. Old John knelt down and opened one of the doors. 'This is what we calls the kettle box, lad, some folk a-calls it a pan-box. We dunna use it now since we've a-bin 'ere, like, but when we wuz a-travellin' yer Granny kept a pot or two in thur an' a bit've food, like.' He reached into the box and pulled out a round tin with a piece of stick protruding from the top. '*Dik* at this, lad, this is me axle grease tin. It's a-what I used t'grease the axles of the wheels with.' He pushed it back into the box and closed the door, remarking, 'I baint a-used that in many a yer.'

Sticking out horizontally from the back of the wagon was a rack covered by a canvas sheet that was fitted just under the window and came down and covered it completely. Jumping up from his kneeling position Little Jimmy bumped his head on the underside of it. 'What's this for, Granfer?' he asked, rubbing his head with his hand.

'This lad is what we calls the cratch,' and he pulled the canvas sheet to one side to reveal it. On one side was a large bulging hessian sack.

'What's in there?' asked Little Jimmy.

'That's me 'arness, lad – an' I baint a-used that fur many a yer neither, a gud set an' all it is, Giddin've London set, 'tis all red morroca an' 'oss shoe buckles, an' plaited reins – I 'ad a man 'ere t'other day a-tryin' t'buy it, but I dussn't a-want t'sell it, like. We used to carry everythin' an' anythin' on this old cratch 'ere, like, even an old *treader* (bicycle) I used t'shove up on thur.' With a wistful look in his eyes Old John pulled the canvas sheet back down over the cratch, and they walked round to the front of the wagon.

Walking up the steps he removed one of the polished brass-fronted lamps that sat in brackets either side of the doorway. 'Now I knows yu'll find this interestin', lad, *dik* at this.' And Old John pulled out the long stem from the bottom of the lamp which revealed the top of a coiled spring. Putting his index finger on it he pushed the spring up and down. 'Now doos yu know what that's fur?'

'No, Granfer.'

'Well I'll a-tell yer,' Old John said with a smile. 'Inside them lamps is candles, an' as they burns down this spring a-pushes 'um up, like. A few times yer Granny an' me's 'ad 'um lit up when we wuz a-gooin' somewhur an' a-got caught out with darkness a-comin' on us, but most times when we wuz pulled up somewhur I'd a-tek 'um outa the brackets an' a-put 'um in the wagin in case the *muskro* (policeman) comed t'us t'shift – an' then I'd a-tell 'im I cuddna until the marnin' 'cause I 'addent any lamps, like.' And Old John let out a loud laugh, coughed and spat. 'We used t'ave a little red 'un an' all, that 'ung on the cratch at the back, but I sold that yers a-goo t'a hantique man 'cause we never a-used it, like, but yer Granny 'uddent part with these, no 'er 'uddent, she loves a-polishin' 'um.'

Never had the children run wild in the woods or splashed about in a brook. And never had they had the strict discipline that their grandfather handed out to them. Jim Lock, now no longer called 'Little Jimmy' as he was when a child, has requested that certain aspects of those first few days be omitted from the story, but a little can, however, be mentioned.

At first the children were subdued, then they ran wild; Katie cutting her legs badly on bramble thorns. Little Jimmy playing cowboys, riding his imaginary horse tried to spur the steed into jumping the brook, but did not reach the grassy bank on the other side and landed up in the middle of the brook, soaked and with a badly grazed knee. Old John and Genty loved to see them running wild, but on occasions they both answered their grandparents back in a cheeky manner, Little Jimmy using a few swear words. This neither of them approved of and amidst screams and tears the children felt the hard hand of Old John. His father has been described as a charming, modest yet knowledgeable man, who was known throughout the borders as 'Gentleman' Lock, and was a man who had never been known to utter a swear word, and Old John was the same. 'Me faarthur 'uddent 'ave it, an' I baint a-gooin' t'ave it neither,' were the words he scolded the children with, as he dished out the punishment.

Genty fussed around them in a grandmotherly way, giving them hugs and kisses and declaring to Old John, 'The dear blesseds, they'm jest like dear little fox cubs a-scamperin' about, that they is, God love 'um.'

It took time for them to adjust; they missed their mother, but after a short period thoughts of their past home slowly dwindled and they settled down to the daily routine and lifestyle. They were both exceptionally bright children and had inherited, thankfully, more of their mother's genes than their father's, and both of them had their mother's facial features and colouring.

Life here in the country was so exciting for them, they had learned to respond to their grandfather's whistle, and were now absorbing Romani words that their grandparents used, and were putting them into their conversation, much to the pleasure of the old couple.

Katie loved her little wagon (which Old John had pulled alongside their own, so that she would feel more secure at night). 'It's me little nest,' she had christened it. Little Jimmy acted the tough little man and was quite content to sleep on the camp bed in the tent. 'I 'ent scared of being in there alone at night,' he had said, but secretly, for a while, he was – pulling the blankets up over his head when he got in his bed at night.

He had formed a bond with Nell, and the dog had formed a bond with him, and when off the chain followed him about incessantly. And now he had formed a bond with his grandfather, who he was beginning to respect and who was quickly becoming his hero.

'Granfer knows everything, don't he, Katie? He must be the cleverest man in the whole world,' he had said, to which Katie had replied, 'I loves Granny's cooking.'

The old couple's worries were now lessened; the children had settled in well. Love and discipline, discipline and love had paid off.

CHAPTER 5

JUST ONE SUMMER

This chapter, consisting of sixteen stories, deals with the daily life the children experienced in that one summer of 1961 – their education into the old fashioned Romany ways of their grandparents. The daily happenings, the characters that they met (now all sadly long gone), the stories that were told around the fire in the evening time, a few of the songs that were sung, and a few of their grandfather's fiddle tunes. An education far removed from *gaujo* society of today that was to be their salvation and serve them well for the rest of their lives.

Love, respect, discipline, courtesy, civility, a sense of morality, resourcefulness (sometimes in a hostile environment a small untruth has to be told to some *dinili gauji* [silly non-Gypsy] in order to survive and put food in the belly), and 'laughter', all being the main components.

The final story, 'The Ancients and the Blood-Red Beads' reflects another aspect: old Black Britty utters the words 'Always be proud of what you is.' That is something that Jim (Little Jimmy) and Katie certainly are.

BILLY SMITH AND HIS GRINDING BARROW

'*Mush vellin'* (man coming), Granfer,' called out Little Jimmy. He was playing in the brook when he looked up to see a stranger approaching.

'It's Billy Smith! Well my blessed Lord! Put the kettle on, gal,' Old John shouted to Genty, 'Lena's Billy's 'ere.'

Little Jimmy's eyes followed the stranger as he made his way over the brook on the plank bridge.

' 'Ello son,' he said, and made to 'square up', giving Little Jimmy a pat on his cheek.

'He's a comical *mush*,' Little Jimmy thought, 'I wonder why he's got that big overcoat on? It's not cold today.'

' 'Ow's yu goin' on, brother?' Old John greeted him. 'We 'eard yu an' the missus wuz in a *kair* (house) over Welshpool.'

'You're lookin' well, brother,' came the reply. 'Aar, me and my Selina's in a council house now. She likes it, but it's a-stiflin' me, my John.'

'What's yer a-doin' all the ways out 'ere then?' Old John asked quizzingly. 'Come on over t'the fire, *mush*, Genty's got the kettle a-boilin'.'

Billy put his hand on Old John's shoulder and with a smile said, 'I'm out with me barrer agin.'

'My blessed Lord, yu baint a-pushed it all the way from Welshpool, 'as yer?'

'No, man,' replied Billy, 'me son's brought me back to these parts in his van – I've been out a few days now.'

'Whur's yer barrer to?' asked Old John.

'Left it just inside the gate behind the 'edge so's it can't be seen, yu can't trust folks these days, my John, and I've a-got all me bits of *covvels* (things) tied on it.'

'Bring it over 'ere, man, an' bide with us, yu knows yer welcome.'

'That's kind of you, my John – but I wants to stop in all me old places – you'll understand, *mush*. I'll *jall* up the lane later and *atch* by that little copse, like I did years ago.'

Katie and Little Jimmy had gathered round the fire and Genty was handing out tea.

'Nice to 'ave tinned milk again,' remarked Billy. 'We 'as the cows' stuff now, milkman brings bottles up to the house an' all. These *chavvies* is your gal's, 'ent they?' (He was careful not to speak Addy's name, knowing the old couple would be upset by the mention of it.) 'I 'eard they was a-stoppin' with you. You'm Little Jimmy and you'm Katie, 'ent you?'

They both nodded, their dark eyes studying Billy the Grinder. Billy was in his sixties, on the short side, his face was round, with big sideboards coming nearly down to his chin. His hair was greased back and unlike Old John, who always wore his neck scarf, Billy wore a neck-tie, the collar of his shirt looking a bit grimy. His old cord trousers were crumply but were half hidden by his enormous overcoat. Billy was again out plying his trade as a knife grinder round the small border villages. In the late afternoon he'd pull up in some secluded spot (and just up the lane from Old John and Genty was one of his favourite old places). He'd tie a piece of canvas sheet to the side of his barrow, pulling it out like a tent and folding the remainder back to the barrow to make a groundsheet for him to lie on. This he would sleep under. He'd then light his little fire, boil his can of water for tea, and fry a bit of bacon or meat which he'd eat with a big chunk of bread. He'd then sit by the fire and smoke until wrapping himself in his blanket (fully clothed – even his boots were kept on) and settling down for the night.

Early next morning he would re-kindle the fire, make his tea, eat a chunk of bread and cheese and then wash up, which consisted of 'a shave'. Billy was always clean-shaven – he'd told his son, many years ago, 'you can't do business with a dirty face – you don't want the dear people to be *a-trashed* (frightened) of you when you knocks on their doors, now do you?'

Little Jimmy kept staring at the big long overcoat Billy was wearing. Why would he wear such a thing on such a warm day? His 'wondering' was answered when Old John remarked, 'That's a *kushti chukka* (good coat) yu'm a-wearin', Billy, must'v belonged t'a real *rai* (gent) – it's proper tweed is that, who'd yu *mong* (beg) it off? We wuz sick've seein' yu in that old black 'un!'

'I was a-callin' over Acton Scott day afore yesterday,' Billy began, 'and I *monged* it off'n this *bori rai* (big gentleman) – and when I sez a *bori rai* I means a real *bori rai. Dordi!* a proper gentleman he wuz – musta cost some *luvva* (money), eh my John?'

'*Owli,*' came the reply, 'that's quality, tis that, yu wunna get cold a-sleepin' in that, *mush.*'

Genty was busy preparing a corned beef stew and asked Billy to stop a while and join them in the meal, which he accepted graciously and then said, 'Afore I forgets, my John, I "called" a butcher's shop in Oswestry a bit back, our Joe took me in his van. Must 'ave bin one of me half *dinilo* (foolish) days 'cause they sharpens their own, don't they? Anyhows, this butcher, he sez to me: "You don't make skewers, does you, 'cause we could do with some?" I don't, I sez, but I knows a man who can, when I sees him next I'll a-ask him.'

'Do you want a-do some for the *mush*, John?'

'Aar, I'd do 'im a gross or two; Maurice could drop 'um in t'im, 'e calls round that way. Tell yu what, Billy, we'll all 'ave a stroll up the lane later this evenin', see 'ow yu'm settlin' in, like. There's a *kushti* elder in that copse grown nice an' straight, I'll bring saw up an' cut a chunk – might as well strike while the iron's 'ot … afore I forgets.'

'Can we go and see your barrow, Uncle Billy?' the children asked politely.

'Sure you can, kids, but don't you go a-playing with it now – t'would break me heart if anything happened to it.'

'Don't yu two be long,' their grandmother called out. '*Hobben* wunna be more'n a 'alf 'our.'

The children ran up the field eager to see this mysterious thing called a 'barrer'. And there it stood, just inside the gate behind the hedge, hidden from the lane. Little Jimmy and Katie stopped in their tracks and looked at this glorious thing in amazement.

'I never seen nothing like it, have you Jimmy?'

'Never!' he replied. 'Painted up nice, 'ent it?'

'Look at all that shiny brass,' said Katie, 'I wouldn't want to polish that!'

Billy's Grinding Barrow was a two-wheel push-barrow, easier to get about with than the old-fashioned one-wheel 'kick up' barrow. It stood on two bicycle wheels, a third one, without tyre and inner tube, being used for the drive wheel to turn the grindstones (a chunk of lead wrapped round the spokes gave it more drive). It was pushed by two handles either side, and across these was a board used for a seat, your feet going onto two treadles that chains were attached to, that went up to the crank of the drive wheel. To conceal this wheel was a fancy cover with the words 'Grinder' painted either side. Billy had spent some time making his barrow and had chamfered all the wood with his peg knife and painted it very colourful – adding old brass knobs all over the cover and sides.

'Look, he's got a dear little pot and frying pan hung up inside, and this must be all his bits of *covvels* he was talking about.'

Little Jimmy poked the long round parcel wrapped in canvas that was tied across the seat. Just then they heard their grandfather's whistle and hurried back to sample Genty's corned beef stew.

After the meal, Billy thanked Genty, sat and had a smoke with Old John and together they talked of 'private' matters. The afternoon had flown by and Billy said, 'Reckon I'll *jall* on up that *bitta drom* (little lane) and get meself *atched* (stopped) up for the *rarti* (night),' and with that he got up from the fire and, looking at Little Jimmy and Katie, said, 'You two be good now – and look after these two old *bengs* (devils) now, won't you?' And with a chuckle he was on his way.

'We'll see yu a bit later,' called out Old John.

After Genty had done the dishes, with the help of Katie, who was now expected to do woman's work, they chained up Nell, and then sauntered up the lane to where Billy was '*atched* up'.

'Thur's a pretty sight, my Genty – been a long time since Billy wer *atched* by that ash tree. *Dik* at that, *chavvies*, yu might never a-see another sight like that.'

Billy had got his canvas sheet secured to the barrow. He'd cut a hazel rod about seven feet long and fixed this on the top side, then tied the sheet to it which then gave him ample space for his night's accommodation, and was seated cross-legged by a tiny smokeless fire, the little pot by its side.

'That's a dear little *yog* (fire) he got, Granfer, why don't he make it bigger?' Little Jimmy asked.

'My son, that *yog* is big enough fer 'is needs, an' it dunna give off no smoke t'bring *gauji foki* round inquisitively,' replied Old John.

'It's *kushti* 'ere, ent it, *mush*?' Billy said as he raised himself up from the ground. '*Dordi!* there's some *shushis* (rabbits) about. Makes me mouth water just *a-dikin* (looking) at 'um.'

Billy sitting quietly by his little fire had observed the many rabbits chomping their way along the verge, not bothering about his presence.

'I see you brought the bow saw, where's that elder tree, my John?' I'll *jall* with yu and give yu a hand.'

Leaving Genty and the children squatting round the fire they disappeared into the copse, Old John leading the way.

' 'Ere 'tis, Billy!'

And Old John stood before a lovely straight-grained elder.

'If I cuts it just about thur, that'll do.'

And Old John proceeded to saw through the trunk which was about eight inches in diameter. It came crashing down and then he sawed off a piece about three feet long.

'That's more'n enough fur us, brother,' he said.

Billy looked a bit concerned. 'Farmer won't mind then?'

'*Kekka* (no),' Old John replied. 'No one ever comes in 'ere, an' any old 'ows, Farmer is a *kushti mush*, *koms* (likes) us 'e duz, yu knows? We can do no wrong in his *yoks* (eyes). *Dordi!* 'e's a *kushti mush* – an' so wuz 'is faarther.'

They made their way back to Billy's *atchin tan*, Old John with his arm through the saw and over his shoulder, the elder log under his other arm. After sitting chatting by the little fire for some time, Genty said, 'It's a-time fer these *chavvies* t'be in *woodrus* (bed), we ought t'*jall* on, my John.'

'I shan't see you in the morning,' Billy said, 'I'm *jallin'* on up this way,' and he pointed up the lane. Grass grew in the centre of the narrow lane as hardly any traffic used it.

'I loves these old lanes,' Billy said, 'it's our bit o' country, ain't it?'

They bade goodnight and Old John and Genty and the children sauntered back home. As they got near they could hear Nell barking. 'Summat's up – someone's about.' Old John's voice sounded worried. Hurrying on, they could see an old blue Commer van parked in the lane by the gate into the field.

'Wonder who that is?' said Old John.

Just then a figure appeared on the other side of the gate. It was Billy's son, Joe.

'Ave yer sin me dad, Uncle John?' he asked. 'I've bin all over the place lookin' fur 'im.'

'Aye lad, we 'ave, we just left 'im up the lane.'

'Thank God,' he replied, 'me mam's been took bad and put into hospital. Our Mary's with her and she's askin' for him.'

Genty, very shocked, said, ''Ospital, oh! my dear blessed Selina! What's up with 'er, lad?'

'It's her chest again, they says it's the fags,' Joe blurted out.

'Thur now, it's they boughten fags what's a-done it. I's sin it afore, lad – yer dad's just up yonder, go quick now, lad.' Genty's voice sounding urgent. Joe jumped into his motor and with a cloud of smoke coming from the exhaust, was gone. Genty's eyes turned to John. 'They boughten fags, my John, that's wot's a-done fer Billy's Selina.'

'Nar – never in this world, baccer never done me no 'arm,' replied Old John, as he coughed and spat in the hedge, 'it's that 'ouse what's a-done fur the dear poor 'ummon.'

The following morning Old John and the children walked through the wood, along the edge of a field and came out onto the little lane with the grass growing in the centre.

'Joe's old van must'a bin the fust motor up this old lane fur years, it's a pretty old place baint it? *Dik* 'ere, this is whur Billy 'ad 'is bit've *yog* last evenin'.' And Old John pointed to an area of flattened grass under the overhanging branches of a hazel bush.

'You can't really see where the fire was, Granfer, he's stamped it all down and put grass over it,' Little Jimmy was examining it closely.

'*Owli*,' came the reply. 'Billy's an old-fashioned *mush*, 'is dad wuz the same, when they shifted 'e alus stamped the fire out an' put grass over it, thought it'd 'ide whur they'd a-stopped, but *dordi*, anyones can see whur yu've a-stopped – but that's what 'e did an' that's what 'e thought.'

As they walked on down the lane Katie remarked, 'Billy's barrer's pretty, 'ent it, Granfer? Has he always done grinding?'

'Aar, 'e 'as an' all, so did 'is dad – 'e 'ad a proper built barrer, big wooden wheels it 'ad. 'E must've a-pushed that barrer all over Worcestershire, Shropshire an' a lot've Wales an' all. Nice old *mush* he wer, 'im an' 'is missus, Old Lena, is a-buried down thur in Bromyurd (Bromyard).'

'Does he only sharpen knives, Granfer?' asked Little Jimmy.

'Lad, that man can sharpen anythin', anythin' at all. Knives, scissors, axes, choppers, brushin'-'ooks, lawn mowers – yu name it, an' Billy'll sharpen it. An' 'e doos a good job an' all. Goos back t'the same 'ouses 'e's a-called afore an' gets more *booty* (work) from the *foki*. 'E's a good old *mush* an' most of the *gaujos* likes 'im; 'e's alus polite t'um, an' 'e makes 'um laugh with the stories 'e tells 'um – aar, they likes Billy with 'is big long overcoat. Well, most of 'um doos. 'E's alus a-worn a long overcoat, never sin 'im without one.'

'What do you mean "most people" likes Billy?' Katie asked with a frown.

'Well gal, some people likes us an' some people dunna like us. I remembers yers agoo, we wuz up Montgomery way, we wuz a-stoppin' up this dear little lane with Billy an' Selina. 'E wuz a-callin' this village with 'is barrer, an' my Genty wuz a-callin' the 'ouses in the same village with 'er basket've pegs I'd a-made. Any old 'ow, I'm a-sittin' on this little wall a-waitin' fur my Genty, all peaceful like I wuz, just a-sat thur smokin' me pipe when I *diks* all these *chavvies* around Billy, tauntin' 'im they wuz, shoutin': "Give us a tune, mister." Afore I can a-do anythin' up comes yer Granny a-shoutin' at these brazen *chavvies*. Well, they turns on 'er a-shoutin', "Dirty Gyppo" an' "Gyppo, Gyppo, lives in a tent, can't afford t'pay no rent." Then these women comes out an' a-starts on yer Granny.

81

Well now, afore I can get over t'um yer Granny is a-cursin' 'um an' all! I 'eard one of 'um say she'd a-call the police! *Jall on, jall on,* I'm *a-penin'* (saying) an' still yer Granny is a-cursin' 'um. I got 'er under the arm an' I'm a-draggin' 'er up the street followin' Billy an' still 'er's a-cursin' 'um. None on us ever went to that village agin – but I did 'ear tell that some've 'um *foki* 'ad 'ad some bad luck.'

A long drawn out *Doooordi!* came from Katie. 'Can me Granny really put curses on people, Granfer?'
'I dunna know if she can or iffn she canna,' replied Old John, 'but some funny things 'as a-'appened t'people that's upset 'er.'
That evening, before the children went to bed, Katie, who'd been thinking of this all day, said, 'Granny, can you really put curses on people?'
'Oh my dear child, whatsoever put that in yer dear little 'ead?' came the reply.
'Tell 'um what yer dad told yu about yer old Granny when yu wuz all down Eve-e-shum (Evesham) way all on them yers agoo, my Genty.'
'No, I dunna a-like to, my John.'
'Goo on, 'ummon, *chavvies*'ll like it,' urged Old John.

And so Genty began her story: 'Well now, we wuz all down Eve-e-shum a-pulled on this old farm. I wer only a young gal at the time. Every year we pulled on t'this farm fur the pickin', like. We 'ad done since the Lord knows when. There wuz a few other families pulled in too, but as usual we alus liked t'stop by ourselves. Me old gran is with us – that's yer great-great-gran I'm a-talkin' about. Well now, we wuz at the end've the pickin' an' me old gran wuz a-doing *kushti* with the townspeople a-doin' 'er *durrakin* (fortune-telling); some

82

'ouses she wuz a-goin' back to week arter week a-weavin' 'er magic. Farmer seemed a nice old *mush* an' we knew we wuz alus alright t'shift from thur when we liked. Well now, me old gran 'ad a-got these *gaujies* a-eatin' out-a the palm've 'er 'and, an' 'er wuz a-takin' some *luvva*, I can tell yu. She'd got these *gaujies* all lined up fer weeks t'come, a-weavin' 'er old spells, a-reckonin' we could bide whur we wuz fer several weeks t'come. Well now, this one mornin' she walks past me dad, who's a-talkin' t'the farmer. "Mornin' Granny," says 'e. "Hey, Granny, is it true that you people can put curses on people?"

"Curses?" sez me old gran. "Oh my dear blessed man, don't be so silly – curses indeed!"

'Well now, later that mornin' me gran's a-talkin' t'me dad, an' she 'appens t'say, "What did the Farmer want with yu this mornin'?"

"He came t'say as we've all got t'shift tomorrer mornin', as some a-them young lads over yonder 'as a-bin up t'mischief an' a-given 'im a load've mouth."

"Shift in the mornin'?" says me gran. "What about all me lovely *gaujies* I'm *a-durrakin* in the town? That farmer is a proper *beng*, 'e is … I shall burn a bit've salt fur 'im tonight!"

'Well now, that's one've the stories about me old gran, she wer only a little 'ummon, smoked a dear little clay pipe, 'er face was as black as that *kavvi* (kettle) over thur an' she 'ad these little black *yoks* (eyes), all snakified they woz.'

'Did burning salt do anything to the farmer, Granny?' Katie asked, after an intake of breath.

'Well now, when we went back to that farm the next yer the farmer was all a-shrivelled up an' 'e wuz a-walkin' with a stick, honest t'God 'e wuz, an' I'll a-tell yu summat else. They young lads as was brazen t'the farmer never did no good with 'umselves, they alus seemed t'ave bad luck. Now *jall* on an' get in them blankets. Curses! oh my dear Lord, dunna yu a-worry about such things, there baint nothin' in this world that can 'arm you two – you'm "special", like.'

Maurice turned up a week later, he'd 'called' round Craven Arms and a few surrounding villages for scrap metal and his lorry was well loaded up. 'I'll have a good 'weigh-in' tomorrow,' he said quietly to Uncle John as he sat drinking tea round the fire. Maurice was never one to boast blatantly, but he was well pleased with his day's work. 'I saw Billy's Joe the other day and he said to tell you that his mam was out of hospital and back home – they put her on some pills or summat and gave her a 'puffer' thing so's she can get her breath, like. His dad said to tell you he'll be back up that dear little lane next year.'

Poor old Selina outlived Billy – he died that winter. He never did get to *atch* up his pretty little lane, with the rabbits and foxes. Billy was buried in his overcoat and after the funeral, Joe burnt the Grinding Barrow.

A Wet Day – and Flower Making

It was one of those 'Border' days – fine misty rain … 'miserable old weather' as Old John called it. Last night, before going to bed, he had placed the old piece of corrugated iron over the outside fire, propping it at an angle against the kettle-iron, to keep the fireplace dry.

As usual, he was always up first to get the fire going and get the kettle on for tea. This morning he had lit the Queenie stove in the tent and was sitting waiting for the kettle to boil. A murmur came from under the colourful Welsh blanket. 'Yu can bide whur yu'm to fer a bit longer, lad, I'm a-mekin' the *meski* (tea) and yu can 'ave a cup in yer *woodrus t'sarla* (bed this morning).' Little Jimmy rolled over in his bed and a muffled little voice said, 'Thanks, Granfer.'

The tea was made, and Old John poured a dish for Genty and took it up into the wagon. 'Drizzly old weather, gal, it's in fur the day,' he said in a mournful voice. 'Gloomy old weather' always made him gloomy. Next he took Katie a cup, and said, 'Bide whur yu'm to, gal, until yu smells the bacon.' Little Jimmy was sitting on the edge of his bed, smothered in the huge Welsh blanket, with just his little face peering out, when Old John re-entered the tent.
'Nice and warm in here, Granfer.'
'*Owli*, lad, it'll be a day in 'ere fur us all,' replied Old John as he handed Little Jimmy his cup of tea. 'Reckon I'll get them flowers

done t'day and outa the way, yer Granny told that dear lady in the market as she'd take 'um in this comin' Thursday.'

'Lucky we cut the sticks yesterday, wasn't it Granfer?'

'Aar lad, I could a-smell this bit've weather a-comin' in. Get yerself up now, yer Granny'll be 'ere in a minute.'

Doing as his grandfather asked, Little Jimmy was up and his blankets were folded with the pillow on top. He then ran down to the brook and splashed water on his hands and face. Old John smiled as he watched him, ' 'E's turning into a proper Gypsy boy,' he said to himself. 'I'll send 'im off t'get some privet stems a bit later on, 'e'll like that.'

Genty was now up and 'busying' herself in the tent. As Little Jimmy ran in she handed him a bowl of hot water and said, ' 'Ere, lad, tek that to yer sister an' tell 'er t'be quick, I'm a-gettin' *hobben* on.' Without a word, he did as his grandmother asked. Over the past weeks he and Katie had found out (with the occasional slap) that their grandparents' commands were to be obeyed, and they were now enjoying this different lifestyle, both bristling with health and vitality.

'Thur's some 'eat a-coming outa this stove, my John,' Genty said as she took off one of the ring plates and put the cast iron hoop-handled frying pan on over the flames.

'Aar, it's that stag oak (very hard dry branch of oak) that I dragged back t'other day, thur's a load thur in the sack in corner that I cut up, I told yu I could a-smell this rain a-comin' couple've days ago.'

Genty looked up at Old John and smiling, said, 'Me old mam said when I wuz a gal, iffn yu 'as 'im, gal, 'e'll alus look arter yu … an' yu 'as, my John – now get outa the way an' a-let me get this bit've *baulomass* (bacon) a-cooked.'

The smell of bacon frying was irresistible, and the children were soon sitting quietly munching into doorstep slices of bread with crispy-edged bacon on top. Genty had topped up the old enamel teapot and it was now gently bubbling away on top of the stove. Stewed tea was what they liked – with plenty of sugar. At first the children had pulled faces at this beverage, but now they'd got a liking for it and were sitting drinking their second cup of the day.

'I likes four spoonfuls of sugar in mine now,' remarked Little Jimmy. Katie rebuked him by saying, 'You shouldn't, our mam said it's bad for your teeth.'

Old John grinned and said, 'Never in this world, gal, *dik* at my *danders* (teeth), they'm all thur baint they? An' *dik* at yer Granny's, she's a-got all on 'urn, 'cept one.'

At the age of 73 Old John still had all his teeth, albeit a little nicotine-stained.

'Mind yu, yer Granny's cousin Ayfie down thur in Gloucester don't 'ave good teeth, do 'e gal?'

And Genty replied, No 'e dunna, my John, they'm all little black stumps. Last time we seed 'im 'e said landlord of the local *kitchima* (public house) uddent a-serve 'im any *livena* (beer) in a glass, 'e'd only let 'im 'ave a bottle t'drink.'

'Does he have lots of sugar, Granny?' asked Little Jimmy worriedly.

'No 'e don't, my John, do 'e?' Genty said, looking at Old John.

'*Kekka* (no), I reckons it's all that black baccer that he chars (chews),' came the reply.

Little Jimmy looked relieved. 'I shan't be chewing any of that,' he thought to himself.

'Did yu bring the washin' bowl back when yu come to the tent, gal?' Genty asked.

'I did, Granny, it's propped up outside – I swished it in the brook as well,' Katie replied proudly.

'That's *kushti*, gal, *jall* an' get it fur yer old Gran, will yu?'

Returning with the 'washin' bowl', Katie handed it to her grandmother, who poured some hot water into it and said, 'I'll just *jall* up in the wagin fer me wash. Yu do them dishes, gal, while I'm gone.'

Old John and Little Jimmy sat quietly watching Katie as she carefully washed the dishes. 'Musn't get the table too wet,' she kept thinking, 'Granny don't like it.' She dried the crockery with care and then hung the teacloth on the string line behind the stove pipe. Then she picked up the 'dishes bowl' and carried it outside to empty it, and swish it in the brook.

'I'm glad we'm men, Granfer,' Little Jimmy whispered.

'*Owli*, lad,' Old John said quietly with a smile, 'we'll do our bit've *booty* (work) when I've a-finished this pipe've baccer and the women folks is out've the way. Yer Granny said to me earlier on that she wanted yer sister all t'erself fur a bit t'day; so they'll *jall* up in the wagin an' we can 'ave this 'ere cosy tent all t'ourselves, like.'

'What does Granny want her for, Granfer?'

'Oh! they'll be a-talkin' women's talk I shudna a-wonder, lad, nothin' t'do with us.'

Little Jimmy looked puzzled, but said no more. Katie appeared in the doorway, her hair glistening with misty rain. Two pairs of dark eyes greeted her. ' 'As you been talking about me?' she asked.

'Talkin' about yu, gal? Whatever giv yu that idea?' replied Old John.

'Well yer *yoks* looks all shiftified and you'm both very quiet.'

'*Dordi!* Canna two *mushes* sit all a-quiet like without some 'ummon a-thinkin' they'm up t'no good?' and Old John started to laugh so rigorously that it made him cough. And coughing always made him spit. There was a sizzling sound from the stove as a well-aimed stream of saliva hit it right in the middle of the grill front.

'You'm a good spitter, Granfer, 'ent yur?' Little Jimmy said admiringly.

'I baint a-sin our Nell this mornin' 'ave yu lad?'

Little Jimmy pointed to his bed, walked over and raised one side – there curled up was the dog, one eye looking at them.

'That's where she sleeps, Granfer.'

'My blessed Lord, that *jukkal koms tutti* (dog loves you), don't 'er now?'

'I loves her too, Granfer – she looks after me at night.'

'Well chuck 'er outside now lad, yu'll be a-mekin' 'er too soft, like.'

Little Jimmy picked Nell up in his arms and carried her out, putting her down on the wet grass. She stood there for a few seconds, gave a little shiver, and then, picking her feet up high out of the wet grass, made her way over to the wagon where she curled up beneath it – one eye watching Little Jimmy as he re-entered the tent. Katie had disappeared up in the wagon with her grandmother and Old John and Little Jimmy now had the tent to themselves.

'Let's get them flowers a-done outa the way,' Old John said with a smile. 'Give us that old bag from under the table thur, an' then bring us them elder sticks we cut yesterday, I chucked a bit've sheet over 'um last night. They'm at the back of the wagin – an' bring that bit've sheet an' all.'

Little Jimmy staggered into the tent with the bundle of elder sticks, the old canvas sheet trailing behind him.

'Eh *dordi!* you've a-got that old sheet all wetified, my son,' Old John said with a chuckle.

'It was wet already, Granfer, it's still drizzlin' out there, you know,' Little Jimmy replied, sounding a little hurt. And Old John chuckled louder.

'Put it down thur in front've the stove, lad, so's all the shavin's'll go on it.'

Little Jimmy did as he was asked, and then sat on the edge of his bed to watch his grandfather make the flowers. Old John had taken Little Jimmy with him yesterday to cut the sticks. They had walked to the little copse up the lane with the grass growing in the middle of it. It was one of Old John's favourite 'cutting' places … and he'd earned some money from it over the years, it had given him the materials for wooden skewers, clothes pegs, wooden flowers and 'crocket' hanging baskets. By some miracle of nature nearly all the wood in this little copse grew straight – just how Old John liked it. And within no time at all Old John had cut his lovely straight elder sticks – just over an inch in thickness and about two feet in length. These he had cut in half when they returned home, twelve inches to make two flowers, and they were now on the floor beside him, on the left hand side of the old milk bottle crate he was seated on. From the old bag he produced his well-worn " 'osses-'ead 'andle" peg-knife, and rubbing his thumb over the blade-edge declared, 'Aar, that'll do – alus keep yer peg-knife sharp and yer flower knife blunt.'

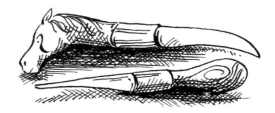

Little Jimmy, head in hands, sat watching from his seat on the edge of his bed.

'*Dik* 'ere, lad, this is 'ow it's done,' and with that Old John held the peg-knife in his right hand and placed it against his right knee, holding it rigid. With his left hand he picked up one of the elder sticks and swiftly pulled it against the knife blade. The bark flew off in long strips about seven inches long as he kept turning the stick. Soon all the sticks had been 'shaved up' and were lying clean end in front of the stove.

'We'll let 'um bide thur a bit to tek the sliminess off 've 'um lad, an' I 'as a smoke, an' yu pours yer old Granfer a drop've *meski* (tea) – that old *piri*'s (teapot) a-bubblin' well.'

Little Jimmy poured the tea, and handed his grandfather his dish, then poured himself a cup, putting his four spoonfuls of sugar in. He'd mastered the art of pressing his thumb on the top of the tin of milk and it came spurting out of the hole with every press. Old John watched, and smiling, said, 'It's a bit like milking a cow, baint it, my son?' and they both laughed.

'Put that bit've *kosht* (wood) back in the 'ole, lad, otherwise yer Granny'll be upset. 'Ere, tek this dish an' I'll a-get on with the flowers.'

Reaching in the old bag he took out his flower knife.

'It's all worn away, Granfer,' said Little Jimmy, looking at the thin tapered blade.

'*Kekka* (no), lad, it's supposed t'be like that (the end of the blade was no more than ¼ of an inch wide), *dik* 'ere,' and with that Old John rubbed the blade across his throat. 'Blunt that is, so blunt yu could ride that to Much Wenlock an' it 'udn't 'urt yer!'

'Why is it like that, Granfer, a knife's no good if it 'ent sharp?'

'Well that's whur you'm wrong, my son, a flower knife is supposed t'be blunt, otherwise it wanna curl the petals. *Dik* 'ere.' And with that Old John picked up his peg-knife and a piece of elder. 'Watch this,' he said, and with that he drew the stick against the sharp blade. A long straight piece came off. Then he held his flower-knife and did the same thing and a long curly piece came off. 'See, it baint no good with a sharp *churri* (knife), although I've a-sin folks a-mekin' 'um with a sharp knife – but the flowers a-looked like a dahlia, but mine looks like a real chrysanthemum, an' the *gaujies* love 'um, that they do. An' that dear lady in the market keeps a-buyin' 'um, don't she?'

'What's she do with them, Granfer?'

'She 'as a shop up thur in Brumijum (Birmingham) an' she sells 'um thur – so 'er told yer Granny. The dear lady gets on well with yer Granny, she does. They'm alus a-stood thur a-*rokkerin* (talking) together on market day – all secretive, like. It's *kushti* an' all 'cause yer Granny teks a bit've *luvva* (money) from 'er. Afore yu two come 'ere, yer Granny sold 'er four dozen of me "crocket" baskets.'

'How many's four dozen, Granfer?'

'Forty-eight, my son, but I made fifty an' told yer Granny t'give 'er the extra two at no charge, like. It keeps 'um sweet, then they comes back fer more, yu see. Aar, she come an' collected 'um an' all, an' 'er brought me an ounce've baccer. The dear lady! An' the baccer cost more than them two baskets – so yu sees, my son, thur's more than one way t'skin a *matchiko* (cat).'

And Old John gave Little Jimmy a wink and a smile. Not quite sure what his grandfather meant, he nevertheless smiled and winked back.

'Any old 'ow, this *rokkerin* (talking) wunna get yu *chavvies nevi chokkers* (children new shoes), we'd better get on with these 'ere flowers, my son.'

And with that Old John picked up his flower-knife, held it against his right knee and with his left hand started to draw the clean end of the elder stick up and down the blade. Starting with little cuts he gradually worked the stick further back, up and down the blade, turning the stick as he went. Soon a big ring of curly petals had appeared. He stopped and 'tickled' them out. 'If yu does this, lad, it meks a big flower, see?' And then he was off again, up and down the blade curled the petals; all the time Old John was working the blade further up the stick, which was now getting much thinner.

'She'll break off in a minute, so I'll finish 'er with little petals now,' Old John's head was nodding back and forward with the rhythm of the cuts. Suddenly the flower head broke off and fell to the floor. Little Jimmy rushed and picked it up.

'It's like a real flower, Granfer.'

'Smell it, lad,' replied Old John, 'it'll smell a lovely fresh smell; better to me old *nok* (nose) than the bestest rose from any genlemun's garden.'

Little Jimmy sniffed it, but didn't make any comment … 'It don't smell that nice,' he thought.

After about an hour Old John had a little rest, 14 flowers (5" wide, 3" high) were in the basket by the table, Little Jimmy having picked them up and placed them gently in there as they fell to the floor.

'That's about 'alf done, my son, my left arm's a-hurtin' a bit' so I'll stop an' 'ave a little smoke.'

He'd just finished lighting up when Genty and Katie appeared in the doorway, Katie laughing so much that tears were streaming down her cheeks. Genty was holding her bottom, looking serious, and trying not to laugh too.

'Granny's slipped down the steps of the wagon, Granfer,' she managed to blurt out, 'and she's a-hurt her *bul* (bottom).'

'You've a-come down them steps front'ards, baint yu, my Genty? I keeps a-tellin' yu t'come down back'uds (backwards), it's yer own fault if yu've a-hurt yer *bul* – an' dunna a-ask me t'rub no Elemans in it!'

'Yu'll 'ave t'do summat about they steps, my John. They goes all slippified when they gets wet.' Genty was trying to keep a straight face, but suddenly burst into laughter. That set Little Jimmy and Old John off … and laughing always made Old John cough, and coughing always made him spit. This time his aim was not so good and a sizzling sound came from the old black kettle on top of the stove. All laughter stopped.

'*Dordi!!!*' exploded Genty, 'yu *mokkadi* (dirty) old *mush*, whatsoever does yu think yu'm a-doin', man? Get that *kavvi* (kettle) outside this instant.'

Sheepishly Old John did as Genty asked, murmuring as he went out, 'Me old *yoks* is a-gettin' *waffedi* (bad).'

'He 'ent such a good spitter as I thought,' Little Jimmy whispered to his sister. Then the three of them started to laugh again.

'While yu'm out thur yu can get that *yog* a-goin' fur me – I wants t'put the pot on very soon.' Genty shouted to Old John.

'I'm a-tryin' t'get me flowers a-done, 'ummon,' came the reply.

'Yu wants t'eat t'day, don't yer? Get it a-goin', man,' Genty shouted to him. 'Thur's still a bit've smoke a-comin' out from under the iron sheet, it'll only tek yu a minute.'

'Yu'm all a-crochety 'cause yu a-'urt yer *bul*, my Genty ... an' it's yer own fault I'm a-tellin' yer.'

Within a few minutes a pungent plume of smoke was rising from the stick fireplace. Old John always kept his firewood covered with an old canvas sheet to keep it dry, even in summer time, and now he was putting larger pieces on – even a bit of his beloved stag oak. 'That'll keep 'er quiet fer a bit,' he said to himself as he went back to the tent. Pausing at the entrance, he called Little Jimmy and said, 'Lad, I wants yer t'do a special job, like.'

'A special job, Granfer?'

'*Owli* – a special job, my son, an' yu've a-got t'be very cunnin' an' careful when yu does it.'

'Whatcher want me to do, Granfer?' Little Jimmy replied excitedly.

'Now what I wants yer t'do is *jall* down t'the little churchyard – keepin' outa sight, like – an' on the left as yu goes in the gate is a privet 'edge. Now what I wants yer t'do is get me about 35 stems've privet from that 'edge. Not little 'uns, mind, I wants nice tall 'uns. 'As yer got yer *churri* in yer *putsi* (pocket) that I giv yer?'

'*Owli*, Granfer.'

'Is it sharp, lad?'

'*Owli*, Granfer.'

'Now cut 'um like I've a-showed yer in the copse t'other day, bend 'um towards yer, an' pull the sharp edge've the knife up – nice an' clean, like.'

'Do you want me to go now, Granfer?'

'*Owli*, lad – most folk'll be 'avin' thur bit've dinner, an' it should be quiet, like. Mind nobody *diks* yer now.'

Little Jimmy put on his jacket … and was gone.
'God love that grandson a-mine,' Old John said aloud.
'What yer on about out thur, my John?' came a voice from the tent.
'Nothin' gal, I'm a-comin' in t'finish me flowers. 'As yer made some more *meski*, I'm
a-fair parched, I've a-cleaned that old *kavvi* well, baint I?' and he chuckled to himself.

Genty had indeed made a fresh pot of tea which sat gently bubbling on top of the stove. Old John took his place on the old milk crate ready to finish off the flowers, and a dish of tea was handed to him.
' 'Ere yu is, man,' Genty said as she handed it to him. 'Bodge up a bit so's we can get t'the table t'sort this *hobben* out.'
Old John moved his milk crate, uttering no word.
'*Jall* and get that 'ock a-bacon outa the meat safe, Katie gal,' she ordered.
Katie was sitting on the edge of Little Jimmy's bed watching her grandfather intently. She was mesmerised by the rhythm of the knife blade going up and down the elder stick, forming the pretty curls, and made no attempt to move. Genty turned from the table, 'I baint a-gooin' t'tell yu again, gal, *jall* an' get the *baulomass* outa the meat safe now. *Jall* on, *sig, sig* (quick, quick).'
Katie leapt to her feet and ran over to the meat safe nailed to the old oak tree.
'I wonder which one she wants?' she thought as she opened the door and looked in. She sprinted back to Genty: 'Them two that

96

we boiled yesterday, Granny, do you want the one we've started to eat, or the other?'

'Yu'm a dear child, baint yu gal? Come 'ere.' and Genty gave her a big hug. 'Bring the one we baint cut yet, gal.' And Katie sprinted back to get it.

By now Genty had chopped up four onions and put them in the big cast iron pot, together with a big dollop of lard, and she was carrying it over to the outside fire.

'Come an' keep yer *yoks* on this, gal,' she said to Katie, as she put it on the kettle iron. 'Just a-keep a-stirring it, gentle like, while I chops up the *mass* (meat).'

Katie was pleased the fine drizzly rain had stopped. 'I don't like rain,' she thought, 'but me Granny don't seem to mind, she always says if you worry about the rain – you'll starve.'

Genty came back with a large dish of chopped up bacon that she'd cut from the big hock, and tipped it into the pot. 'Just keep a-stirrin' it, nice an' gentle, gal,' she said, 'I'll be back in a minute.'

'*Dordi!* I mustn't let it burn,' Katie thought, and she swung the pot over to the side of the fire. Genty saw this as she came back. 'Yu'm gettin' t'be a good little cook, gal,' and Katie beamed with pride, saying, 'I didn't want to get a clout for lettin' it burn, Granny.'

Genty emptied two tins of tomatoes into the pot, then some boiling water from the kettle, and then sprinkled three Oxo cubes in. 'Keep yer *yoks* on that, gal, an' give it a gentle stir now an' again,' and she disappeared back into the tent. She reappeared again with the large dish filled with chopped carrots and potatoes which she tipped into the pot and, taking the big spoon from Katie, gave it all a stir up, then added more water.

'*Jall* an' get us that 'alf a cabbage offn the table, will yu Katie?' she asked.

Handing the cabbage to her grandmother, she watched as Genty halved it in her hands and then, holding a half over the pot, she sliced it in, doing the same with the other half. 'You'm good with that knife, Granny, I'd be frightened of cutting myself.'

'*Kekka*, gal, t'is easy … an' me old *vasts* (hands) is 'as 'ard as nails, gal,' Genty replied. 'Now *jall* an' get us the salt an' pepper an' that little cardboard box of me 'erbs from the wooden box at the back've the table.'

Salt, pepper and herbs were added and Genty gave it all a final stir and put the heavy lid back on the pot. 'We'll just a-let 'er simmer thur now, gal,' she said.

'Are we having "humpty dumptys" in it, Granny?'

'Only if yu does 'um,' came the reply.

Katie and Little Jimmy loved dumplings, and Katie was now expert in making them.

'I'll go and do them now, Granny,' she said.

'Try not t'mek too much mess, Katie gal,' Genty said, smiling to herself.

Katie scampered off to the tent, and when Genty arrived she was already making her 'humpty dumptys'.

Into the big dish she had counted out eight big spoonfuls of flour, four big spoonfuls of suet, and added a pinch of salt. Then she sprinkled some of her Granny's herbs in, added some cold water, and started to mix with the big wooden spoon, adding a drop more water as she wanted it until she'd formed a firm dough. Then she dipped her hands in the flour bag and gently made eight round balls, which she placed on a plate and covered with the tea cloth. Old

John was having a rest from his flower making and sat quietly smoking his pipe, watching Katie make her 'humpty dumptys'.

'I 'ope yu washed yer 'ands, gal, afore yu started they dumplins.'

'They'm clean, honest to God they is, Granfer – I washed them this morning,' came the reply.

'*Dordi!* It's a good job they'm gooin' t'be boiled,' he said.

Little Jimmy came back with the privet stems, the bottom of his trousers and jacket sleeves soaking wet. 'I've got 'um for you, Granfer – and nobody saw me,' he said rather breathlessly, 'I runned all the way up the lane just in case anybody was walkin' down.'

'Good lad,' replied Old John. 'Fill that bucket with *pani* (water) from the brook an' put 'um in thur, we'll put the heads on 'um t'morrer.' Little Jimmy did as he was asked and, coming back into the tent, said, 'I'm soaked, Granny, every time I cut one of them stems the water come off them all over me arms.'

' 'Ere, get it off, lad,' and Genty helped him to take the jacket off, hanging it at the back of the stove pipe to dry.

'The grass is long by that hedge as well,' he said, '*dik* at me trousers. *Jall* outside a minute, Katie, while I changes them.'

'I've seen yer dear little legs before,' she said, as she went out of the doorway, laughing.

'Women's funny creatures, 'ent they, Granfer?'

'They are, my son – dunna reckon I've ever understood 'um.'

'Yu'm lucky t'ave a good 'un, my John – baint yu finished them flowers yet, I wants t'get this place tidied up, man,' Genty said with a little laugh.

The 2½ dozen (30) flowers were finished and Old John rolled up the canvas sheet with all the shavings and pointed sticks in it. *'Jall an'* tip this lot in the wood, my son, will yu?' he said to Little Jimmy. 'Can't I chuck it on the fire, Granfer?' he replied.

'My dear blessed Lord! Does yu never remember anythin' we tells yer … elderberry is very …'

And Little Jimmy, jumping to attention, said, 'VERY UNLUCKY TO BURN.'

'Owli! Yu've remembered now; never, never, never burn it, my son, it'll bring bad luck – *jall* and chuck it in the wood like I asked yu. 'Ow long'll *hobben* be, my Genty?'

'I should think we could put the dumplins in now, don't you Katie?' replied Genty, making Katie feel important.

Katie carried the plate of 'humpty dumptys' over to the fire, and Genty placed them in the simmering pot, replacing the heavy cast iron lid. 'Tell yer Granfer we can *hol* (eat) in about 'alf an 'our, an' then give Nell that hock bone offa the table, gal. An' then cut four slices've bread an' get the dishes out've the cupboard an' put 'um on the table an' get four spoons out an' all.'

'Dordi! You'm always tellin' me what to do,' came a little voice, as she hurried off to do it.

Genty's ham stew was a success, Little Jimmy having a second helping of it, and eating three of Katie's 'humpty dumptys'.

'You'm a *kushti* dumpty maker, Katie,' he said to her, as he stuffed half of a stodgy ball into his mouth.

'Granny says I'll make some *mush* a good wife when I'm older,' came the quiet reply.

The meal was finished, dishes done, and Old John decided to dye half of the wooden flowers ready for putting them on the privet stalks in the morning. 'The lady said she wanted 'alf on 'em pink, dinna she, my Genty? An' the other 'alf natural, like.'

'*Owli*, she did, my John, I'll go an' get some bits've crepe paper fur yu.'

And with that she went over to the wagon, returning with a handful of red crepe paper bits that she'd saved from last making red paper roses. Old John had put the old dyeing saucepan on the stove, and the water was boiling as Genty returned. The handful of red crepe paper bits went into the saucepan, and Genty gave them a stir with a bit of stick. She then took the saucepan off the stove and put it down on the floor by the doorway to cool down a bit.

Katie had been watching this intently, and remarked, 'It's gone a lovely red colour, Jimmy, red's me favourite colour.'

'Aar, but it wunna make the flowers red, gal, it'll only mek 'um pink, like. Beetroot or blackberry dyes 'um darker,' said Old John as he lit his pipe, filling the air with the strong smell of 'Condor' tobacco. He then reached for the basket of curly-headed flowers and put it down beside him. 'Give us that newspaper yu gets offn Mrs Davies every week when yu calls t'see 'er, my Genty.'

She reached into a cardboard box for the paper, and before handing it to Old John, opened it to the page that showed a photograph of a magnificent bull, standing at its head a gentleman dressed in a smart suit and sporting a bowler hat.

' 'Ere yu two, *dik* at this, yu can read. What's it say under that bull?'

'Hereford Market,' they shouted out.

'There yu is, my John, I said it was that.'

'I knowed that, gal, I've a-seed "Her-e-Furd" a-painted on the *pookerin-coshts* (signposts) enough times in me life, a-pointin' in that direction, to *jin* (know) what it is.'

'Yu'm alus a-windin' me up, man,' came the reply, and Genty handed over the newspaper, which Old John opened up and placed on the floor before him. Genty reached for the saucepan of dye and placed it on the paper, then reached for the teapot.

'You'll be a-wantin' a drop've *meski* soon I suppose, my John?' she said.

'Aar, gal, me old throat's a-fair parched, that it is.' And with that he took one of the flowers from the basket and, holding the stalk end between his thumb and forefinger, dipped the head in the dye, gave it a little shake, and put it stalk down on the paper. He then took another one, but this time twirled the edges in the dye, giving the flower a two-tone effect. And so he carried on, until stopping, said.

'What's a 'alf 've 30?'

'Fifteen,' came the reply from the children.

'An' 'ow many 'as I done?'

The children started to count the pinky flowers on the paper.

'Thirteen,' said Katie.

'No it 'ent,' said Little Jimmy, 'it's fourteen.'

'No it 'ent,' said Katie, 'it's thirteen.'

'Eh *dordi! dik* 'ere at these two, an' theys 'ad schoolin' an' all – 'ow many's thur, my Genty?'

Her eyes quickly scanned the flowers. 'Fourteen, my John.'

'Told yer so,' Little Jimmy said as he gave his sister a poke in the ribs, and Katie let out a yell and said, 'I'll getcher for that.'

' 'Ere, gal, 'old this in yer fingers an' just a-dip the edges,' and Old John handed Katie the last flower.

'I wanted to do that last 'un,' Little Jimmy shouted out.

'*Dordi!* I just canna win, can I gal?' and he threw a smile at Genty as she handed him his dish of tea. Then she picked up the ends of the paper and placed it on the table.

'Yu teks pride in a-mekin' them flowers, don't yu now?' she said.

'Aar, an' yu teks pride in *bikkin* (selling) 'um an' a-getin' the *luvva*, don't yu?' replied Old John with a chuckle.

A sizzling sound came from the red hot grill bars of the stove.

'Good shot, Granfer!' shouted Little Jimmy.

UNCLE EZIKIAH
(AND THE HORSE CHARMER'S MELT)

'I enna a-told yer about me old Uncle Ezikiah now 'ave I? I dunna a-like t'mention 'is name – God rest 'is soul, the dear man – but I shall 'ave to, otherwise yu wunna a-know who I'm a-talkin' about!'

It was evening time, and as usual Old John, Genty and the children were sitting around the fire, and Old John was in a storytelling mood again.

'That's a funny name, Granfer, why was he called that?' asked Katie.

' 'Cause it wer 'is name, gal, but 'e wer known as Ezzie, an' a comical old *mush* 'e wer too, an' a clever man with 'osses 'e wer. 'E used t'buy 'um an' a-sell 'um like nobody's business. Any old 'ow, we'm all a-stoppin' round Llanidloes – over that bit've country (and Old John waved his hand in the direction of the sun going down). Me uncle Ezzie and me Aunt Caroline 'ad a-come down t'this bit a-country, as I'm a-tellin' yer about, an' 'ad *velled* (come) down from north Wales. They wuz a-stoppin' on thur own, in a pretty little place, not so far from whur we wuz a-stoppin', so they could 'ave a little stroll over t'see us or we could 'ave a little stroll over t'see them, like.'

'Any old 'ow, it wuz a Saturday night, an' me an' me brother David decides t'walk inter the town an' 'ave a drop of *livena* (beer) at a *kitchima* (public house) what's a-known as the Red Lion. Nice old place it wuz, an' thur was never no trouble nor nothin'. When we wuz round that way we alus went inter that Public an' the *mush* knowed us an' was a civil man, as yu might say.'

Old John stopped his story and, pointing to the kettle by the fire, said, '*Jall* an' put a drop of *pani* (water) in thur lad, I'm fair parched, I am!'

Little Jimmy returned with the kettle of water and put it on the kettle-iron over the embers. Old John reached for some thin dry sticks to put under it, but before putting them on the embers, said, 'I've a-told yu afore lad, alus put the *kavvi* on the *saster* (kettle-iron) with the spout pointin' away frum the wind – yu must a-listen t'yer old Granfer, lad – it'll boil quicker if yu does!'

'There's no wind, Granfer,'

'Thur's a dear little breeze, my son, an' that's enough t'slow 'er down.'

Little Jimmy turned the kettle round, saying, 'Will that do?'

'That'll do, lad. Now, whur wuz I?'

'You was in the Public with your brother in … Clan … Clan summat-or-other, I can't say it, Granfer.'

'It's Clan-id-loyce (Llanidloes), lad. Aar, me an' me brother David is in the Red Lion, an' we'm sat at the back've the room at a pretty little round table – cast iron it wer – with a polished wooden top, lots've Publics 'ad 'em. Any old 'ow, we'm a-sat thur with our *livena* and we'm 'avin' a smoke an' a talk, when we *diks* the *wooder* (door) open, an' who should *vel* (come) in but uncle Ezzie. All the *foki's sherros* (people's heads) is a-turned, an' thur *yoks* is on him. *Dordi!* 'e wer a figure of a man, I can tell yu. Thur 'e stands, upright an' smart, with 'is big 'ookey *nok* (nose) a-stickin' out an' under it 'is big droopy tash with the curled-up ends, a-dressed in 'is big old tweed jacket with the big patch pockets a-bulgin' an' the belt a-fastened across the back, 'cause 'e never used it, like, an' across 'is weskit (waistcoat) pockets 'e 'ad 'is big gold timepiece chain – thick as me little finger it woz, with all on these gold sovereigns a-danglin' offn it. 'Is black silk *diklo* (neckscarf) is a-wound twice round 'is neck an' a-tied in a bow, an' on his 'ead 'e's a-wearin' 'is best black *stadi* (hat), a proper furry velour it wer. Now 'e dunna *dik* us 'cause 'is old *yoks* warn't that good an' we'm sat at the back an' it's a bit smokified in thur any'ows. Well, we watches 'im *jall* up t'the bar an' 'e gets 'is pint an' turns round.'

'Call 'im over,' sez David.
'*Kekka*,' I sez, 'I wants t'*dik* if 'e gets up to 'is mischief with the *gaujos*.'
'What do yu mean?' sez David.
'I seed 'im do a comical thing in a Public up thur by Ruthin yer or two back,' I sez, 'an' I wants t'see if 'e does it in 'ere. Keep yer *yoks* on 'im now.'

'Well now, 'e's a-turned from the bar with 'is pint an' 'e's a-lookin' fur somewhur t'sit 'imself down. 'E *diks* one *mush* at a table like owern an' 'e's a-*jallin* over to it. Well the *mush* sees 'im an' without further ado 'e ups an' moves t'another. So uncle Ezzie, 'e sits at this table all on 'is own like. Well now, 'e puts one leg over t'other and takes 'is *stadi* off an' a-puts it on 'is knee, an' I can see the *foki a-dikin* (people looking) at 'im an' a-starin' at 'is dear little kiss curls a-danglin' thur on 'is forehead.'
'What's kiss curls, Granfer?' asked Katie.
'Uncle Ezzie wer real old fashioned, gal, 'e alus 'ad 'is 'air cut very, very short, like a worn out shavin' brush, but 'e 'ad these dear little curls left a-danglin' on 'is forehead – lots've the womenfolk used

t'ave 'um. Yu curled 'um with yer finger an' thumb with some soapy washin' water.'

'Any'ows, 'e *jins* (knows) the *foki is a-dikin* at 'im, an' 'e starts t'put on a show. Fust 'e teks out 'is *swiggler* (pipe) – and a *kushti* 'un it wer too. It wer a Meerschaum, like me best 'un – but bigger. The bowl wuz held by a big eagle claw, an' it wuz a bendy stem 'un. Well now 'e puts this *swiggler* on the table, an' then 'e teks out 'is black baccer twist, an' tekin' 'is pocket knife 'e cuts bits off iner the palm of 'is 'and, an' puts the baccer an' knife back inter 'is weskit pocket. Then 'e rubs the baccer up, like I do with me flake baccer in palm of left hand (index finger and middle finger of right hand put through thumb of left hand – and rub!). Then 'e teks 'is pipe an' fills 'er an' a-lights up. An' all the time the *foki is a-dikin* at 'im, so arter a few puffs 'e teks the pipe outa 'is *mui* (mouth) an' 'olds it out fer the *foki* t'admire – lookin' away from it like, as though 'e's a-thinkin' a-summat else.'

'Any'ows, brother David is a-gettin' a bit impatient like, an' 'e *putches* (asks) "whatcher waitin' fur?" I sez 'ang on a minute an' keep *a-dikin* at 'im. So we does an' then the *mush* that 'ad got up offn the table gets up, 'e duz, with 'is empty glass, an' meks t'go t'the bar. Uncle Ezzie's little black *yoks* is on 'im, an' then 'e ups an' follers 'im to the bar an' stands thur right next t'im while 'e's waitin' t'be served.'

'*Dik akai* (look there),' I *pens* (says) to David, '*dik* 'im *rokkerin t'the gaujo* (see him talking to the non-Romany).'

'What's 'e a-*penin* (saying)?' David sez.

'I'll tell yu,' I sez. 'I was right close t'im in that Public at Ruthin an' I 'eard every word.

Dik at 'im thur, 'e's *mongin* (begging) the *mush* fer a pint. 'E's a-sayin' *You'm a nice kind gentleman, 'ent yu sir, is the nice kind gentleman going t'buy me a pint? Dik* at 'im, 'e's a-keepin' it up, *dik akai*! 'E's got 'is 'and on the *mush*'s shoulder now – there yu are, look, thur's two pints on the bar. Watch as 'e puts 'is 'and in 'is pocket an' brings out 'is big wad've notes – there, 'e's a-doin' it now.'

'What's 'e sayin'?' sez David.

' 'E's a-sayin' – eh *dordi! dik* at 'im a-lickin' 'is fingers an' pullin' a note off – 'e's a-sayin' *For being such a nice kind gentleman, you're t'ave this pint on me!* Aar, me uncle Ezzie was comical, like.'

'Any'ows, after that we calls 'im over an' 'e's a-buyin' us *livena*, wudna let us pay no *luvva* – no 'e 'udent. Well now, the *mush* rings the bell an' 'e calls out "time gentlemen, please". Well, we dunna feel like gooin', but we duz, 'cause it wer a *kushti* old *kitchima* an' we wuz sensible enough not t'cause any trouble, like. Any'ows, we *jalls* outside an' the cold air it 'its me, an' I'm a-wobblin' thur like; uncle Ezzie an' me brother David is only *posh motto* (half drunk), but I'm a bit more like. Well now, uncle Ezzie's 'oss an' trap is a-tied up outside an' they 'oists me inter the back an' then the two've 'um sits on the seat an' away we goes. *Dordi!* Could uncle Ezzie 'andle a 'oss! An' this *grasni* (mare) was no exception. 'E 'adna got any lights on the trap, but that never a-bothered 'im. We flew over the bridge an' round the bend an' I'm a-tossed an' a-turned all over the place. Next thing I knows, 'e's pullin' the mare up all skiddified like, an' I tumbles outa the back right by the side've our wagin. "Get up!" 'e shouts to the *grasni* – an' they'm gone!'

'Well now, I manages t'crawl t'the front've the wagin an' I'm a-shoutin' fur yer Granny t'let me in.' From the other side of the fire,

Genty said, 'An' I told 'im 'e could bide whur 'e wer to – baint that right, my John?'

'Aar, 'er did an' all, yer Granny 'as a cruel streak in 'er sometimes.'

'Where did you sleep, Granfer?' Katie enquired in a worried tone.

'I curled up like a little *jukkal* (dog) I did, right thur between the shafts, an' slept like a babby. Next mornin' I woke up all shiverified, like, covered in dew I wuz. I crawled over t'the *yog* an' a-got it gooin', a real good blaze I got 'cause I was so cold, like. Any'ows, I gets the kettle a-boilin' an' manages t'get the *meski* made. Then I goes up inter the wagin an' 'ands yer Granny 'er mornin' tea, tryin' t'be all nice t'er, like.'

'That taught 'im a lesson, my gal,' Genty remarked, looking at Katie, 'an' when Uncle Ezzie 'eard 'e did laugh, I can tell yu!'

Little Jimmy had been sitting there hanging on every word of the story.

'Uncle Ezzie sounded a comical old *mush*, Granfer – tell us more about him.'

'*Owli*, 'e wer a nice old man, 'e wer different t'me dad, like chalk an' cheese they woz. An' 'osses, *dordi!* 'e wer some 'oss man, I can tell yu. Knowed all about 'um 'e did, dealt in 'um from right up in north Wales thur, down inter Gloucester, 'e did. Yu know I said 'e wore this big old tweed jacket with bulgy pockets?'

'Yes,' said Little Jimmy, 'I remembers that.'

'Well now, do yu know what 'e carried in one a-them bulgy pockets?'

'His *flurta* (catapult),' Jimmy replied.

'Well aar, 'e alus a-carried a catty, but what I'm a-gettin' to is, 'e 'ad 'is "charmer's melt", kept it in a round tin, 'e did.'

Before Little Jimmy could utter a word, Katie shouted out, 'What's a "charmer's melt"?' followed by her brother asking the same question.

'Well now, I'll a-tell yu, but this is *secret*,' replied Old John.

Katie's eyes were opened wide. 'Secret, Granfer?'

'Yes, very secret, very, very secret.'

The children were on the edges of their seats, waiting in anticipation for their grandfather to continue.

'Me uncle Ezzie could a-do anythin' with a 'oss – all 'e 'ad t'do wuz open the lid've that tin an' a-let 'um smell what was inside.'

'What was it, what was it, Granfer?' Little Jimmy asked excitedly.

'I dunna think I'm a-gooin' t'tell yu, 'cause it's *too* secret, like,' Old John said, looking very serious, but inwardly smiling to himself.

'Granfer, please tell us,' the children wailed.

'Well, me old throat's a bit parched, an' I think we should 'ave a drop've *meski* (tea) … an' I'll a-think about it.'

Little Jimmy leapt to his feet and put the kettle, which was warm in the embers, onto the kettle-iron, spout facing away from the 'dear little breeze'. Old John smiled, and Katie leapt to the cupboard on legs and put out two tea dishes for her grandparents and the two cups that she and Jimmy used. In her haste she accidentally tipped the glass sugar basin and a little of the contents spilt onto the oilcloth. Genty had been watching her, 'Push that sugar inter yer 'and, gal, an' chuck it on the fire. It'll mek it burn good, a spoonful on a wet day'll 'elp any fire along.'

Katie and Jimmy sat bent over with their faces in their hands, looking at the kettle, and looking at their grandfather mournfully. Old John sat looking into the fire, making out to be very serious.

Suddenly he said in a low drawn-out voice, 'I dunna know if I should tell yer or not.'

By now Genty had made the tea, and as she handed Old John his dish she said, 'Yu is such a tease, yu is. Go on an' tell the *chavvies* an' put 'um outa thur misery. Just a-*dik* at 'um sat thur, all as good as gold, like.'

Old John took a sip of his tea and said, 'Well, I've been a-thinkin', an' I will tell yu, but I dunna want yu t'go a-blabbin' this around, 'cause it's our secret yu understands.'

'Tell us, Granfer, we won't tell a living soul, will we Katie?'

'No we won't, no never we won't,' came the reply.

'Well now, a "charmer's melt" is …' and Old John paused, with a twinkle in his eye, to take another sip of his tea. 'A "charmer's melt" is very special like, an' not many folks 'as 'um,' and he paused again to take another sip.

'Eh *dooooordi!*' cried Little Jimmy as he pushed his leg out, catching the end of a smouldering log, sending ash over his grandfather. Old John brushed the ash from his jacket, saying, 'If yu lets me I'll a-tell yu. Now when a mare 'as a dear little foal she licks it all over, t'get it nice an' clean like. Now all on this stuff as she's a-licked off the dear little foal forms up inter a ball, an' she swallers it. Now, if you'm clever an' quick an' knows about 'osses yu can get this ball afore 'er swallers it … an' that's a "charmer's melt". An' that's what uncle Ezzie 'ad in that tin've 'is, an' as I sez, 'e only 'ad t'let a 'oss a-smell it an' it 'ud foller 'im anywhere.'

'Have you got one, Granfer?' asked Little Jimmy.

'No I baint, lad, never needed one, I wer never no 'oss dealer. We 'ad 'um, as yu knows, t'pull the old wagin about, but they wuz only old *grais* (horses), nice an' quiet like. I'm fond've *moilas* (donkeys), I am, like me old dad an' granfer. They wuz donkey an' tent men, an' I grew up t'life with the pack donkeys – aar, I'm a-fond've a dear little neddy, I am. Now uncle Ezzie, 'e warn't keen on 'um; 'osses it alus wer with 'im, an' my dear Lord, 'e knowed 'is job, that 'e did. 'E earnt sum *luvva* from 'um, but 'e got a bit too comical once, went round sayin' 'e was a-buyin' 'um fer the Army – t'get 'um a bit cheaper, like. Well, one old *rai* (gentleman), 'e complained t'the *muskros* (police), an' they come an' a-got 'im an' locked 'im up – right over in Wales it wer – but that's another story! Pour us a drop more *meski*, gal, an' I reckons it's way past these *chavvies' woodrus* time (children's bed time); *dordi*, me old throat is a-fair parched.' And Old John coughed and spat into the fire.

A SHUSHI FOR THE POT AND THREE
DOZEN CLOTHES PEGS

'Yer Granny wants a *shushi* (rabbit) fur the pot, lad, yu an' yer sister baint a-never a-tasted rabbit I bets, 'as yer?' Little Jimmy answered 'no'.

It was early afternoon and Old John was sorting out his rabbit snares. 'These is med've brass twisted wire, lad, 'uddent think so, 'ud yer 'cause brass is all yeller an' shiny, baint it? But they 'enna no gud iffn they'm like that, they 'as t'be all dullified like these is.' And with that Old John put half a dozen snares, with pegs attached, into the big inside pocket of his old tweed jacket.

'Doos yer wanna come fur a stroll with me an' a-see 'ow I *lells a shushi* (catch a rabbit)?' Old John, with a smile, said to Little Jimmy – knowing full well that the answer would be 'yes'.

Half way up the hedgerow of the grassy field at the back of the wood Old John stopped and beckoned Little Jimmy to lie down in the hedge with him.

'What's we doing, Granfer?'

'Jest yu keep yer *yoks* fixed on the bottom've that little ash tree up thur by the gate, lad, an' yu'll a-see somethin' in a minute or two.'

'What, Granfer?' Little Jimmy whispered.

'I knows thur's an old fox 'avin' a little sleep under that little tree, a-sunnin' 'isself, like. It's one've 'is places that 'e likes – now watch.'

Old John wet his lips and put them on the back of his hand, just down from his thumb, then with a sucking action made a squeaky noise (which imitated a rabbit in distress). The old fox rose slowly from his sunny position and with a stalking motion made his way down the hedgerow towards them, Old John still making the squeaky noise until he whispered to Little Jimmy, 'Jump up an' a-frighten' 'im.' Little Jimmy leapt to his feet, and in the blink of an eye the fox had disappeared through the hedge.

'Iffn we 'enna careful old sneaky'll 'ave our *shushi* tonight, lad, yu scared 'im gud an' proper, that yu did.'

They crossed over the little lane with grass growing in the centre and entered 'Old John's copse', where they made for the far corner which had a thick thorn hedge as its boundary. 'Git yerself through thur, lad,' Old John said as he pointed to a thin gap, which they both squeezed through, coming out onto a small grass field. Walking slowly down the hedgerow Old John pointed out the 'rabbit runs' that came from the hedge into the field.

'Ere's a gud 'un, lad, now keep back 'ere with me, like, an' a-watch wot I'm a-doin'. See on this run whur the rabbit a-jumps an' the grass is a-patted down, now 'e'll alus a-jump in the same place, so we puts the wire in between them marks like, at the end've the last jump.'

Reaching up to the hedge Old John cut six thin sticks to act as prop pegs and gave them to Little Jimmy to hold, then he took one of the snares from his inside pocket and with his thumbs and forefingers made it into a pear shape. Taking the wooden 'tether' peg he pushed it into the ground on the side of the run at the end of the 'jump marks'. Then taking one of the prop pegs from Little

Jimmy he put his knife blade in the top and made a small slit. This he then pushed into the end of the snare where the cord was attached, then he pushed it into the ground not far from the peg. The loop swung over the rabbit run about four inches from the ground.

'I sets 'um by eye, lad, but that's about as 'igh offn the ground as yu wants 'um,' and Old John held out the palm of his hand, 'an' I'll tell yu summat an' all, that's 'ow 'osses is a-measured, 'ands they calls it, four inches meks one 'and. Pull a bit a-grass up frum over thur an' put it over the top of that peg, lad, t'ide it, like.'

Old John set another four snares down the hedgerow, then picking up a piece of dead branch said, 'Ere's another way,' and he took the last snare from his pocket and removed the wooden peg from it. He then attached the cord to the centre of the branch. 'This is wot we a-calls a drug (drag) stick.' Setting the snare in the run he put the branch by its side. 'Iffn we catches one 'ere, *shush*'ll drag that stick up t'the 'edge, an' 'e wunt a-be able t'goo no further, like.' Little Jimmy nodded his approval, in an admiring way.

'We'll goo back 'ome a different way, lad, I wants t'cut some sallys (willow), the dear lady in the market 'as a-asked yer Granny fur three dozen pegs. Baint a lot, I knows, I usually a-meks 'um by the gross (twelve dozen), but it'll bring another shillin' (5 pence) in.'

Not so far from the small brook was a wet area where willow grew in abundance, and this is where Old John and Little Jimmy headed. Lovely straight growth willow stems were soon cut and the pair headed home, timed perfectly for the meal Genty and Katie had prepared. That evening, sitting around the fire, Little Jimmy's mind was on rabbits. 'I wonder if we've caught one yet, Granfer?'

Old John gave a chuckle. 'One is all we wants, lad, or maybe a couple – what I generally doos about this time is t'ave a little stroll around t'see if any've the wires 'as a-bin moved, like, but seein' 'as we only wants one we wunna a-bother, we'll a-git ourselves offn early in the marnin'.'

Full of excitement, Little Jimmy couldn't wait for morning to come. He was up before his grandfather, and had the fire rekindled and the kettle boiling when Old John emerged from the wagon. Tea was made, and as usual Old John took Genty hers in the wagon, Little Jimmy following suit and taking Katie a cup. The kettle was re-filled and hung back over the fire ready for the women's washing water, then the pair were off to see what had been caught.

The first snare along the hedgerow held a dead rabbit caught cleanly round the neck. Little Jimmy raced ahead, 'These 'ent got nothin', Granfer,' he called out.
Old John laughed as he pulled the pegs from the ground and put them in the big pocket of his jacket. The last snare attached to the dragstick had vanished.
'This one's gone, Granfer.'
'Look in the 'edge, lad,' Old John called out.
Little Jimmy looked at the hedge and saw the dragstick branch held firm against it, then he heard the frantic noise. 'This one 'ent dead, Granfer.'
Old John pulled the stick and out came a rabbit caught round its middle; in one deft action the hard hands cleanly broke its neck. Taking his knife Old John cut a slit behind the rabbit's one hind leg, then pushed the other leg through it. ''Ere my son, yu can a-carry this 'un – put yer finger through them legs.'

They walked back up the hedgerow to where the first caught rabbit lay.

'We'll a-leave summat fur that old fox, lad, 'cause 'e baint a-took our dinner, 'ave 'e now?'

Taking his knife he slit the belly of the two rabbits, then with the help of his index finger shook the innards out at the bottom of the hedge. 'That's what we calls paunchin' 'um,' he said, as he wiped his finger on the grass, 'old slinky'll like t'get 'is old *nok* around that lot.'

He cut a slit behind the rabbit's hind leg and, like the other one, pushed the other leg through it, putting his finger through the joined legs and making the rabbit easily carried. They sauntered slowly home, Old John remarking 'Yer Granny'll be 'appy, my son; rabbit stew fur us all t'day, an' yer Granny doos a gud 'un an' all.'

And Genty was pleased. 'We baint a-'ad a *shushi* fur ages 'as we now?' she cheerfully said as Old John deftly skinned them, then asked Little Jimmy to dispose of the skins 'out thur in the wood'. Katie had been quietly watching the skinning of the rabbits. 'I likes to see little bunnies scampering about, Granfer, all happy playing together.'

'Aar, an' yu'll a-like eatin' 'um an' all, gal,' came the reply.

'Put that *tassamangri* on the *saster* (frying pan on the kettle-iron), gal, an' a-put a chunk a fat in it,' Genty called to Katie, as she cut the back and front legs off the two rabbits. Then she broke and cut the bodies in half, washed them, and fried them in the pan. When all the meat was nicely sealed she put it in her big black heavy cast iron pot, which stood on the edge of the fire embers. Next she gently fried a load of sliced onions, and when they were done 'just soft' she added them to the meat in the big pot. 'Bring me salt, pepper an' me 'erbs from the tent, gal.' Katie, doing as she was asked, returned with them and Genty sprinkled the salt, pepper and dried herbs over the meat and onions, poured in some boiling water from the kettle and gave it all a stir, then she placed the heavy cast iron lid on the pot and said, 'It can bide whur it's to now gal, while we gets the vegitables done.' And she pushed the pot a few inches more into the embers.

'Is we having '"humpty dumptys" in it, Granny?' Katie asked.

'*Owli*, gal – but we dinna bother about they until s'arternoon.'

At the side of the tent Old John and Little Jimmy were sitting on the grass, with the willow sticks that they had cut yesterday, that were to be made into clothes pegs for the 'dear lady' in the market. They were busy stripping the bark off the sticks, 'rinin' 'um', as Old John called it ('rinin' meaning rinding – taking the rind off). By inserting the thumbnail into the bark it could be pulled off in long strips.

'They'm all wet an' slippery now we've stripped them, Granfer.'

'Aar, we 'as t'do summat about that, lad, otherwise they goos a *chikli* (dirty) colour, an' that 'enna no gud t'the likes a-we.'

Taking an old piece of rag he rubbed the sticks up and down with it, then fashioned them into a tripod shape by tying a bit of binder twine round the top of them. 'We'll leave 'um thur t'dry out in the sun fur a while, lad, *jall* an' see 'ow them women's a-getting' on, an' see iffn yer Granny'll mek us a drop've tea, like.'

Later that afternoon, before the meal was ready, Old John started to make the clothes pegs; Little Jimmy watching intcntly. First he banged his old well-worn 'ground block' into the earth with the use of his well-worn 'beater'. Taking the pile of peeled willow sticks, that had now dried out a fair bit and were a clean white colour, he placed them on the grass beside the 'ground block'. Sitting on the grass, with the 'ground block' before him, he picked up one of the sticks, put the cut thick end on the block, put his 'chopping off' knife blade on it, and hit the back of the blade with the beater – the end was chopped off cleanly and square. Next he put the stick back on the block and cut off just over a foot in length – this he used for a measure for the rest of the sticks, and he soon had eighteen lengths cut.

From his old bag he took out long strips of tin, just under ⅜" wide, that he had previously cut from used tin cans. These he used to bind the two ends of the cut sticks; by bending over the end of the tin strip he put it a small way down from the end and knocked it in with his small hammer. Then twisting the strip round a few times he formed a spiral; making a small hole in the spiral end with his awl, he inserted a tiny gimp pin nail and knocked that in. Then he bent the tin strip back over itself, put it on the block and gave it a blow with the hammer, and by bending it back and forwards with his finger and thumb it broke off cleanly.

This he then did to the other end of the stick, and very quickly the eighteen lengths were finished.

'That's what we calls "tinnin' 'um",' Old John said as he looked up from his work at Little Jimmy, who nodded knowingly.

'Some folks only puts one piece've tin round the top've the peg, but these is better, they looks better an' they is better, like. Now we 'as t'chop 'um in 'alf. Some folks 'as a measurin' stick, but I doos 'um by eye.'

Picking up one of the sticks he placed it on the block, put the knife blade in the centre, and chopped it in two. Little Jimmy picked them up and put them side by side – they were the same length, all but a fraction.

Old John chopped all the sticks in half, making thirty-six pegs (three dozen).

'Now comes the nice bit, lad, we 'as t'mouth 'um. Collect 'um all up an' put 'um 'ere by the side a-me.'

Doing as he was asked, Little Jimmy collected the tinned-ended one-peg-lengths up, and placed them on the left hand side of his grandfather. Picking one up, Old John pushed his peg knife (with the 'osses-'ead 'andle) into the top of the un-tinned end and gave it a little wiggle. The blade slid down the slit, then almost like magic, he turned the blade round in the slit, raised his right knee, held his knife against it, and pulled the peg backwards at an angle against the sharp edge of the knife. A V-shaped piece flew out. He then inserted the blade again, and did the same on the other side.

'That's "mouthin' 'um", lad,' he chuckled, 'all we 'as t'do now is pull the knife blade over the mouth, on both sides, an' that'll mek 'um nice an' round, an' the womenfolk wunna snag thur washin' on 'um, like.'

Within a few minutes all the clothes pegs were finished. Little Jimmy sat watching in amazement at the speed his grandfather worked. Reaching for one of the unused peeled sticks, Old John made a small knife cut in it, slightly on the angle, about six inches from the end. He then placed the stick against his raised knee and pulled it back towards him, which caused the small knife cut to spring open with a 'crack' noise. Inserting his index finger into the slit he proceeded to pull the stick back and at the same time pushed his index finger along the slit. A long thin strip came off.

'What's that for, Granfer?' asked Little Jimmy.

'T'put the pegs on, lad – watch.' Picking up a peg he pushed it onto the thin strip and soon the three dozen were neatly in line on it. He handed the long strip of pegs to Little Jimmy, saying, 'Put 'um in yer Granny's basket in the tent, lad, an' then ask 'er 'ow long *hobben*'ll be – I'm 'ungry now, an' yu must be an' all.'

The rabbit stew, complete with dumplings, was a great success. Genty gave each of the children the 'back' part of the rabbit (really meaty and tender) and they loved it. Little Jimmy was all for going out again the following day to catch more.

'Yu dunna a-want 'um too often, lad, jest now an' then, like, otherwise they tastes "samey" an' they dunna taste as gud as a-wot yu've jest a-eaten, like,' Old John remarked philosophically!

THE ONE-MAN CIRCUS

Coming back from town one Thursday, the children shouted to their grandparents, 'Look, look!' and there on the edge of the village pulled up on the verge was a little bow tilted cart and two donkeys tethered and grazing contentedly.

'I know who that is,' said Old John, 'that's Old Fred Abel, the one-man circus. We'll *jall* on over an' a-see 'im.'

The cart, just big enough to sleep in, had the word CIRCUS roughly painted on the canvas, and as they all approached Old Fred got up from a stool by the side of it.

'*Doooordi!*' said Little Jimmy, for Old Fred was a colourful character. Grubby, to say the least, with a large beard and sporting a battered black top hat. Two dogs were chained to the cart, leaping in the air and barking ferociously.

'Don't you *chavvies* get too close t'them *jukkals* (dogs), or the old *mush*,' Genty said in a soft voice, 'yu might get *joovers* (fleas/lice) from 'um – and 'im.'

' 'Ow's yer goin' on then?' was Old John's greeting.

'Aaaal r-r-r-right,' came the reply. 'N-n-n-nice weather, ain't it?'

'Yu gets about a bit, dunna yu? Last time we seed yu wuz over Kiddy-minster (Kidderminster) way, yers agoo.'

The children stood by their grandmother, silently, with mouths open. They had never seen such a sight.

'Are yu open fer business, old mate? Be nice iffn yu'd give me grandchildren a bit've a show,' Old John was smiling and winked his eye as he took a shilling (5 pence) from his pocket.

'Y-y-y-yes, aaal r-r-r-right,' came the reply.

Old Fred had a bad stutter and kept his sentences short, although when shouting at the dogs to be quiet he didn't appear to have a stutter at all. Walking over to the black and white collie, Fred unchained it. Katie squeezed her granny's hand, saying, 'He won't get me, will he?'

'*Kekka*, my gal, the man knows what 'e's a-doing,' said Genty reassuringly. 'We've a-sin 'im do this afore.'

Both dogs had now ceased their barking, and were looking at Fred attentively. With just hand movements Fred made the collie sit, and then from a wooden box he took a mouse, and by the tail lowered it onto the dog's nose.

'He'll eat that mouse,' Little Jimmy whispered.

But not at all. For several minutes the mouse sat on the dog's nose and the dog just remained still. Then Fred picked it up and put it back in its box. Next he unchained the second dog, a brown and white mongrel, and it followed him to a space about ten feet from the other dog and sat quietly. Fred then produced an iron hoop on a frame which he placed between the two dogs. Going over to his cart he came back with a drum, and then started to beat it. First one dog ran and jumped through the hoop, running round the seated dog, and then back to its place – swiftly followed by the other dog doing the same thing. Round and round they went until Fred stopped beating his drum. Little Jimmy and Katie clapped their hands, shouting, 'That was *kushti*. Them *jukkals* is clever, 'ent they? We'll train Nell to do that when we gets home.'

'Yu baint a-goin' t'do that, now watch the man,' Genty replied in a louder voice.

Fred chained the dogs up again and then produced another wooden box from the cart. From it he took a black and white coloured rat. 'Oh! *Dordi!*' Little Jimmy said alarmingly, 'I hates them things, we had them in the yard in Wolverhampton. Mam says they'm the worstest, unluckiest creatures in the world.'
'That they is, son,' Genty replied, 'an' don't yu ever go an' speak the name've 'um – it's very unlucky, my son.'
'Mam told us that,' said Katie, 'they puts a shiver all over me body.'

Fred walked over to his donkeys and placed the 'longtail' on the nearest one's head. It just sat there blinking, making no move to escape, then he put it on the donkey's back and with hand movements made it run up and down.
'I can't a-bear to *dik* at it, can you, Jimmy?'
'No I can't,' he replied, and Katie squeezed her Granny's hand. Old John had heard the children and said, 'That'll do fer now, Fred, show's over, an' thank yu kindly fer a-showin' the children.' He pressed the shilling into Fred's dirty hand, noticing the long dirty fingernails with some disgust.

As they walked up the lane Little Jimmy looked at his grandfather and said, 'He was a dirty old *mush*, wasn't he, Granfer? But his *jukkals* was clever, wasn't they? Who is he, Granfer?'
'Old Fred's been on the road a long time, my son, dunna know why, but I've a-seen a few men like 'im in me time. Some on 'um took t'travellin' arter the war – I suppose they just cudna settle, like. But

I suppose Fred's doin' what 'e wants t'do, an' 'e dunna 'arm anyone, do 'e?'

'How does he boil his kettle and cook his food, Granfer? I didn't see no fire.'

'Did yu notice that little square tin 'e 'ad with two bars on top?'

'No, I didn't, Granfer.'

'Well yu should keep yer *yoks* open, my son.'

'What was it for, Granfer?'

'That little tin is fer 'is fire, 'e puts dear little bits've *kosht* (wood) in it then 'e puts 'is pots on the top. Dunna use so much that way, dunna leave a fire mark, an' dunna get in so much trouble with the *muskros* (police). When I was a *chavvi*, 'bout as big as you, we 'ad the big tents in the winter time an' most on us used what we called a 'fire bucket'.'

'A fire bucket? What, a tin like Fred's?'

'No, an old bucket with 'oles knocked in the sides an' we 'ad the fire in it, with a couple've iron bars across the top like Fred 'ad. I sin 'um danglin' under the cratch've many a wagin in me time – *kushti* see, 'cause they 'ad the 'andle on.'

'Why don't we use one, Granfer?'

'Well my son, we got plenty've *kosht* whur we'm to, an' yer granny an' me likes a bit a-fire on the ground, like, *kushti* t'sit round baint it? We cudna live without it, my son.'

That evening, before the children went to bed, Little Jimmy said, 'You don't think one of them "longtails" is going to sneak into the tent when I'm asleep, do you?'

Old John smiled. 'Not with Nell about they wunna. We baint seen one fur years, 'ave we, Genty?'

'No, we baint,' came the reply.

After lighting his pipe and spitting into the fire, Old John said to the children, '*Vel* (come) over 'ere an' I'll tell yu summat that yu might find interestin'. I've a relation up in Liverpool, works in the Docks as a "longtail" catcher – 'e dunna like the things, but 'e dunna bother about 'um too much 'cause the *foki* pays 'im well. One day I was a-chattin' t'im an' I sez, "Clifford, 'ow's that longtail job a-goin'?"

'*Kushti*,' 'e sez, 'an' I meet some interesting *foki* when I'm a-doin' it. Do yu know, I was talking to this *mush* the other day an' 'e told me that thur's a dear little island right out in the sea – only a few rocks it is, no grass, no plants, no nothin' – but thur's loads've longtails that lives on it.'

'What do they live on?' I *putches* (asks) 'im.

'Well,' he sez,'thur's little pools've rainwater that collects in the rocks so they can 'ave a drink.'

'But what doos they eat?' I sez.

'I'm about to *pooker* (tell) yu,' 'e sez, 'these 'ere creatures 'as long pink tails, very pink,' 'e sez, 'an' do yu know why?'

'No,' I sez.

'Well I'll tell yu,' 'e sez. 'They uses thur tails fer fishin', fer catchin' crabs– an' that's what they lives on.'

'Now what d' yu think a-that?'

'*Doooordi!*' came the reply.

126

The Pipe

'That's a beautiful pipe you're smoking, Granfer, why do you smoke it only on a Sunday?' Katie was 'in Old John's face', having a real close-up look at this magnificent pipe.

'If yu sits down by yer brother, I'll a-tell yu,' replied Old John.

He cleared his throat and spat in the fire. 'This 'ere pipe is a bit special like, an' I must've 'ad it … ohh, let me see now … well, it must be over forty yer.'

He held it in his hand, admiring it. It brought a lot of pleasure to Old John and yes, he did smoke it only on a Sunday.

'This 'ere is a Meerschaum *swiggler* – made've a special white clay, but t'look at it now yu udden't think so, 'ud yu?'

The pipe was indeed a Meerschaum, and over the years it had gone a golden brown colour. The bowl was carved with a castle scene and prancing from the bowl, along the stem, was a pretty little pony, the mouthpiece having an ornate silver band around it.

'I only smokes it on a Sunday because it's special; I likes it, you likes it, yer Granny likes it, in fact, everyone that's ever a-seen it likes it, an' I likes t'take care've it, I dunna want t'get it *poggered* (broken) now, do I? An' it's the sort've thing that could easy get bust if I wer t'drop it an' sit on it or summat.'

Old John held the pipe out for the children to examine.

'Just you *dik* at that dear little *grai* – the *mush* who carved that knew about 'osses now, didna 'e?'

'It's really pretty, Granfer, how did you get it?' Katie's big dark eyes looked pleadingly into her grandfather's.

'Well I'll a-tell yer,' replied Old John. 'Me cousin Noah 'ad it. We was all stoppin' round Lentwardine at the time. 'Is sister, me cousin Esmeralda, had *rommered* (married) a real *bori rai* (big gentleman) from Bridgnorth. The marriage 'adn't a-lasted long, they wuz alus a-fightin' with each other. She wer only a gal an' 'e wer old enough t'be 'er *daddus* (father). Any old 'ow, she runned off an' a-left him. Now this *bori rai* 'ad a friend an' like this *rai*, 'e thought this old life of owern was *kushti*, an' 'e wuz always a-comin' round t'us people, sittin' round the *yog* an' a-askin' questions, like. We didna mind too much 'cause 'e alus 'anded round the baccer pouch an' brought a bottle've *tatto pani* (whisky). Well, this one day 'e turns up an' 'e's smokin' this 'ere *swiggler* that yu'm a-looking at, proud as a peacock 'e wuz with it in his *mui* (mouth). Now I warsn't thur at the time, but Noah said that everyone's *yoks* was on that *kushti swiggler*, an' 'e really wanted it. This *rai* 'ad 'is little notebook out a-wantin' *Romanes* words an' Noah says t'im: "My *rai*, I knows some real old words I'd a-tell yu." An' then 'e whispers in 'is ear, "an' I'd a-tell yu the 'great secret' if yu'd trade me that old pipe you'm a-smokin'."

'This *rai* gets all excited, like an' says "*owli*". Noah tells 'im some *lavs* (words) an' the *mush* writes 'em down, then Noah beckons 'im away from the others.

"My *rai*," 'e *pens* (says), "what I'm about t'tell yu I wants yu t'promise yu'll never tell anyone" – all secretive like.

"I promise," says the *rai*.

So Noah gives 'im a real good *hokkapen* (lie), an' they shakes 'ands … an' Noah got the *swiggler*.'

'But how did you get it, Granfer?' shouted out Little Jimmy.

'I'm a-comin' t'that in a minute. Race over to the tent an' ask yer Granny t'come an' brew up some *meski* fer us. Kettle's boilin' an' I'm all a-parched.'

The children ran over to ask their Granny and Old John smiled to himself – he was a good storyteller. Genty brewed the tea, and after a few sips he could see the anticipation on the faces of the children, so he began again:

'We wuz all stopped t'gether gettin' ready fer the whinberry pickin', over Newcastle way, t'other side've Clun. Well, cousin Noah is bragging one day that 'e wer the bestest man with a *flurta* (catapult), so I ups an' sez t'im, "My cousin, yu reckons yu'm the best man with a *flurta* an' I challenges yu."

"What yu goin' t'give me if yu loses?" 'e sez.

"Me 'ookey-bladed peg knife with the 'osses-'ead 'andle," sez I – I knowed 'e liked it – "an' if you loses, I wants the *swiggler* yu 'ad offn the *bori rai*."

I really, really wanted this old *swiggler*.'

And Old John gave it a loving rub with his thumb.

"What we goin' t'shoot at?" sez Noah.

Well that mornin' I'd found one've me goldfinches dead in the cage, so I goes over an' gets it. "Shoot at that!" I sez.

Sez Noah, "That's easy."

"Not so fast," sez I, an' I picks up a bit've stick we'd got fer the fire with a 'Y' at the top. I puts it in the ground an' puts the dear little *chiriklo's* (bird's) 'ead in the 'Y' an' sez "knock 'is 'ead off."

'Now Noah knew I could use a catty, all on us could, but 'e didna know 'ow good I was. For yers an' yers I'd a-practised with me brothers – we used t'collect a bucketful've stones an' practise fer 'ours. Brother Reubin would chuck a big stone, 'bout as big as a rabbit's 'ead, along the ground an' it got I could 'it it every time, even a certain leaf on a tree I could knock off.

"Who's goin' fust?" sez Noah.

"You can," sez I.'

'*Dordi*, I was a bit worried 'cause I knowed 'e wuz good. Any old 'ow, 'e pulls the elastic back an' 'e lets 'er go – 'e 'it the stick, an' when we goes over to have a *dik*, the dear little bird 'ad still got 'is 'ead on. Now it's my go (from his right-hand jacket pocket Old John took his catapult, unwound the elastic, held the peg in his right hand at arm's length, and pulled the elastic right back with his left hand, right past his left ear).

I pulled right back like this an' then I let 'er go.'

'Did you knock the bird's head off, Granfer?' shouted Little Jimmy with excitement.

'Yes, I did my son, an' the stick never moved – an' that's 'ow I come by the beautiful *swiggler*.'

'You're the best shot in the world,' said Katie.

'Maybe,' replied Old John, 'but what Noah didna know was that I 'adn't used a stone, I'd used a steel ball-bearing. I was pally with a *mush* who worked in Newtown, an' 'e'd given 'em t'me. *Kushti* they wuz, just the right weight an' all shiny an' round. *Dordi!* did they go!'

Old John took a brand from the fire and lit up, smiling to himself. 'Will you make me a catty, Granfer? I want to be as good as you,' Little Jimmy said enthusiastically.

'Aye son, I will,' said Old John, 'it's about time yu 'ad one, we'll have a *dik* round the 'edges soon an' I'll a-cut yu a nice little peg, an' when we goes t'town next week I'll get some thin elastic. Yu'd never be able t'pull this back.'

THE BACCY TIN

Old John took his round shiny tobacco tin from his bottom left waistcoat pocket – that's where he kept it, that's where he'd always kept it, the bottom left pocket. Top left pocket was for his pocket watch, or, as he called it, – his 'timepiece'. Top right pocket was for his pocket knife, and bottom right was for his matches. This is how it had always been with Old John, and how it had been with his father too. Little Jimmy and Katie sat watching, waiting for the 'magic' tin to open. Holding the round tin in the palm of his left hand, he said, 'Acki, acki, acki, whur's me baccy?' He then raised his right hand up past the tin … and the lid mysteriously flew open. The children loved to see this, and always said, 'Please tell us how you do it, Granfer,' and Old John's reply was always the same: 'I canna a-tell yu – it's magic! – an' if I wuz t'tell yu then the dear Lord wud be all upset with me.'
'Would it work if you didn't say those strange words, Granfer?' asked Katie.
'No, it uddent,' Old John replied. 'You watch now.'

And with that he closed the lid and, uttering no word, raised his hand past the tin. The lid remained closed, then he said, 'Watch!' and he said the magical words, raised his hand – and the lid flew open. (Old John's tin was the old style round 'pigtail twist' tobacco tin; by squeezing the sides the catch was loosened and the lid flew open.)

'Will you tell us what the magic words mean, Granfer?' Katie implored in her best pleading voice.

'Well, I *could* a-tell yu, but I dunna know if I'm a-gooin' to,' said Old John with a smile.

'Please tell us, Granfer.'

Old John had really got them now, and he said, 'Well alright, yu've a-twisted me arm an' I'll a-tell yu.'

The children sat, spellbound, watching and waiting as Old John took his time filling his pipe and slowly lighting it with a brand from the fire.

'Oh come on, Granfer, tell us, we're waiting,' Little Jimmy said impatiently.

'Yu'm gettin' t'be a proper little *mush* baint yu my lad, just yu wait a minute now.'

And Old John took more time lighting the pipe.

'Well now, it's like this see. Yers and yers ago – yer mam wuz only a babby at the time – we wuz a-stoppin' on this old common, down country it is from 'ere, 'Artlebury Common (Hartlebury) it's a-called. Any'ows, thur wuz other folks a-pulled on this common, thur wuz 'Arry Tintack an' 'is family …

'Harry Tintack?' Katie butted in. 'That's a funny name.'

'Aar well, yu see thur name is Smith, but everyone calls 'um Tintack.'

'Why?' Katie asked.

'Yu'm alus a-wanting t'know summat baint yer gal? – well I'll a-tell yu. They got the name way back then 'cause every mornin' when 'Arry's missus went off with 'er basket a-callin' the houses, 'e'd call arter 'er "don't forget me tintacks".'

Katie butted in again. 'What did he want tintacks for, Granfer?'

'Fur makin' 'is pegs, gal, but the dear little nails baint tintacks – but 'Arry called um that. Now, wherever in the world wuz I?'

'On the common,' Jimmy replied. 'Bide quiet, Katie, I wants to know about the magic words.'

'Aar yes,' said Old John, 'we wuz a-pulled on this old common an' so wuz 'Arry Tintack an' 'is family, an' so wuz Stranger Price an' 'is family, an' so wuz Acki Price an' 'is missus. Now all we kept a-hearin' from whur Acki was *atched* wuz "whur's me baccy?" 'E'd keep a-shoutin' this to 'is dear little missus all day. An' that (Old John winked and tapped the side of his nose) is whur them magic words comes from, from the very lips of me dear old "cousin" Acki. 'E loved 'is baccy; I can picture 'im now a-rollin' they dear little *tuvlers* (cigarettes) of his; an' while I a-thinks've it, I'll tell yu summat else that 'appened on that old common.'

'Thur was a little *budiker* (shop) up in the village, it wer the front room've this dear old lady's 'ouse; 'er only sold baccy an' sweets, *dordi!* I can smell that little shop now – real *kushti* it wuz, all baccer an' sweety smell. Any'ows, she sold "black baccer" an' I wuz partial t'it, like me old dad wuz. So this one day I thinks t'meself I'll *jall* over the common an' through the pretty little copse whur thur wuz a path a-leading t'the road. The long way round to the village like, but as I sez, it wuz a nice day an' I thought I'll tek me time.'

'Any'ows, I gets t'the little *budiker* an' sure enough, the dear lady 'ad plenty've "black baccer". She 'ad a counter right across the little room with a little flap in it so 'er could get through t'open an' lock the door, which 'ad a dingly bell on it, otherwise *foki* (people) could've *jalled* in an' a-*chored* (stolen) all 'er stuff, 'causc she used t'sit in 'er kitchen 'avin' 'er cups've tea, like.'

'Any'ows, the dear old lady asks what I wants an' I sez "Four inches've black baccer, lady please".'

'Four inches, Granfer, whatever do you mean?' Katie blurted out.

'*Dordi!* Yu'm an inquisitive child, I'll never finish this 'ere story. On the counter wuz a brass ruler, screwed down it wer, an' yu asked fer 'ow many inches've baccer yu wanted – this baccer come in a roll, 'bout as thick as me little finger t'was, an' they'd cut off 'ow many inches yu wanted an' then a-weigh it on they lovely old brass scales. An' then yu paid fur it!'

'Any'ows, I'd got me baccer an' wuz a-walking down the street, t'go back like, when I passes the *kitchima*. I thought t'meself I'll think I'll 'ave a pint of *livena* an' sit under that old yew tree outside – they warn't too partial to us people in this old Public – an' I'll 'ave a smoke with me new fresh baccer. Well, the man served me, an' I takes me *livena* and a-goos an' sits under this yew tree, an' I'm a-smokin' me baccer an' I'm real happified, an' I thinks t'meself, maybe I'll just 'ave another fer the road. So I duz. Then I looks at the coppers I 'ad, an' thinks maybe I'll just 'ave another cus I've got the *luvva*.'

'Any old 'ows, I've a-supped me *livena* an' a-smoked some of me new baccer, an' I thinks t'meself I'd better be gettin' back t'get the *yog* a-gooin' an' the kettle on ready fer yer Granny comin' 'ome from 'er callin'. So I thinks t'meself I'd best goo back the short way, which wer straight down this little lane opposite the *kitchima*. So off I goes an' I'm all happified an' I starts a-singin' a little song t'meself, an' I'm ploddin' on down this old lane when I stops dead in me tracks. *Dordi!* I sez, whatever can that be?'

'What was it, Granfer, what was it?' shouted out Katie.

Old John held up his right hand index finger, the tip of which was burnt black from years of tamping down the burning tobacco in the bowl of his pipe, and nodded to Katie.

'I'll tell yer if yu bides quiet an' lets me. Well now, all across this dear little lane is these blacky brown marks. I'm a-lookin' at um an' I thinks t'meself – whatever can they be? Well now, I'm a-lookin' an' a-lookin', me *yoks* is a-tryin' t'work out whatever they can be. Then I *diks* that the grass is all flattened down on the bank at the side've this little lane, an' then I notices these scuffy white marks on the edge've the lane where the grass is all a-flattened. *Dordi!* I sez t'meself, I *jins* (knows) what this is.'

'What was it, Granfer?'

Again Old John held his index finger up at Katie and said, 'I'm not a-gooin' t'tell yu now.'

'Sorry Granfer, but I'm so excited and I wants to know.'

'Well I'll a-tell yu. Yu knows that "black baccer" that I've a-bin a-talkin' about? Well some folks likes to charr it (chew it), an' when yu charrs it yu 'as to spit the juice out, like. Even when yu smokes it yu likes t'ave a little spit now an' agin.'

'Any old 'ows, I *jinned* what it wer.' And Old John paused and looked at the children's faces and smiled to himself.

'An' now I'll a-tell yu what it wer. It wer two people who'd a-laid on that grassy bank an' I could a-tell that by the scuffy marks on the road, it wer the iron on the 'eels've thur *chokkers* (boots) what 'ad a-scuffed the road, see? An' them blacky brown marks wuz baccer spit. They'd a-sat thur on that grassy bank charrin' baccer an' a-spittin' across that dear little lane t'see who could spit the furthest. Now what do you think've that? An' I'd a-workd out who it wer an' all. I'd a-though t'meself it must be old Matty an' Annie, an' I'd a-worked out that they must be *atchin* down by the pool whur they alus *atched* when they wuz round this way – an' I'd a-worked out that they musta bin up to that dear little *budiker* an' bought some black baccer as I'd just a-done.'

'Any'ows, I carries on down the lane, an' sure enough, in thur by that dear little pool under some bushes is Matty an' Annie's tent, a bit've smoke a-rising up from thur little *yog*, and thur old pram parked alongside.'

'A pram, Granfer? Did they have a babby?'

'No gal, they never 'ad no babby, they wuz too old fur that. That old pram was fur a-carryin' thur tent rods an' canvas, thur blankets, an' all on thur bits've *covvals* (things) as they 'ad. That's 'ow they used t'move about, like – they never went too far mind, they wuz localised as yu might say. Any old 'ows, I gives 'um a shout as I passes. *'Ow yer gooin' on?* I shouts. An' they gives me a wave of thur 'ands. They wuz dear old people, but not the sort as we liked t'*atch* up with, yu understands.'

'Well, I gets back to the wagins an' gets the *yog* a-gooin' an' gets the kettle on, just in time fur yer Granny a-comin' 'ome – otherwise thur'ud a-bin trouble. Well yer Granny, she fries a bit've *mass* (meat), and we 'as our *hobben*, an' I'm still a bit *motto* (drunk), like. So I *jalls* up in the wagin an' I gets me old fiddle an' I a-tunes 'er up, then I sits down by the *yog* an' I starts a-playin'. A drop've *livena* alus makes me play that old fiddle better, Well now, I'm really makin' 'er sing an' yer Granny, she gets the bit've playwood (plywood) offn the cratch an' she chucks it down by the *yog* an' she says, "Give us the Gypsy Hornpipe (Wrexham hornpipe), my John". An' she starts a-dancin' – tippity tap, tippity tap she's a-gooin'. Yu didna *jin* she wer *kushti* on 'er *peeris* (feet), now did yu? She's the bestest, is yer Gran. *Dordi!* can 'er dance!'

'Any'ows, the others who was *atched* close by, they 'ears the music an' they all *jalls* over, an' they'm all a-sittin' round the *yog*, enjoyin' umselves like. Then yer mammy – she wer only a little 'un – she sez, "I'll give yu a song, *dordi!*" Yer mammy was only a bit've a gal then, but my dear Lord, she 'ad the prettiest voice.'

And Old John went quiet for a bit. 'Any'ows, Isaac, 'Arry's lad, 'e gets out 'is mouth organ an' 'e's a-blowin' an' a-suckin' at it an' a-givin' us some *kushti* tunes. Then old Rosie, she sez t'Stranger, Samson's lad, she sez, all a-sentimental like, "Give us that dear old song *Who'll Break the News to Mother?*" Well, Stranger, 'e teks 'is *swiggler* from 'is *mui* an' in 'is croaky voice 'e sang that dear old song, an' Rosie is a-sat thur a-moppin' 'er old *yoks*. An' then yer Granny, she gives us the old Jimmie Rodgers' song *Letter Edged in Black* an' old Rosie, she's a-moppin' 'er old *yoks* agin. *Dordi, Dordi!* she wuz a pretty sight. So I plays um summat a bit lively like, an' we'm all a-laughin' an' a-jokin' – aar, we 'ad us a real good night that night. They wuz *kushti* old times, don't yer know …'

'Any'ows, afore yu *jalls t'woodrus* (goes to bed), I wants yer both t'ave a goo at a-openin' this old baccer tin've mine. I wants t'see if yu've a-got the magic in yer.'
Old John took the tin from his pocket and held it in the palm of his hand.
'Now yu both knows the words now, don't yer?'
'*Owli*,' they replied.
'Say 'um then, one, two, three.'

In unison Little Jimmy and Katie whispered, 'Acki, acki, acki, where's me baccy?'

The lid flew open.

'We did it! We did it!' they shouted.

'Thur now, oh my dear blessed Lord, yu two's a-got the magic in yer, on my life yu 'as.' Old John chuckled to himself as the children ran over to their Granny.

'We've got the magic, Granny, we've got the magic in us!'

'*Mi-Duvval* (my God)! What's ever yer Granfer bin up to now, he's a-getting' wusser in 'is old age, I swear 'e'll turn us all into *dinilos* (fools) afore too long!'

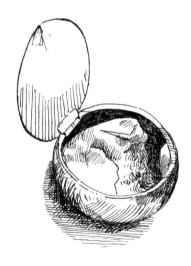

Who'll Break the News to Mother?

While shot and shell were screaming
Across the battlefield,
The boys in blue were fighting,
Their noble flag to shield.
Then a cry from our brave captain
Said, 'Boys, the flag is down.
Who'll volunteer to save it from disgrace?'
'I will,' a young boy shouted,
'I'll save the flag or die!'
Then rushed into the thickest of the fray,
Saved the flag, but gave his young life,
All for his country's sake.
We carried him back and heard him softly say,

Chorus: "Just break the news to Mother
            She knows how dear I love her
            And tell her not to wait for me,
            For I'm not coming home.
            Just say there is no other
            Can take the place of Mother,
            Then kiss her dear sweet lips for me,
            And break the news to her."

From afar, a noble general
Had witnessed this brave deed.
'Who saved the flag? Speak up, boys.
'Twas a noble and brave deed.'
Then a cry from our own captain said,
'Sir, he's sinking fast.'
Then slowly turned away to hide a tear.
The general in a moment
Knelt down beside the boy,

140

And gave a cry that touched all hearts that day:
' 'Tis my son, my brave young hero.
I thought you safe at home.'
'Forgive me, father, for I ran away.'

Chorus: "Just break the news to Mother
                    She knows how dear I love her
                    And tell her not to wait for me,
                    For I'm not coming home.
                    Just say there is no other
                    Can take the place of Mother,
                    Then kiss her dear sweet lips for me,
                    And break the news to her."

Letter Edged in Black

I was standing by my window yesterday morning
Without a thought of worry or of care
When I saw the postman coming up the pathway
With such a happy look and jaunty air

Well he rang the bell and whistled while he waited
And then he said Good morning to you Jack
I little knew the sorrow that he brought me
As he handed me a letter edged in black

With trembling hand I took the letter from him
Broke the seal and this is what it said
Come home my boy your dear old father wants you
Come home my boy your dear old mother's dead

The last words that your mother ever uttered
Were tell my boy I want him to come back
My eyes are blurred, my poor old heart is breaking
As I'm writing you this letter edged in black

Those angry words I wish I'd never spoken
You know I never meant them, don't you Jack?
May the angels bear me witness I am asking
For your forgiveness in this letter edged in black

I bow my head in sorrow and in silence
The sunshine from my life it all has fled
Since the postman brought that letter yesterday morning
Saying come home my boy your dear old mother's dead

As I heard the postman whistling yesterday morning
Coming down the pathway with his pack
Oh he never knew the sorrow that he brought me
When he handed me that letter edged in black

There'll Come a Time

Why are you sad papa my darling?
Why are those tears falling today?
Why do you look at me so strangely?
Have I done wrong? tell me I pray

Oh no, my child, you are an angel
There's not a heart truer than thine
But I'm afraid someday you'll leave me
Just as your moma did, there'll come a time

There'll come a time some day
When I have passed away
There'll be no papa to guide you
From day to day

Let me know all papa my darling
Tell me I pray of mother dear
Where has she gone, why did she leave us?
Why is her name never called here?

It seems I can feel her dear arms about me
And her sweet lips pressed close to mine
I'd give this world only to see her
I pray to heaven will there come a time

Oh there'll come a time some day
When I have passed away
There'll be no papa to guide you
From day to day

By Charles Kassell Harris (1867-1930)

THE TALKING DOG AND AUNT BECKY'S CAT

Old John and the children were squatted down on their haunches, backs against the wall of Church Stretton Post Office. Katie had pulled her skirt tightly around her legs before squatting down as her mother had taught her to do when she was very small. 'Cover yerself up you brazen gal,' had rung in her ears so many times and now, like all the women folk, she did it automatically. By Old John's side was Genty's cross-over arm basket, filled with groceries and he was keeping his eye on it, thinking of the meat pudding Genty would make on Sunday.

Genty was still in the market, talking as usual to the 'dear lady' who bought Old John's hanging baskets and flowers from her. Each week the 'dear lady' had some problem to discuss with Genty … and Genty would always 'advise' in her soft-spoken *durrakin* (fortune-telling) voice. Returning to Old John she would wink her eye and say, 'I've a-took some *luvva* from the old *rauni* (lady) again, my John.' And Old John would reply, '*Dordi* – the dear lady – she buys us most of the *hobben* every week, don't she, gal? … the dear kind lady.'

Suddenly, Little Jimmy exclaimed, '*Dik at that jukkal* (look at that dog). *Dordi!* that's the funniest *juk* I've ever a-seen.'
A rather smartly dressed, well-to-do woman had walked past them with a Pekinese dog on a lead. She had passed them as though they

were invisible, and made no acknowledgement of Old John's 'Mornin', Lady'.

'What sort of *jukkal* is that, Granfer?' Little Jimmy's head was turned watching the dog (and its owner) waddle down the pavement.

'That's what's known as a Pekinese, lad, comes from somewhere over the seas I think – yu dunna see many've 'um about, it's only the posh old *raunis* and *raklis* that 'as 'um, like. They baint no good fur nowt, 'uddent be no good fur sniffin' out a *hotchi* (hedgehog) or bushin' out a *shushi* (rabbit), 'ud they. They'm only good fer the *foki* t'ave as petty things. Me Aunt Caroline 'ad one that could talk.'

'Talk, Granfer?' Little Jimmy exclaimed in a puzzled tone.

'*Owli*, well she *penned* (said) that the *bitta jukkel* (little dog) could *rokker* (speak) any old 'ow.'

Katie had been listening to the conversation, and excitedly said, 'Tell us about the dog that could talk, Granfer.'

'You'll 'ave t'wait t'ear about that,' replied Old John, ' 'ere comes yer Granny.'

Genty was coming up the street, looking very pleased with herself, smiling and nodding to the country folk that recognised her. Rising up from his squatting position to greet her, Old John said, 'Yu alus looks pleased when yu've a-sin that lady.'

And Genty winked her eye at him. 'I've a-took a *kushti* bit've *luvva*, my John.'

'*Dordi* – the dear kind lady,' came the reply.

Genty picked up the basket, putting her right arm through the handle and the leather strap over her shoulder to ease the weight, pulling the basket up onto her hip. Then they all made their way to the bus stop just in time to catch the bus for the return journey home.

Little Jimmy and Katie sat in the seats in front of their grandparents, and Katie kept turning round asking Old John to tell them about the talking dog. 'Tell us about the *jukkal* that could *rokker*, Granfer – tell us, tell us.' Her voice was getting louder, and Old John said sternly, '*Kekka rokker*, the *foki is a-dikin at tutti* (don't talk, the people are looking at you).' Katie turned round, head bowed, and was silent for the rest of the journey.

'Whatsoever yu bin fillin' thur little 'eads with now, my John?' Genty said quietly, '*rokkerin jukkals?*'

'*Owli*, gal. you remembers me Aunt Caroline's little *jukkal* now, don't yer?'

'Oh! my dear blessed Lord, that I do, my John,' and she gave a little chuckle. 'I could a-tell 'um about me Aunt Becky's *matchika* (cat) an' all – *Dordi!* they'd a-like that, t'was a long time ago, my John.'

'It wer an' all, gal,' he replied, 'they dear people an' them days is long gone … long gone.'

Once off the bus Katie was her usual boisterous self, skipping up the lane, taunting Little Jimmy and making him chase her. The barking of Nell greeted them as they made their way over the plank bridge.

'I loves this old place, my John,' Genty said as she put the heavy basket down in the tent doorway.

'Aar, it's 'ome, baint it gal? We'm lucky, baint we?'

A thin plume of smoke was rising from the smouldering log that Old John had covered with wood ash, and he went over and gave it a kick, freeing the ash from it. A few thin dry sticks were placed over it, and then with his old tin tray he flapped the fire to life again. Putting on a few bigger pieces he took the kettle and filled it from the water jack which stood on the table outside the tent.

'I'm a-puttin' the *kavvi* on fur *meski*,' he shouted to Genty, who was busy packing away her groceries. 'Let Neil loose, lad, afore 'er strangles 'erself a-dancin' on the end've that chain,' he shouted to Little Jimmy, as Genty was shouting to Katie to 'come an' put this *mass* (meat) in the safe fur me, gal'.

They ran to get their jobs done, knowing that their grandmother always had something for them in the bottom of her basket.

Standing like two little soldiers in the doorway of the tent they were soon rewarded with the market day treat. Two bananas were produced and handed to the children.

'Eh *Dordi!* Monkeys eats them,' cried out Little Jimmy, and he pranced about pretending to be a monkey.

'*Kekka rokker* that *nav*, *chavvi* (don't speak that name, boy) – it's unlucky, *really* unlucky to say that name,' shouted Genty. 'Dunna use that name again, lad, you'll bring bad luck on us all.'

Little Jimmy stopped his imitating, saying, 'Is you serious, Granny?'

'By the dear blessed Lord I am, lad, *jall* an' ask yer Granfer t'spit three times in the fire an' turn 'is bit've *luvva* over in 'is pocket – do it now, lad, an' be quick about it.'

Old John had heard the commotion and had already done the deed before Little Jimmy asked him.

'Yer Granny knows about these things,' was all he said.

All this time Katie had been standing motionless by the tent, her mouth and eyes wide open.

'You is a witch, 'ent you Granny? I knowed you was – can we eat the 'nanas now?' she said.

'Come 'ere yu two,' said Genty and she put her arms round the shoulders of her two little grandchildren.

'I didna a-mean t'shout, but thur's many things in this old life of ourn that yur a-got t'learn. *Jall* on and eat yer 'nanas now – but remember never t'say that word again, won't yu?'

After drinking their tea and munching on a big slice of fresh white crusty bread and cheese and onion, Old John and Little Jimmy trundled off to the farmyard to fill the churn with their drinking water. Katie was sitting by the fire peeling potatoes for the meal of the day. 'These peelings shrivels up in some funny shapes when they'm drying, don't they Granny?' she said as she threw a handful onto the flames.

'Aar they do, gal, an' I'll a-tell yu what they'm really good fur as well. Iffn yu 'as an iron pot that's a-goin' a bit rusty, like, chuck all yer fresh peelins in with some water, an' a-boil it up fur a few hours, then chuck it out. Then get a bit've rag an' dip it in some water, then dip that in the ash from the fire an' rub it on the inside of the pot. Then swish it out, an' then boil it up with water, an' it'll come all lovely an' clean, like.'

'I'll remember that, Granny,' she said, but her mind was on 'the talking dog'.

'Granny, will you ask Granfer to tell us about the 'pickle sneeze' dog that could talk *please*? – 'cos if I asks him he'll say "well I might or I might not" – all teasified like and make us wait and wait and wait. And I really wants to know.'

'I will, gal,' replied Genty, 'he do tease a lot, don't he? He's alus a-done it. If we gets 'im well fed when 'e an' yer brother comes back 'e'll be all happified an' it wonna tek 'im long t'a-start 'is storytellin'. An' I'll a-tell yer about me Aunt Becky's cat an' all, an' we might get 'im t'get that old fiddle out – 'e baint a-played fur a while now, 'as 'e?'

'No he 'ent, Granny, he says his fingers is gettin' 'maticky.'

Age, and a life in the open air, with daily manual work had, over the past few months, made playing the fiddle more difficult for Old John. By the time Old John and Little Jimmy returned Genty had boiled and then fried the sliced potatoes and onions and they were now keeping warm in the big cast-iron pot by the side of the fire. Pork belly rashers were now in the swing-handled frying pan and Genty was cooking them as they all liked – well done with crunchy edges. Katie had cut four big slices of crusty bread, and was busy buttering them as her grandmother called out, 'Is them dishes ready, gal?'

'*Owli*, Granny,' came the reply, and Genty took the pot and pan over to the cupboard table and dished up, giving Old John his first as she always did.

The meal was finished, the dishes washed, and the little group took their places around the fire. Katie's big dark eyes kept looking at her grandmother, and then they strayed over to her grandfather and she gave a little nod of her head, and then her eyes went back to her grandmother with another little nod of her head. Genty had got the message.

'My John, is yu a-gooin' t'tell the *chavvies* about that *rokkerin jukkal*?'

'I wuz just a-thinkin' about that, my Genty,' he replied with a smile. 'I'll just a-fill me old *swiggler* fust.'

Katie's dark eyes looked towards heaven, and Genty gave her a smile and a little wink of her eye. A cloud of strong-smelling tobacco smoke filled the air and Old John coughed and spat in the fire. Little Jimmy had been sitting quietly looking into the flickering flames, listening to all this and suddenly exploded with, 'Is you goin' t'tell us about that *jukkel* or 'ent you, Granfer?'

'*Dordi!*' said Old John, 'yu's getting' t'be too much've a man, yu is,' and he burst out laughing. 'I is, an' I'm a-gooin' t'tell yu now, so pin yer *kans* (ears) back an' bide quiet … or I shannent.'

Katie's eyes again rolled heavenwards.

'Well now, started Old John, 'I'm a-gooin' t'tell yu about me old Aunt Caroline's little *jukkal* – God rest her soul … and that dear little dog an' all.'

'We knows that, Granfer,' Katie said in a haughty manner.

'*Dordi!* An' yu's a-getting' t'be a right little madam an' all my gal,' said Genty. 'Now bide quiet or 'e wonna a-tell yu, will yu my John?'

No I shanna, my Genty – I'm a-thinkin' twice about it now.'

'Sorry, Granfer, *pleeese* tell us,' and Katie looked pleadingly at her grandfather.

'*Dordi!* them *kaulo yoks* (black eyes) 'ull melt any man's 'eart … they'm just like our Addy's,' he thought as he smiled at her.

'Well now, I've a-told yer about me Uncle Ezzie, baint I? Well me Aunt Caroline was 'is wife, an' when Uncle Ezzie died – God rest 'is soul – she 'udent 'ave the wagin burnt; they *yogged* (burnt) the tent an' all on 'is stuff, like, but she stayed in 'er wagin, an' a good 'un an' all it were. It were what we calls a Bill Wright wagin, with big wheels at the back an' all carved fruit an' flowers a-gilded on it an' a lovely *grai* (horse) a-carved an' a-gilded on the door. Now 'er son, me cousin Varnon an' 'is missus an' *chavvies*, they stops with old Caroline, an' they all travels together, 'cos the old 'ummon canna 'arness-up, like, an' manage the wagin on 'er own. So me cousin Varnon, 'e yokes up an' takes charge've everythin' for 'is old mam, like, an' when they shifts 'is missus Margery she drives thur little wagin an' thur boys drive the carts, an' they'm all 'appy t'gether. Any old 'ow, me old Aunt, she still manages t'get about a-callin' an' a-*durrikin* (fortune-telling) – an' a *kushti durriker* she wer' an' all – they alus 'ad plenty've *luvva* an' *kushti mass to hol* (plenty of money and good meat to eat). Well, as the yers passes she gets older, as all on us do, an' she starts a-gettin' a bit peculiarified, but she still goos out *a-durrikin* the *gaujos*, like. Any'ows, this one day she comes 'ome an' she teks 'er *mongin gunner* (begging sack) offn 'er shoulder an' a-puts it down – an' guess what pops out?'

'A little "pickle sneeze" *juk*, Granfer – it was, wasn't it?' shouted Katie.

'*Owli*, it were an' all, gal, a little Pekinese came outa that old *gunner* a-shakin' itself an' a-runnin' about. "Wherever did yu get that, mam?" Varnon asks 'er. "I've a-called that big house end of the village t'day," she sez, "an' the dear lady 'as a-gived it t'me."

Well now our Varnon is a bit *trashed* (frightened) about this, an' 'e's sure that 'is old mam 'as *a-chored* (stolen) it. "You'll 'ave t'tek it back, mam," 'e sez, "we canna 'ave a *jukkal* like that with us." Well the old 'ummon she swears on the dear Lord's life that the lady a-gived it t'er, an' she starts a-causin' a rumpus, an' a-sayin' 'ow she'll do 'erself in, an' a-swearin' an' a-cussin'. Varnon said it were terrible to 'ear. "What's we to do?" he sez to Margery. "I thinks we should scarper outa this county," she sez. An' they did, they yoked up an' wuz gone, an' they ended up right up thur in Anglesey, an' that's whur they bided to until me Aunt left this earth.'

'Was that lovely wagon burnt when she died, Granfer?' asked Little Jimmy.

'No it warn't, lad. Me Aunt Caroline took 'er last breath on the dear Lord's earth in a tent, same as me Uncle Ezzie did, an' they *yogged* that. Aar, it were a lovely wagin. Uncle Ezzie 'ad bought it from one've the Burtons – they alus 'ad good stuff, an' Varnon sold it back to the family an' as far as I knows it's still in thur yard in Birkenhead, up thur in Cheshire.'

'But what about the dog *talking*, Granfer?' Katie said impatiently.

'Eh *dordi!* I'd forgotten about that,' Old John replied. 'Well now, Aunt Caroline loved this little *jukkal*, fed it on the best've food, let it sleep in the wagin on its own little cushion, she used t'brush it an' comb it, an' she'd alus 'ave it on 'er lap a-pettin' it, like, an' a-talkin' to it. Any old 'ow, the dear 'ummon, she got more an' more peculiarified, an' it got to 'er a-talkin' an' a-answerin' the *juk* as though it were a-talkin' back t'er. I can see 'er now, sitting on the front've the wagin with the little *juk* on 'er lap a-talkin' to it an' a-answerin' it, like. "I's got a nice bit've *kanni* (chicken) fur yer tea today Pogo," she'd say – "what's that, you wants *baulomass* (pork)? Well now Pogo, I's a-got it specially fur yer – what's that yu sez, yu 'ad chicken yesterday? – no you didn't Pogo, you 'ad the best bit of *baulomass* yesterday … I thinks you'm a-goin' a bit *divvy*," she'd say. Poor old 'ummon, it were 'er that wuz a-gooin' that way. She told everyone that the little *jukkal* could *rokker*, but when yu went t'er an' a-asked 'er t'mek the dog talk, she'd say, "Pogo 'as been a-*rokkerin* non-stop all day, 'e's fair made me 'ead bad, I've just a-scolded 'im an' a-told 'im to 'ush his *mui* – *dik* at 'im thur all a-sulkified." Or she'd say that 'e 'ad a sore throat or summat.'

'So the little *jukkal* couldn't really talk then, Granfer?'

152

'No, course it cudna, gal, but me dear old Aunt a-thought it could, an' we all 'umoured 'er on, like – the dear old soul. She still insisted on gooin' out a-*durrikin* right up to the time as 'er old legs give out – but Margery alus went with 'er, and 'udent let 'er tek 'er *mongin gunner*. An' yu 'ent gooin' t'believe this, but it's true, that little *jukkal* died the same day as me old Aunt, an' our Varnon went into the churchyard when it wer' dark an' a-buried little Pogo in the grave t'be with 'er, like. Pour us some *meski*, my Genty, will yer, me old throat's a-fair parched … then I'll bide quiet an' yu can tell 'um 'bout yer Aunt Becky's *matchiko* (cat).'

They all sat quietly drinking their tea, when Little Jimmy said, 'That lady with the Pekinese that we saw this morning was a rude lady, won't she, Granfer? She never spoke to you, did she? And you was real polite when you said mornin' to her.'

Old John smiled. 'I *diked* 'er a-comin' down the street, an' I *jinned* the sort she were. I alus speaks t'um – to annoy 'um, like. People like that might look poshified, but they baint got no breed t'um. They thinks they'm better'n anyone else, but when they dies they gets the same size little piece've ground as we does. Yer Granny 'ere dunna a-like 'um, does yu my Genty?'

'No I dunna, my John,' came the reply.

'Nasty *gauji* people they is – if I can ever sell 'um anythin' I alus puts a few coppers on extra, I likes t'try an' 'urt 'um in the pocket.' Both children nodded appreciatively and Katie said, 'Tell us about the cat, Granny.'

Old John coughed and spat in the fire. 'Yu two listen 'ard t'yer Granny now, 'cause this is a good 'un she's a-gooin' t'tell yu.'

'Well now,' Genty began, 'me old Aunt Becky – I think she wer me great-aunt, but I'm not rightly sure 'cause it wer' a long time ago – 'ad a cat. Now a cat is a funny sort've animal fer us people t'ave, but me old aunt an' uncle wer tent people, an' when yu lives in a tent they little mouseys can be a bit've a nuisance sometimes, so maybe they thought a cat 'ud be a good idea, like. Well now, after a while me old Aunt she fell out with this *matchiko*. The blessed thing was alus a-getting' on 'er food 'amper, an' when it did catch a little mousey it 'ud chew it up on thur bed blanket, an' the old 'ummon was a-really gettin' fed up with it. So this one day she sez t'er 'usband, she sez, "My Appy, you'll 'ave t'get rid've this *matchiko* afore I doos it some 'arm."
"I will, my Becky," he sez, "t'night I'll put it in a sack an' I'll goo over this old common we'm a-stoppin' on an' I'll chuck it out."

Well now, 'e doos just what I've a-told yu, and do yu know, the next mornin' the blessed cat is back, sitting by the fire embers, sittin' thur as bold as brass it wer. "My Appy," me old aunt sez, "yu'll 'ave t'tek the blessed thing further afield." So that night me old uncle Appy 'e puts the cat in the sack an' off 'e goos across the common an' down these dear little lanes, miles 'e walks, an' then 'e thinks t'imself this'll do, an' 'e chucks the cat out. Well now, when the old couple crawls outa the tent the followin' mornin', what doos they find?'
'The cat,' shouted Little Jimmy.
'*Owli* lad, the blessed thing 'ad a-found its way 'ome agin. Me old aunt she starts a-cussin' me old uncle an' she's a-sayin' 'e baint no good at nuthin', an' she's a-really a-givin' 'im some stick. "My Becky," 'e sez, "dunna goo on so; t'night I'll goo even further afield where the blessed thing'll never find its way back." So that night me old uncle 'e puts the cat in the sack again an' 'e puts it over 'is

shoulder an' off he goos. 'E goos over the common, but in a different direction, an' 'e walks an' 'e walks an' 'e walks – miles an' miles an' miles he goos, fur 'ours an' 'ours an' 'ours. 'Ventually 'e thinks t'isself this'll do, an' 'e chucks the cat out. Well now, 'e turns 'isself round an' starts a-walkin' up this dear little lane, an' then down another dear little lane – an' it's a dark old night, with just a dear little bit've moonlight – when suddenly me old uncle 'e thinks t'isself, "Oh! my dear blessed Lord, I dunna know whur I'm to." 'E'd gone and got 'isself lost! Just up this little lane 'e can make out in the moonlight a *pookerin-kosht* (signpost) on a crossroad, but that wanna no *kushti* t'im, 'cause like us 'e cuddna a-read a word. Well now, 'e sits 'isself down an' 'e leans 'is back agin this old *pookerin-kosht* an' 'e 'as 'isself a little smoke an' 'e's all a-worried, like, when suddenly, in the moonlight, he *diks* the cat a-comin' with its tail 'eld 'igh in the air. "*Dordi!*" 'e sez t'isself, "I'm saved, I'm saved." An' do yu know what 'e done?'

'What?' shouted the children.

'Why, 'e follered the blessed thing all the way 'ome.'

Silence fell – Little Jimmy and Katie sat staring at their grandmother. Suddenly she started to laugh and so did Old John. Laughing made him cough and the sound of a coughing laugh made Genty laugh more vigorously. The sight of their grandparents laughing made the children laugh – but they weren't quite sure what they were laughing about!

THE FISHY STORY

Old John and Little Jimmy had been on their daily excursion to the farmyard for water, Little Jimmy leaning on the side of the half milk churn trying to push, but making Old John's efforts to keep the old pushchair straight more difficult. They were almost home, when Katie came running up the track shouting, 'Granny's cooking us fish today!'

'Whur's 'er got *matchi* from, gal?' asked Old John.

'A *mush* I 'adn't seen before brought them, says he's me Uncle Benny. Smart he was, in a nice shirt with a tie,' replied Katie.

'Aar, Benny, that's yer Granny's brother's boy. 'E is smart an' all, alus dresses well does our Benny. Is 'e still thur, gal?'

'No, Granfer, he only popped in for a minute, gave Granny the fish, and said he was off to see about a job.'

Genty's nephew Benny was engaged on barn spraying and was a good 'grafter'. He owned a nearly-new J-type Bedford lorry and a tidy 'Eccles Traveller' trailer, and everything about his turnout 'twinkled'. To 'call' the farms he'd bought a smart, modern car, which his wife Elsie drove when they moved, with Benny driving the Bedford, pulling the trailer.

Genty was beaming when they arrived.

'Our Benny's just a-bin an' brought us some trout, my John.'

'I gathers that 'ummon, where's they a-stoppin' to?'

' 'E says they'm pulled on a lay-by this side've Hur-e-furd (Hereford) down by Hope under Dinmore. Says 'e just a-done one farm yesterday an' was off t'see another, said 'e cuddna bide long as farmer 'ad agreed t'see 'im.'

'My dear Lord, that lad do rush about now, don't 'e? – 'e's a "goo aheader" 'e is, makes yer proud now, don't it?'

Old John smiled and puffed on his pipe. 'Did 'e say whur 'e'd a-got the *matchi* from?'

'I never asked 'im, my John, but yu knows what 'e's like a-sneakin' about at night, that lad loves it now, don't 'e?' When I seed Elsie last she said she warn't a-goin' t'cook 'im another *shushi*, said 'er's sick've the sight've rabbits!'

That afternoon saw Katie helping her Granny to get the meal ready. 'You cut that skin on them *puvengris* nice and thin now, gal.'

Katie had been cutting the skin off the potatoes in chunks, much to her grandmother's disapproval. The peeled potatoes were washed and then put in the pot over the fire to 'parboil'. After a while Genty gave them a prod with a knife and declared, 'They'm done now gal, bring us that dish over.'

After tipping the water out, Genty poured the potatoes into the big dish and said, 'Put 'um on the table in the tent, gal, they can cool down a bit in thur.'

Carrying the big dish carefully to the tent, Katie placed it on the table on the right hand side of the doorway. She looked across to Little Jimmy's bed. 'He's folded them blankets nice and tidy,' she thought. Genty had taught Jimmy how to fold his blankets, piling them on one end of the little camp bed and putting his pillow on top. Genty was always one to have her place looking nice and tidy.

'I'm glad I don't have to fold my blankets up every morning, all I has to do is smooth them out and fluff up me piller.'

Katie was lucky to have her own little fixed bedplace at the back of her little wagon, where there was no need to fold her blankets every morning. She liked her little 'nest' as she called it, and was really proud of the thick pretty rug that Maurice had given her for the floor.

'Is yu day-dreamin' in thur, gal?' came a shout from Genty. 'Bring that bag've flour outa the wooden box at the back've the table.'

Genty had cleaned the fish and was now standing in front of the outside cupboard on legs, by the fire; the top of which was covered in red and white check oilcloth. The cupboard contained the tea dishes, cups and plates, sugar, and tinned milk (with only one hole punched in the top and a bit of stick pushed in the hole) – 'to save earywigs a-gettin' in,' as Genty said. (The children had found it difficult to operate the tin at first, but had now got the knack of 'hold in one hand, thumb on top, press thumb down and the milk spurtled out'.) The cutlery being kept in an old silver-plated bottle holder on the top. Genty had placed her 'rollin-out' tray on the check oil cloth and was ready to flour it and coat the fish ready for frying.

'Watch 'ow I does this, gal,' she ordered, and Katie nodded at her grandmother as she took the four trout and coated them in the flour, sprinkling salt and pepper on them.

'They can bide thur fer a bit now, goo an' see if them *poovers* 'as a-cooled down enough.'

Katie ran to the tent and put her finger on a potato.

'They're still a bit hot, Granny.'

'They'm ready,' thought Genty, who was taking the big cast iron hoop-handled frying pan over to the fire. 'Bring us me 'eavy pot, gal, an' put it down by the side've the fire.'

Katie struggled to carry the cast iron pot. 'I mustn't drop it, me Granny loves this pot,' she thought. 'Only the other day she said she could never get another one like it.'
'Put it just down thur, gal, by them embers,' said Genty, and Katie did as she was told. The pan was now on the kettle-iron and Genty put a large lump of lard in it.
'Run an' get me the *puvengris* now, gal.'
Katie liked helping her Granny, who said, 'It's fur yur own good, my gal, no nice young Gypsy boy will want yu when youm older if yu canna cook 'im a *kushti* bit a-*hobben*. Now *jall* and get them *puvengris* quick, the fat is a-meltin'.'

Running back with the dish of potatoes Katie did as she was asked, and put them on the ground next to her Granny, who picked one up in her left hand and, knife in her right hand, sliced them into the hot fat, turning them over with an old metal spatula.
'They'm lookin' nice and brown, Granny.' Katie was watching every move.
'Open that lid, gal.'
Katie, with a bit of rag, took the heavy iron lid off the pot by the side of the fire. Genty scooped up the fried potatoes with the spatula and transferred them into the pot.
'Put that lid on quickly, gal,' demanded Genty as she sliced the remaining potatoes into the hot fat. When all were cooked she put more lard in the pan and asked Katie to bring the tray of trout over, which she did at great speed, as by now the smell of food was really

making her feel hungry. Old John and Little Jimmy had returned with a pile of firewood each. Old John always used his old horse halter for carrying firewood (he'd lie it on the ground, put all the sticks over it, then pull the end through the loop and hoist it up onto his back). He'd made Little Jimmy a little halter of his own by plaiting baler twine, and Little Jimmy felt 'quite the man' carrying his own bundle of sticks.

'You've a-timed that well, my John.'
'Aar, Little Jimmy 'ere said 'e could smell *hobben* from way back thur in the wood.'
Genty then put two of the trout in the pan, Katie watching intently, cooked them on one side, turned them over to cook the other side, and then said, 'Open that pot, gal.'
Again the lid was taken off and Genty put the two trout in to keep warm. She fried the other two and said *"Obben*'s ready, my John.'
The big pot was taken over to the check oilcloth-covered cupboard table, where Katie had laid out four dish plates. Genty served up, saying, *"Ere yu is, my John'* (she always served her man first). 'I'll tek meat offn the bone fer the *chavvies*, I dunna want 'um t'get any bones stuck in thur dear little throats.'

Katie and Jimmy stood there waiting, mouths watering, then they were handed their meal which they took to the fire and munched hungrily. Genty, following them over, asked, *"Ow does yu like matchi*, then?'
With a full mouth Little Jimmy answered, 'Oh! *doooordi!*'
And Katie with a smile said, 'I likes fried *poovers* best! – I did they, Jimmy.'
'Shan't eat 'um then,' he replied ungraciously – but he did!

'Yu needn't 'elp me with them pots, Katie gal, yu did well 'elping with the cooking; come 'ere gal.' She gave her a big hug, then said, 'Yu get off with yer brother now an' 'ave a little play.'

The children ran towards the wood with Nell at their heels. Genty watched them go and, turning to Old John, she said, 'They've a-settled in well now, my John.'

'Arr they 'ave, the dear little lambs,' he coughed alarmingly and spat into the fire. 'Katie is so like our gal when she was that age, baint she?'

He was gazing into the fire watching a small burning stick in the embers turning into a perfect horseshoe shape.

'That's an omen fer sure,' he said to himself.

Returning from playing in the woods, the children sat down round the fire. Nell, exhausted, lay down next to Little Jimmy. The boy and dog had formed a close relationship, and Little Jimmy was content in his mind that no 'longtail' creature would sneak about with Nell on guard. Looking at his grandfather he remarked, 'I like fish, Granfer. Have you ever caught them?'

'Caught them!' said Genty. 'Lad, you're a-lookin' at the best fisherman in England an' Wales.' (Genty was prone to exaggeration.)

'I've a-done a bit in me time, lad, fished with rod an' bottle,' smiled Old John.

'How do you mean, Granfer – 'bottle'? Do you mean a beer bottle or something?'

'I do, lad. Want t'ear 'ow t'do it?'

Little Jimmy nodded.

'Well now, this baint no good in a river, but it's *kushti* in a pool or pond whur yu knows thur's *matchi*. Now what yu doos is, yu gets a bottle an' yu fills it with water – just enough so as it will bob in the water with the neck out, like. Then yu bungs in a cork an' yu pushes feathers inter the cork – not big 'uns or little 'uns, but medium 'uns, like. Then yu gets yer fishin' line with 'ook on end an' a dear little bit've lead jest above it, an' yu ties the end t'the neck a-the bottle, an' a-leaves the other end a-dangling below the bottom. Then yu gets a bit've string or a rubber band an' yu puts it round the bottle towards the bottom like, which will 'old the line in place. Then yu ties a piece've string, a very long piece've string, t'the neck. Yu puts yer bait on the 'ook an' yu chucks the bottle inter the pool – a-holdin' end've string, like. Then yu ties this end onto a bush or summat an' yu 'ides yerself an' 'as a smoke, or yu *jalls* off an' comes back later, *rarti* (night) time is *kushti* as no one can *dik* it, can they? It's a good 'un, lad, see – the wind a-blows them feathers an' that bottle it *jalls* all around the pool. You *jalls* back an' "hauls the bottle t'shore", as yu might say, an' iffn yu'm lucky yu 'as a nice *matchi* fur yer *hobben* that day.'

As Genty handed Old John his dish of tea he said, 'A-talkin' a-fish brings t'me mind when we wuz a-stoppin' with me cousin Caleb Lee an' 'is family, near Corwen up thur in Wales, yu remembers my Genty, don't yer? It wer yers agoo, I minds yu an' Annie a-sittin' by the *yog* a-whisperin' t'each other all secretive like.'
'I remembers, my John, an' I knows what yu'm a-goin' t'tell *chavvies* an' all.'
'Whatcher goin' to tell us, Granfer?' Katie blurted out in an excited voice.
'Well, as I sez, we wuz a-stoppin' with me cousin Caleb an' Annie up by Corwen, an' we wuz *atched* in this pretty little spot, right by the side've the river Dee. Farmer used t'let us bide thur, 'e warn't

no trouble, an' 'e an' Caleb was good pals as yu might say. 'E never said nowt about Caleb a-fishin' nor nothin'. Caleb an' me's a-pullin' these *matchi* out an' yer Granny an' Annie is a-cookin' 'um an' we'm 'avin' a right good time. Well, one day who should turn up but 'nother've our relations. It wer Horace Wood from over thur in Bala, jest a-passin' by, like. Well now, 'e's a-sat by the *yog* a-'avin' a drop've *meski* with us, an' 'e starts a-laughin' t'isself.

'What's up?' I *putches* (asks) 'im.

'Want t'ear a funny story?' he *pens* (says) t'us.

'*Owli*,' we sez, 'must be a good 'un the way you'm a-*savin* (laughing) t'yerself.'

'It is, oh! it is,' 'e scz.

'You knows me brother Valentine now don't yu?' '*Owli*,' we sez.

'Well,' he sez, 'month or so back 'e wuz in trouble with the Water Bailiff – cost 'im a bit of *luvva*, it did, an' 'e warn't a 'appy man. 'E sez to me, 'e sez, I'm a-gooin' t'ave that *mush* – an' 'e did last week.'

'What'ud 'e do?' we *putched* 'im.

'I'll tell yu,' 'e sez, all a-smilin', like. ''E got 'is big long mackintosh an' cuts the bottom of the right-'and *putsi* (pocket) open with his *choori* (knife).'

'Why'd 'e do that?' interrupted Caleb.

'Yu'll see in a minute,' 'e sez an' 'e carries on, ''e crept down t'the lake in this old mac of 'is, an' 'e took 'is rod an' all. Now 'c's a-lurkin' thur, waiting fer Bailiff t'come inter view. At last he *diks* 'im, an' 'e strides out inter the water. 'E never a-minded a-gettin' 'is *chokkers* (boots) and *hollivas* (socks) and *bulengris* (trousers) wet, no 'e didn't. 'E went out inter the water till it come up above the bottom of 'is coat … an' then he started to fish, an' 'e can fish an' all. 'E's a-pullin' 'um out, an' 'e's a-puttin' 'um in 'is right-'and *putsi*. Well a-course the *matchi* is comin' out've the bottom of 'is *putsi* and a-swimmin' away. Well now, Bailiff is *dikin* this an' 'e thinks t'isself, "I've got you again, my lad." So he *jalls* an' gets the *muskro* (policeman), as a witness t'im a-takin' *matchi*. They stands thur a-watchin' Valentine. Then Bailiff sez, "He's got four or more, come on".'

'Well 'e calls me brother out an' 'e accuses 'im of takin' four or more fish.

'I 'ent got no fish,' he sez, 'I warn't fishin', I was just a-practisin' me technique – I demands yu search me, Sir.' He sez to the *muskro*, 'this man 'ere 'as a-got it in fur me an' is a-causin' trouble.'

Well with that Valentine 'e ups with 'is arms, an' the *muskro* pats 'im all over.

'He 'ent got no fish,' 'e sez.

'I seed 'im,' sez Bailiff.

'Man,' sez Valentine, 'yer old *yoks* must be a-getting' *naflo* (bad), an' fer the life've me I canna understand why you'm alus a-makin' trouble against me. I wuz only a-practisin' me technique, man.' An' with that 'e upped and left them.

''E got 'im, didn't 'e brother?' sez Caleb. '*Dordi!* that's a good 'un, that is.'

'Well now, we wuz all a-sat thur a-laughin', an' then Horace pulls out 'is timepiece an' sez, "Lord, I must be off, gotta see a *mush* about a dog". 'E gets up, thanks us fer the tea an' wuz gone. An' that's the last time I seed 'im, nice man 'e wuz, all on 'is breed wuz. An' that's the end've that story.'

'That was a *kushti* trick, wasn't it?' Katie said, looking up at her Granny.

'It wer, gal, I remember that time well, I liked them times we spent with Caleb an' Annie. An' as yer Granfer sez, me an' Annie spent some time round the old *yog* a-*rokkerin* (talking) together – women's affairs yu understands. I miss Annie, she's been gone a long while now.'

She went quiet and then said, 'Do as yer old Granny sez and *jall t'woodrus* now.'

They went over to their grandfather and, as usual, gave him a big hug. This time his cap fell off and landed in the fire embers. Little Jimmy leapt to retrieve it and beat it on his trousers.

'Sorry, Granfer,' came a little voice from Katie, 'but we loves you.'

Little Jimmy handed Old John his cap saying with a smile, 'I does too old *mush*!' and skipped quickly backwards, as Old John took a swat at him with his cap.

'Dear Lord,' shouted Genty, 'yu can be brazen, yu can. Come 'ere an' give yer old Gran a hug, an' get yerself *t'woodrus* afore I gives yer a smack.'

JUKKAL'S MORED THE BOKRO

Genty called the children over to her one day, '*Vel akai chavvies* (come here children),' she'd called. They came scampering over to her.

'I've a-noticed yu two is *rokkerin Romanes* (talking Romani) a lot lately, I loves to *shoon* (hear) it, it's *kushti* t'me old *kans* (ears). Now what I wants yu t'do – yu *jins* 'ow yer old Granfer likes t'play jokes on folks?'

'*Owli*,' they replied.

'Well what I wants yer t'do is go an' shout *Dordi! dordi! the jukkal's mored the bokro* (dog's killed the sheep). *Dik* at 'im thur, 'e's all sleepified by the fire – go an' do it now!'

They said it to themselves; then crept over to Old John and shouted it out with all their might.

'Oh my dear blessed Lord! Never, never, never, oh! never!' he choked out as he came to from his forty winks and slipped off his milkcrate seat with an old sack on top, knocking the teapot over into the ashes. He lay on his side on the ground shouting 'Where? where?'

The children burst into laughter. He looked round at them, and there by their side stood Genty, hands on hips, rocking from side to side, tears streaming down her cheeks with laughter. 'We got yu thur, my John,' she managed to say.

'My dear blessed Lord, you lot is evil. The Devil 'imself 'ud 'ave a job t'find more evil people than you.'

166

He sat there with his legs outstretched, and then started to laugh himself. 'Now I thinks about it our Nell 'ud never do a thing like that – 'ere, give us a 'and up.'

Little Jimmy and Katie took an arm apiece.

'Up you come, Granfer,' and Old John raised himself up. He hunched his shoulders, put out his arms, fingers outstretched like claws, roared like a lion and said, 'Now I'm a-goin' t'*mor* (kill) you.' The children screamed, turned on their heels and fled in the direction of the wood.

'Now who's had the last laugh, my Genty?'

'You 'as, my John, yu alus do – but my blessed Lord, yu did look comical when yu slid offa that old crate, an' yu big great *dinilo* (fool), yu knows farmer shifted sheep outa field yesterday. Why, yu give 'im a 'and yerself, now dinna yu? But I doubts if you remembers … yu'm getting old, my man!'

MAKING THE CATAPULT

For the past couple of years Old John had been keeping an eye on an ash sapling which was growing on the far side of the little copse. He'd tied the two little upright stems together at the top, to make them grow into a perfect cupped U shape.

A magpie was chattering on a branch of a plum tree on the left hand side of the track as Old John and Little Jimmy were returning from the farm with the milk churn full of water. Saluting the bird, Old John said, 'Mornin' Mr Magpie, 'ow's yer wife?'
'I canna abide they *kakarachies* (magpies), lad,' remarked Old John as he took his catapult from his pocket. Feeling in the other pocket he produced a nice round stone, and a second later the bird had ceased its chattering and was flying across the field.
'You missed him, Granfer,' Little Jimmy shouted, rather disappointedly.
'Aar lad, I missed 'im, me old *yoks* baint as *kushti* as they used t'be – but I scared 'im, didna I, lad?'
'When's you goin' to make me a catty, Granfer? You said you would weeks and weeks ago.'
'Soon, soon,' came the reply, and Old John's thoughts turned to his little ash sapling.

That afternoon Old John raised himself from his milk bottle crate seat by the fire, and without saying a word started to walk towards the wood.

'Where you goin', Granfer, can I come with you?' Little Jimmy said as he came running across to his grandfather.

'No yu canna, lad, I'm on a special errand, yu look arter that kettle an' a-see it's a-boilin' in just over an 'our's time.' And with that Old John disappeared into the wood. Following the hedge on the side of the field he came to the five-barred gate which led onto the little lane with grass growing in the middle, and there opposite was his little copse.

'That ash peg should just about be the right size fer Little Jimmy's 'and,' he thought, as he made his way to the far side of the copse. And there it was. It had grown perfectly, and as Old John had thought, was just the right size for his grandson. With his old curved blade pocket knife he cut the two top branches off, leaving the binder twine binding still on. Then, bending the sapling, with one clean cut he cut it off about a foot from the fork of the Y.

'Eh *dordi*, it's a good 'un an' all,' he said to himself.

Little Jimmy, sitting by the fire, was watching the edge of the wood where his grandfather had disappeared so mysteriously. Suddenly Old John appeared, and Little Jimmy swung the kettle-iron, with kettle suspended, over the flames. By the time Old John reached the fire the kettle was boiling.

'Yu'm a-getting' t'be a good lad,' Old John said with a smile. '*Jall* an' ask yer Granny t'come an' brew us some *meski*.'

'But where have you been, Granfer?'

'*Jall* and ask yer Granny, then I'll a-tell yu,' came the reply.

Little Jimmy sprinted to the tent, and in no time was back to his grandfather.

Old John pulled the left hand side of his old tweed jacket open to reveal the big pocket that Genty had sewn on for him. And there, protruding from the top was the Y of the ash peg. He took it out and Little Jimmy said excitedly, 'Is that my catty, Granfer?'

'It will be, lad, but a good *flurta* (catapult) takes time t'do it proper, like, an' this is a *kushti* little peg, lad – see, it's a –grown t'be a lovely cup shape. *Dordi!* it's a good 'un.'

He held it out before him, eyeing up the two upright stems. Yes, they eyed up perfectly.

' 'Ere, lad, 'old it in yer 'and,' Old John said as he passed it to Little Jimmy.

'*Kekka*, lad, you'm a-holdin' it wrong, come 'ere.'

Little Jimmy was holding the peg in his clenched fist, and his grandfather, taking the peg from him, said, 'Watch now! Yu puts yer thumb on the left side've the peg an' 'ooks yer fust finger round t'other an' them three fingers goos round the stem an' pulls it t'yer palm, like. Here now, yu show me,' and he handed it back to Little Jimmy.

'Like this, Granfer?'

'*Kushti*,' came the reply, ' 'old it still now while I cuts a little mark.'

And Old John cut a little V on the stem just below the boy's hand; then, taking it from him, proceeded to cut V's all the way round, deeper and deeper until it was cut off. Then, with little cuts he formed a clean round end to the stem. Just under ¾ inch up he cut another little round circle of V's, and by clean little cuts formed a knob on the end, leaving the bark in the centre.

'Whatschur doin', Granfer – is you making a catty?'

Genty and Katie had arrived to make tea, and Katie was leaning over Old John's shoulder, knocking his cap to one side in the process.

'Eh *dordi!* – yu'm an excitable child, come outa yer granfer's face now gal, and *jall* an' put out the dishes,' Genty shouted to her.

'I wants to see the catty, Granny.'

'DISHES!' came the reply, and Katie, moodily, took the few steps to the cupboard table and put out the two tea dishes and two cups. Turning round to face the little group, with hands on hips she crossly uttered, 'I'm nothing but a slave, a little slave, that's what I is!'

Genty and Old John looked at each other and burst out laughing. Genty was laughing so violently that she had to sit down, and laughing always made Old John cough, and coughing always made him spit. With tears rolling down her cheeks, Genty, putting out her arms, said, 'Come 'ere my dear child.'

Katie, sulkily, went over to her grandmother who, cradling her in her arms, soothingly said, 'A slave is wot yu baint, an' a-never will be, my gal, but we all 'as things t'do, an' yu'm a real good gal a-helpin' me so much. Yu've a-took t'this old life of owern well, an' all the things yu'm a-larnin' 'ull be good fur yu when yu'm older – now give yer old granny a hug an' a kiss.'

Little Jimmy, who had been sitting quietly by the fire, suddenly said, 'What about me catty?' and they all started laughing again – Katie included, and Old John coughed and spat in the fire.

After drinking his tea, that Katie graciously offered him, and filling and lighting his pipe, Old John resumed the making of the catapult. Taking his knife, he carefully cut off the little branch that grew in the centre of the ash fork, then, just below the fork he cut a circle in the bark, then carefully he cut the bark from the fork and two stems. Then, eyeing them up, he cut the stems off about 1½ inches up from the bottom.

'Thur yu is, my son, a lovely little catty peg.' Old John held it up to show Little Jimmy, who was now beaming with excitement.

'In that bag a-mine under the table in the tent is some sandpaper that Old Fred left when we made yer sister's accommodation – *jall* an' a-get it fur me, lad.'

Little Jimmy rushed to get it, and handed it to Old John who carefully sanded the white peeled top part of the catapult, then finished by sanding the knob at the bottom of the stem.

'We've a-got t'let 'er dry now, lad, bring us yer Granny's big iron pot over.'

Little Jimmy lugged the heavy cast iron pot over to his grandfather who, taking it, placed it on the edge of the fire.

'We dunna want 'er too hot an' we dunna want 'er too cold,' Old John said philosophically.

After a little while he lifted the heavy lid and put his hand in. 'Just right,' he murmured and placed the peg inside and replaced the lid, then pulled the pot further away from the embers.

'Nice an' slow, lad, otherwise she'll crack an' split, an' I dunna a-want that, no more than you, 'cause 'er's a lovely little peg.'

Little Jimmy nodded knowingly.

Later that evening the peg was removed and a piece of string tied to the knob. Then Old John walked over to the clothes line, at the rear of the tent, and tied it on the line. Little Jimmy was at his heels, watching every move.

'We'll let 'er bide thur, lad, fur a couple a-days, like, an' with the bit've sun an' wind 'er'll be ready.'

Two days Little Jimmy thought – I wants it now! Old John could see the anticipation in the boy's eyes and winked at him. 'It'll be a good 'un, lad, an' good things is alus worth a-waitin' fur, an' day arter t'morrer is our day t'goo t'town an' I'll a-get the elastic.'

Friday morning came, and Little Jimmy was up early. He walked round the tent and there was his catty peg dangling in the breeze from the clothes line. He reached up and touched it and felt a little shiver go through his body. After breakfast Old John took Little Jimmy into the wood where grew a pine tree. Taking his knife, Old John removed a hard lump of resin from the bark.
'What's that for, Granfer?' asked Little Jimmy.
'When that's a-melted, lad, it sticks like glue, an' we needs that t'hold the ears in place while I binds 'um.'

It all seemed a great mystery, but Little Jimmy nodded approvingly and thought, with pride, 'me Granfer knows everything'.
They walked slowly back, and Old John stopping, said, ' 'Old yer right arm out an' pretend t'old yer *flurta* in yer 'and – now keep that arm straight at all times. Now with yer left 'and pretend t'pull the elastic back,' and Little Jimmy's left hand went back past his left ear. 'Now, keep that right arm straight, let the elastic goo an' flip yer wrist for'ard.'
Little Jimmy followed the instructions and Old John said, '*Kushti!* remember t'keep the right arm straight an' let yer wrist flip for'ard every time. 'Ere now, watch me,' and he took his catapult from his pocket and demonstrated.
'I've got it, Granfer.'
'Right arm straight an' flip yer wrist, lad,' and Old John wagged his index finger and winked at his grandson.

On their return Old John disappeared into the tent, coming out with his old bag from under the table. Turning to Little Jimmy he said, 'Take they bowls an' stuff offn the table, lad,' which Old John observed was done with great speed. Placing the old bag on the outside table, Old John started to rifle through it. 'I *jins* they'm in 'ere somewhur,' and suddenly he said, 'Aar, 'ere they is,' and he produced two tongues that he'd cut off a worn-out pair of his old brown boots.

'I alus cuts the tongues offn me old *chokkers* (boots), they'm *kushti* fur *flurtas*, then I burns the *chokkers* in the Queenie (stove),' and he gave Little Jimmy a smile.

Little Jimmy watched intently as his grandfather cut two strips from the leather about 3½ inches long and ¼ inch wide. 'Them's fer the ears,' he said, 'reckon they'll be wide enough 'cause it's only a little peg.'

Then he cut a piece five inches long and one inch wide, 'That's fur the pouch – now whur's me rasp to?' And he delved into the bag again and produced an old farrier's rasp (file). Walking over to the fire he put the pointed tang handle end into the hot embers.

'Whatever you going to do with that, Granfer?' asked Little Jimmy, who was now really puzzled.

'Burn the 'oles in the pouch, lad,' came the reply. 'Come on back t'the table now an' watch 'ow I does things.'

Back at the table Old John took the pouch and with his clothes-peg making awl pushed two holes into the leather about ½ inch from the ends. Then, back at the fire he took the red hot pointed end of the rasp and burned the small holes to about ¼ inch diameter.

'*Jall* an' get the peg, lad, an' we'll put 'er ears on.'

Little Jimmy laughed and rushed over to the clothes line and untied the peg. '*Dordi!* it feels *kushti*, Granfer,' he said as he handed it to him. 'I can't wait to try it.'

'Patience, my son,' came the reply, 'in me bag yu'll a-find a piece've cardboard with a load've thin string (harness makers' thread), wrapped round it. Fetch it over, lad, an' they two ears.'

When Little Jimmy returned he could see that Old John had placed the little ball of resin on a stick by the embers of the fire and it was now melting.

' 'And us them ears, lad.'

Little Jimmy handed them over and Old John folded the leather strips in half and pinched them tight.

'That's the centre, my son, now we wants t'leave a loop in top, so we'll put this dear little bit've sticky glue just up t'about thur.'

And Old John, with a bit of thin stick, proceeded to put the sticky resin on the inside of the leather strips, leaving about an inch in the middle. Then he placed the strips on the two forks, front and back, and held them tight between his finger and thumb for a few minutes.

'Now my son, you hold 'um tight fur a bit while I 'as a little smoke,' and Old John carefully handed the peg to Little Jimmy, saying, 'Dunna let 'um slip now, 'old 'um tight whur they is.'

Little Jimmy pressed his finger and thumb together very hard against the leather strips, until at last he said, 'Me hands is really hurting, Granfer.'

'That'll do, lad,' came the reply, '*jall* an' 'ang it on the line fur a bit so's the wind a-gets t'it an' 'ardens it off, like. We'll 'ave us a bite t'eat an' then I'll bind them ears on, an' then yer Granny'll give me a 'and t'do 'lastic.'

Yesterday, on their return from town, Genty had made a currant cake in the cast iron hoop-handled frying pan, and Katie, with her grandmother's help, had made another, which was a little burnt on one side – which Genty soon scraped off with a knife. She had cut thick slices, buttered them and handed, as usual, Old John his first. Handing a slice to Little Jimmy, he said, 'Is this yourn or the one me sister made, 'cause if it's Katie's I don't want it.'

'Thur now, *chavvi*! Thur's a thing t'say about yer sister, she's a good little cook, that she is, an' alus washes 'er 'ands afore she touches anythin', don't yer, gal?'

'I do, Granny, I do. I'm very 'tickler like you is,' shouted out an indignant Katie.

'D'yu want this or dursn't yu, lad?' said Genty as she held it under his nose.

The temptation was too great and he took it, making a 'yum' noise as he took the first mouthful.

'I think this is yours, Granny, 'cause it tastes lovely,' he uttered with his mouth full.

'Thur now, yu bad mannered child, keep yer *mui* closed when you'm a-eatin', just *dik* at yer a-spittin' out they dear little crumbs. An' if yu must know, that's a piece've the one yer sister made.' Katie sat quietly beaming with pride. Genty smiled to herself, as she wasn't sure if it really was the one Katie had made.

Cake and tea finished, it was time to get on with the catapult. Little Jimmy retrieved it from the clothes line and handed it to Old John, who, taking the harness makers' thread carefully bound the leather loops in a fashion known as whipping. Round and round and round the thread went, until just before the bottom of the leather Old John put the end of the thread through a little loop and gently pulled the end at the top, which pulled the loop and thread end up to about the middle of the whipping. Then he cut the two thread ends off. Little Jimmy had watched this in awe.

'Granfer, that is so clever, where did you learn to do that?' he asked.

'Lad, I larnt that a long time agoo offn one of me cousins, our Amos it whar. 'E'd a-gotten 'isself a job at a 'unt kennels up thur in Cheshire it wer, an' one a-the lads wur a-mendin' a whip fur the Whipper-in, an' our Amos 'e a-watched 'im an' larnt 'ow t'do it. An' when we wuz all a-stoppin' t'gether once, 'e showed me – *kushti* baint it?'

Little Jimmy nodded and said '*owli*.'

Old John finished whipping the other fork, then asked Little Jimmy to go and ask Genty to come and help him tie the elastic on. The 'washing fire' was at the rear of the kitchen tent on the edge of the wood, consisting of two rows of old bricks, in the middle of which was the fire. On top of the bricks was a large round galvanised tub with a handle on each side, which was now bubbling away with soapy water and dirty clothes. Genty, sleeves rolled up, was engaged in poking the washing with a peeled nut stick, as Little Jimmy came over to ask for her help.

'That man've mine alus wants some 'elp when I'm busy, don't 'e now?' she said as she handed Katie the stick. 'Keep a-pokin' it, gal, I'll be back shortly.'

Wiping her hands on her pinner she followed Little Jimmy over to Old John.

'My man, yu is a pest, yu is.'

'Thur now, 'ummon, it'll only tek a few minutes, an' the lad's bin a-waitin' all day fur his *flurta*, baint yu lad?'

'I have, Granny,' came a pitiful little voice. Genty smiled at him, 'Give us the string, my John,' she said.

Old John had cut four lengths of twine and handed them to Genty. He'd cut two pieces of the thin elastic to about ten inches in length, and put the ends through the holes in the pouch. The other ends he put through the ears – just enough to fold the end back to the long piece, and he was now holding them in both hands, stretching them apart for Genty to tie with the twine.

'Eh, *dordi!* I've a-done this a few times, lad,' she said as she tied the final knot. The elastic on the two ears was completed and the same manoeuvre done on the pouch. Old John cut off the trailing ends of the twine, and the catapult was completed. Holding the peg in his right hand he pulled the pouch back and stretched the elastic – the ties held in place.

' 'Ere yu is, my son, a little beauty baint she?' and he handed eager Little Jimmy his first catapult.

'Thank you, Granfer, thank you! You must be the cleverest man in the world.'

Old John smiled at him. 'If I was, my son, I'd be a-wearin' a brand new suit 'uddent I? But thur agin, I dusn't suppose a man like that could mek a *kushti flurta* now, could 'e? Thur's just one more thing t'do, my son, afore yu *jalls* off with that catty, an' that's t'give it a drop've oil. Now whur in the world did I put that dear little bottle that I *monged* (begged) offn Old Fred yesterday when we wuz on our way back from town?'

'Yu put it on the footboard of the wagon, Granfer – shall I get it?'

'*Owli*, lad,' Old John replied.

When Little Jimmy sprinted back with the bottle, Old John removed the cork and poured a drop of the oil into the palm of his hand, then, taking the catapult, he rubbed the oil into the peg, which turned it a lovely silky colour.

'It smells nice, Granfer, what is it?' enquired Little Jimmy.

'It's linseed oil, lad, double-boiled linseed oil. Thur's raw linseed oil, boiled linseed oil, an' this 'ere is what Old Fred a-calls double-boiled linseed oil. When 'e wer a-workin' doin' carts an' wheels an' such, 'e alus painted all the joints with it. Said it 'ud mek the stuff last longer, like, an' this oil dries quicker than t'other two. 'Ere now, yu 'ave a goo, keep on rubbin' it in, an' it'll mek yer 'ands nice an' soft, like. Then 'ang it on that bush over thur, not on the line 'cause yer Granny'll be a-puttin' the clothes on it.'

Little Jimmy rubbed and rubbed the oil into the peg and the more he rubbed the silkier it became. Then, doing as his grandfather asked, hung it on the bush to dry out a bit.

'You'm dyin' t'try it, baint yu my son?'

'I am, Granfer, I am! I want to practise and practise 'til I'm as good as you.'

'Put yer jacket on, lad, we'd a-better get yu a load've pebbles t'shoot,' came the reply from Old John.

'What's me jacket got to do with pebbles?' Little Jimmy asked as he returned from the tent wearing it.

'Yu got pockets in yer jacket, baint yer lad?'

'Yes, Granfer.'

'Well, pockets'll 'old pebbles 'unt they! Come on, my son, let's 'ave us a little stroll.'

And with that Little Jimmy followed his grandfather out onto the little lane with grass growing in the middle and onto the road that led into the village.

'Where's we going, Granfer?'

'Jest up yonder is a *bori rai's kair* (big gentleman's house) with a driveway up t'it. Now, the driveway curves round an' yu canna a-*dik* the 'ouse, so the *mush* canna a-*dik* us at the entrance, now can 'e?'

'Granfer, I don't know what you're talking about,' Little Jimmy puzzledly replied.

'My son, when we wuz a-comin' 'ome yesterday yu didna *dik* that the man 'ad 'ad 'is drive all nicely done with pebbly stuff, now did yu? No my son, yu wuz too busy a-playin' with yer sister, a-scamperin' up the road. I wuz a-gooin' t'pick up some've they dear pebbles, but thur wuz two 'ummons a-walkin' by an' a *mush* on a bike was a-comin' – so I left it; but we'll get some now, my son, an' they'm lovely, jest the right size!'

They approached the entrance of the driveway, no one was to be seen up or down the road. Old John bent down and picked up a roundish pebble about the size of his thumbnail.

'Thur yu is, lad, 'unt fur some like that, I'll keep a look-out.'

In no time at all Little Jimmy had both his pockets full.

'*Dordi!* They'm heavy, Granfer, is you getting some?'

'That I am, lad, keep yer *yoks* open,' and with that Old John, eyes darting over the pebbles, half filled the big inside pocket of his jacket, putting his left hand underneath to ease the weight as he straightened himself up.

No one was about as they made their way homeward, which was as well, as Old John appeared to be walking lopsidedly, and Little Jimmy with his pockets bulging, resembled a hamster with its cheek pouches filled with food.

'I'm going to shoot me catty now!' Little Jimmy said excitedly as they walked over the plank bridge.

'Let's put up that old bit a-canvas that I uses t'cover woodpile fust, lad, it'll stop yu from a-losin' them lovely pebbles … 'ere lad, give us a 'and,' and Old John took the sheet and gave Little Jimmy one corner of it.

At the rear of the tent, on the edge of the wood, Old John, with Little Jimmy's help, tied the sheet to a small silver birch tree then across to another. In the front of which he pushed a small stick and on it an old tomato tin. Taking six big strides from the upturned tin he said, 'Bring us that old bucket, lad, an' we'll put us all they lovely stones in it – and then bring yer catty an' a-get a-practisin'.'

Thud, thud, went the stones on the old canvas sheet as Little Jimmy tried over and over to hit the old tin can.

'Keep that arm straight, my son, an' jest let yer wrist flick when yu lets goo. Eye that old can up lad, as though yu was a-chuckin' a stone at it.'

Thud, thud, thud, as stone after stone hit the old canvas sheet.

'I can't hit it, Granfer.'

'Yu will, my son, jest keep a-practisin',' and Old John took a few steps back from his grandson. Taking his catapult from his pocket he put a stone in the pouch and waited for Little Jimmy to shoot again. Old John watched as Little Jimmy, full of concentration, pulled the elastic back, and as he let the pouch go … Old John fired too … PING went the can.

'I hit it, Granfer, I hit it,' Little Jimmy shouted excitedly as he turned to face his grandfather, who burst out laughing. Seeing the catapult in Old John's hand and the way that he was laughing, it dawned on little Jimmy what had happened.

'*Dordi!* Granfer, you's an old *beng* (devil), you is,' he shouted out, which made Old John laugh more, and laughing made him cough, and coughing made him spit.

'Keep a-practisin', my son,' was all he could manage to say.

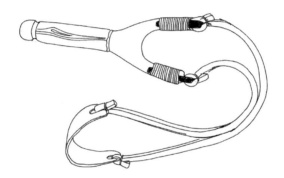

Moodying 'um On

'Well, we wuz down Eve-e-shum (Evesham), just finished the plum pickin', an' as usual, afore we 'eaded back up the borders, we pulled up Blasted Oak Lane. It wer an old stopping place fur travellers an' we usually got t'bide thur fer a week or more.'

'Why was it called Blasted Oak, Granfer?'

'Well, I'll tell yu – there used t'be a big old oak tree that 'ad been struck by lightnin' up this old lane, but it 'ad bin sawn down yers an' yers an' yers ago. But the name stuck – an' still does. Some've the Prices was already thur when we pulled in an' little Mickey Ball an' 'is missus – we called 'im "Little Mickey" 'cause he wer only about five foot 'igh an' I suppose because've that 'e alus tried t'be the big man. We didna a-like stopping by them so I pulled up the lane outa the way. Now, as I said, we usually got a week or two thur, the local old *muskro* (policeman) warn't a bad old *mush*, but we didna a-know that 'e'd died an' thur wuz a young new *muskro* took over. Well, next mornin' 'e turns up – all spruced up 'e wer in 'is new uniform, an' keen t'show 'is authority. We wuz the first've the wagins that 'e come to, an' I could see at once that I'd 'ave t' "moody" 'im.'

'What does "moody him" mean, Granfer?'

'Well, when some *muskro* or *bori rai* (big gentleman) come to be nasty to us, all aggressive like, I'd try an' "moody 'um on" – be all civil an' charmin', like. Sometimes it worked, sometimes it didna, but most times it did, an' they'd see that we wuz nice old-fashioned peaceful people that never done no 'arm,' and Old John chuckled, 'even if they didna know that we'd taken the farmer's 'edge posts an' a-burnt 'um! Little Mickey wer no good at this, he'd fly off the handle at the drop've a hat.'

'Mornin' Mr Policeman, Sir,' I sez.

'E replies, 'How long do you think you're stopping here?' all authorityfied.

'We just finished pickin' the plums, Sir, on farm down road, an' we alus stops 'ere just fur a little rest afore we 'eads up to Shropshire. PC Dixon alus lets us bide fur a couple of weeks, Sir.'

'Well PC Dixon has died and this is my beat now and I'll say how long you're staying,' 'e sez.

'Oh, the dear blessed man,' I sez. 'Will yu please give 'is missus our condolences?' all very sincere, like.

I could see that I was getting' 'im softened up when along comes Little Mickey.

'If you've come t'shift us,' 'e shouts, 'we baint a-goin' until we feels like it. My missus is going t'deliver me an heir any minute, look you now.'

'An' 'e waves 'is arm down the lane, an' thur stands 'is missus with a piller (pillow) stuffed up 'er pinner – she must 'ave been over sixty an' looked a 'undred! It was an old trick an' all the *muskros* knew it. Yer Granny used it a few times, *dordi* Genty, remember that time when yu stood on the top've the steps in the doorway an' the pinner strings come undone an' the piller falls out? *Dordi*, did that *muskro* laugh.'

'That's the quickest delivery in history,' 'e sez.

Anyway, Little Mickey is getting real brazen with this young *muskro*. '*Kekka* I keep *rokkerin* (speaking) but 'e teks no notice.'

This young *muskro* warn't softened up any more an' I can see 'is face goin' a bit red. All of a sudden 'e sez, 'I want you lot off here tomorrow morning.'

Little Mickey 'ad a-narked it fer all on us with 'is 'ollerin' an' a-swearin' an' a-cussin'.

'Early next mornin' this *muskro* an' 'is pals turns up, just as I'm a-backin' the old mare inter the shafts. 'E comes up t'me an' 'e sez, "I saw Mrs Dixon last night and passed on your condolences," an' 'e gives me a little smile an' a nod of 'is 'ead. I thought t'meself, if we pulls up Butchers' Broom Lane next yer, by ourselves, we'll be alright.'

'Why was it called Butchers' Broom Lane, Granfer?'

'*Dordi!* yu keeps askin' questions an' never lets me finish … I'll a-tell yu why. This old lane 'ad butchers' broom a-growin' in the 'edges an' afore yu asks, butchers' broom is a green spiky bush an' we used t'cut it an' sell it t'butchers fur a-cleanin' thur choppin' blocks – used t'sell 'um wooden skewers an' all that we made. Any'ows, the Prices an' Mickey Ball an' 'is old woman pulls off 'eadin' fur south Wales an' we 'eads back up to Shropshire – an' I'll a-tell yu what 'appened when we pulled on "dead *rai*'s (gentleman's) corner" another night.'

'But afore yu *jalls* t'*woodrus* (go to bed),' (and he looked hard at Little Jimmy and Katie) 'who duz yu think was the cleverest man in that story?'

'You was, Granfer,' Little Jimmy shouted out. 'If that Mickey hadn't been so nasty to the policeman you'd have been able to stay, wouldn't you?'

'That's right, that's right,' replied Old John. 'Always remember that – moody the *gauji* on – it'll make yer life a lot easier, an' a lot easier t'tek a shilling from 'um, 'cause without the *gauji foki* we uddent 'ave any *luvva*, now 'ud we?'

THE SCHOOLMASTER, THE RHYME AND THE SIN-EATER

'Mr Lock! Mr Lock!' Fred's lad shouted out as he made his way down the little path towards the plank bridge.

'What is it, lad?' Old John shouted back.

'Mr Lock, I can't stop a minute, but me dad says he's had a phone call from the schoolmaster asking if it's alright to come down on Saturday and give your wagon sheet another coat of paint.'

'Tell yer dad t'tell 'im we look forurd t'a-seein' 'im, lad – an' thank yu fur a-comin' t'ask us,' and Old John gave him a wave of his hand. 'Did yu 'ear that, my Genty? Schoolmaister's a-comin' on Saturday.'

'That I did, my John,' came a voice from the interior of the kitchen tent, 'couldna 'elp not to the way yu two was a-hollerin' at each other. It's a funny thing, my John, I knowed we wuz a-gooin' t'ave a visitor a-comin' t'see us, that's why I bought extra meat t'day fur the pudden. He liked that pudden've mine last yer when 'e come t'put the new cloth on the wagin, now didna 'e?'

''E said 'e did,' came the reply, 'but Old Fred a-told me that 'e said it-a given 'im hindy-jestion.' And Old John chuckled to himself.

'Thur now, thur's a thing t'say, that Fred is nuthin' but a troublemaker, that 'e is. Schoolmaster 'ud never say a thing like that, 'e's a dear kind gentleman, not in the old wide world 'e 'uddent a-say a thing like that – no 'e 'uddent, 'e loved me pudden an' 'e'll have it agin on Saturday, that's fur sure!'

Genty had risen to the bait, and Old John sat chuckling to himself by the fire. Later that afternoon Little Jimmy and Katie arrived back from playing in the wood, and were greeted with the words from Old John: 'Schoolmaister's comin' on Saturday.'

The children looked at their grandfather in horror, and Old John gave them a big smile. 'E baint a-comin' t'get yer inter no school, dunna worry 'bout that. Yu'll like the man an' if yu behaves yerselves 'e'll like yu an' all.'

'What's he comin' for, Granfer? Who is he?' asked Little Jimmy, sounding worried.

'We could make out we was *divvy* (stupid) and then he wouldn't want to bother with us, couldn't we Jimmy?' Katie piped up, sounding worried too.

Old John started to laugh and then coughed and spat in the fire.

'Oh my blessed Lord, jest a-*dik* at you two a-stood thur a-tremblin' an'

a-worrified,' Old John managed to say amid bouts of laughter. 'Come an' a-sit down 'ere an' I'll a-tell yu who this nice kind gentleman is, an' a-wot 'e's a-comin' fur.'

They both took their places round the fire, and Old John looked at their worried little faces and he gave another laugh.

'The man who's a-comin' on Saturday all on us people calls the Schoolmaister, 'cause 'e is one, 'e likes us people an' 'e dunna a-come t'us t'do no schoolmaisterin' – no 'e dunna, an' we likes the man. 'E knows all on ourn ways, an' 'e *rokkers Rumunus* (speaks Romani), so dunna goo a-*rokkerin* behind 'is back 'cause 'e'll *jin* what you've-*penned* (know what you've said). 'E knows all about wagins, like, when 'e baint a-schoolmaisterin' 'e's a-studyin' the 'istory of 'um "galleons of the *drom* (road)" 'e calls 'um, an' 'e's got a *kushti* little wagin that 'e made, an' a decent old *grai* (horse), an' in the summer time 'e an' 'is missus goos about with the horse and wagin an' they stops with travellin' folk all over the place. An' 'e doos the odd bit a-work on the wagins an' 'e 'as a deal a-two, like. I 'ears 'e's a good man t'ave a deal with an' all. When 'e wuz 'ere last yer I sold 'im 'er-what-baint-with-us-no-more's (meaning Addy, who he never mentioned by name) set've London 'arness that I'd a-bought 'er. A good set it were, all 'oss shoe buckles on it. 'E bid me sensible money an' we wuz both satisfied, as yu might say. 'E's a man of 'is word an' all, I tell yu, 'e comed 'ere last yer an' a-put a new cloth on the wagin an' a-give it a coat've paint, like. An' 'e sez "I'll come back next summer an' a-give the cloth another couple've coats". An' sure enough 'e's a-comin' on Saturday t'do the job.'

'Where's he comin' from, Granfer?' asked Little Jimmy, still sounding a bit anxious.

'The man lives right up thur in north Wales, not s'far from whur me dear cousin Izzie lies a-buried, God rest 'er soul. 'E gets about on a motorbike, like, an' yu 'uddent believe the stuff 'e carries on it an' all. Last yer when 'e wuz 'ere Old Fred repaired a couple've wheels fur 'im an' 'e got 'um a-tied on the back've that motorbike sweet as yer like. *Dordi!* it were comical t'see. It were Fred that a-brought 'im t'us in the fust place, he'd a-done some wheels fur 'im before, like, an' that's when 'e brought 'im over t'see us. Me an' yer Granny a-liked the man as soon as we met 'im, an' I sez to 'im as I a-wanted a new cloth on the wagin, an' as I sez, 'e come 'ere last yer an' a-put one on fur us, like.'

'How long will he be here, Granfer?' asked Little Jimmy, sounding a little less anxious.

'I reckon 'e'll be 'ere Saturday an' Sunday, lad. 'E sez 'e's a-gunna give that cloth two coats've paint, then 'e'll 'ave t'get back fur Monday mornin', I'm 'spectin', t'do 'is schoolmaisterin', like.'

Katie had been listening intently to the conversation and, looking at her grandfather, asked, 'Where's he going to sleep?'

'E'll get 'is 'ead down at Fred's place, like 'e done last yer, I'm 'spectin',' replied Old John. 'Fred's missus likes 'im an' all, fusses about 'im like an old mother 'en, 'er doos, an' she's a-pattin' 'er 'air an' a-straightenin' 'er pinner all the time 'e's thur, like. Any old 'ow, I wants yer t'be polite t'the man, like we've a-taught yer, an' a-call 'im Sir when yu meets 'im, an' then arter an 'our a-two, when yu got t'know 'im better, like, yu can call 'im Schoolmaister – 'e'll like that an' all. Yer Granny calls 'im *Raia* (Sir), but I calls 'im brother, an' t'be 'onest with yu, I'd a-sooner 'ave 'is company than I 'ud some of me own breed, that I 'ud. Sensible man 'e is, an' 'e dunna *pukker no hokabins* (tell no lies) neither.'

Around eight o'clock on Friday evening Old Fred heard the sound of a motorbike entering the yard at the rear of their little house in the village street.

'He's here – get the kettle on, Mary,' he called from his comfy armchair by the side of the fireplace. Two knocks sounded on the back door, and old Mary, patting her hair in place, opened it and gave a funny little curtsey. Then, throwing her arms around the startled young man, exploded, 'Oh! we're so pleased to see you again, come on in, boy, kettle's boiling.'

'Come on in here, my friend, and have a pew,' called out Fred. 'Missus has got a bit of supper ready for you.'

The rest of the evening was spent supping tea flavoured with village gossip and chatting about country matters; and Fred and Mary were intrigued to learn why the schoolmaster found Gypsies so appealing.

Early Saturday morning saw Old Fred and the young schoolmaster mixing their own special brew of paint for the canvas roof of the wagon. The schoolmaster had brought two gallon cans of green gloss paint, and Old Fred had sorted out, from his paint shed of the old workshops, a large heavy can of white lead paint and a large can of his 'double-boiled linseed oil'. They mixed the differing ingredients together, adding a bit more of this and a bit more of that, until Old Fred said, 'Looks about right, don't it, shall I chuck in some driers?'

'That would be handy, Fred,' the schoolmaster replied. I want to try and get two coats on while I'm down here.'

They had just finished mixing 'the brew' when Old Fred's lad drove his van into the yard. He greeted them with, 'You two are up early.' 'Lot of paint to slop on today,' was the comment, as he lifted one of the heavy cans up and placed it in the back of the van. Old Fred left his lad to pick up the other heavy can too, which he did with ease.

'I've got the ladder and steps in the van, dad, so if you two are ready we'll be off, I've got a little job of me own to finish off this morning, and I don't want to hang about.'

'My lad's always busy,' Old Fred said, with a big smile … 'keeps 'im out of mischief!'

The little encampment of the Locks was also busy that morning. Old John had risen early as usual, and he and Little Jimmy had already done their trek to the farm and back with the churn of drinking water, and Genty was now shouting orders to the children. 'Put this away, move that over there, empty that washin' bowl, lad, you've a-forgot agin, an' swish that bowl in the brook an' all, Schoolmaister an' Fred'll be 'ere in a minute.'

She had hardly finished the sentence when she heard Little Jimmy shout out, 'Here they is.'

Looking across to the other side of the little brook she saw the three men approaching, Fred's lad carrying the two large heavy cans of paint, the *gaujo* schoolmaster with the ladder on his shoulder, and Old Fred carrying the stepladder and two empty paint kettles. Making their way over the plank bridge they all shouted the greeting of 'Morning!'

By now Old John had risen from his milk bottle crate seat by the fire and was the first to greet them. 'Mornin', Fred, mornin', lad.' Then, turning to the visitor, he put out his hand and said, 'It's *kushti t'dik tutti a-poply, prala* (it's good to see you again, brother),' and shook the outstretched hand offered vigorously. 'I knowed yu'd be back, yu said yu would, an' 'ere yu is now – all on yer. Come on over t'the fire an' 'ave a drop've tea, like, afore yu starts on that old roof of ourn.'

Fred's lad, making his excuses of 'lots to do', made his exit and the new arrivals sat down on the two chairs that had been brought from the kitchen tent ready for them. Little Jimmy and Katie had been standing by the tent watching and listening. 'He don't look much like a schoolmaster, does he Katie?'

'No, he don't,' she answered her brother, 'he looks like some old painty *mush*. Well, one without a *tuvla* in 'is *mui* (cigarette in his mouth).'

Katie's eyes had been scrutinising the appearance of the schoolmaster, who was dressed in a paint-splattered pair of overalls with a paint-splattered old cap on his head, and his old work boots were paint-splattered too. Not the usual attire, one would think, of a schoolmaster!

'Come on over 'ere,' Old John called to them, 'an' meet this dear kind brother've mine.'

The children slowly walked over to the fire, and shaking hands with him said, 'Mawnin', Sir,' Katie adding, 'nice day, 'ent it?'

'And I'm pleased to meet you too,' said 'Sir' as he reached into his overall pocket and produced two bags of sweets. 'Here,' he said, 'my wife has sent these down with me to give you.'

Very politely the children took the sweets, saying, 'Thank you, Mister,' then scampered off in the direction of the wood. Genty had now made the tea, and handed the two a cup before handing Old John his, as was the usual custom when visitors were there.

''Ow did yu an' yer missus know *chavvies* wuz 'ere? Did yu tell 'um, Fred?'

'No I never, John, we was only on the phone a second or two,' Fred replied.

'Missus looked in her crystal ball!' the schoolmaster said with a laugh. 'No, I'll tell you John, I was over Bangor the other week and who should I bump into but Alfie Lock, he's a cousin of yours, isn't he?'

'Aar, 'e is that, brother, a distant 'un at any rate. We calls 'im Menai Bridge Alfie, an' 'e a-told yu, did 'e?'

'Yes.'

'*Dordi!* word soon gets about, don't it now? I reckons some folks knows about things afore they 'appens, that I doos,' and Old John spat in the fire.

The morning sun was now fully shining on the one side of the wagon. 'Time to get the paint on,' remarked the schoolmaster. 'By the time I've done half the top and that side the sun will be round to the south-west and shining on the other, which will be perfect for the job.'

And with that the schoolmaster-turned-painter made his way over to the wagon, put the long ladder up against it, poured some of the paint into one of the wire-handled paint kettles that Fred had brought, took a wide-headed brush from his back pocket and up the ladder he went, 'to slop the paint on'.

'Whistle up Katie fur me, will yu my John? I wants 'er t'elp me a-get this bit've *hobben* ready fur this arternoon. Iffn yu'll excuse me, Fred, I 'ave ter get on.' And Genty made her way over to the kitchen tent.

Placing the tip of his thumb and index finger in his mouth Old John let out the high then low-pitch signal call *joter* (whistle). A few minutes later the children appeared. 'Yer Granny wants yer, gal,' called out Old John.

'Wash yer 'ands, gal, I wants yer t'give me a 'and with the pudden.' Genty was busy in the tent cutting the stewing beef into cubes, then putting them into a bowl with a little flour and some of her 'erbs and salt and pepper. She mixed them up and got them well coated. Katie had washed her hands and was now standing in the doorway of the tent. 'Watcher want me t'do, Granny?' she asked.

'Fill me big boilin' pot 'alf full've water an' ask yer Granfer t'get it a-boilin' fer me – tell 'im t'mek 'isself useful, gal. Then 'ave a look in the kettle box an' bring us me big 'namel basin with blue round the top – the big 'un, not the little 'un.'

By the time Katie came back with the enamel basin Genty had mixed flour, suet and water together and was now rolling it out on her 'rollin' out' tray. ''Ere gal,' she said, 'peel an' slice them onions up fur me, not too thin nor not too thick, like.' Then looking at Katie, she asked: ''Ow much flour an' 'ow much suet, gal?' Straight away Katie replied: 'Eight big spoons of flour and four big spoons of suet.'

'That's *kushti*,' Genty said with a smile. 'So if I puts in ten big spoons've flour, 'ow many've suet 'ud I use?'

Katie stood there thinking for a few seconds, then replied, 'Five, Granny.'

'You'm larnin' well, gal,' came the reply from Genty, who now had greased the inside of the enamel basin and lined it with the suet pastry. Then taking a handful of the sliced onions she put them in the basin followed by a handful of the floured cubed meat, then another handful of onions and so on in layers, until the basin was almost full to the top.

'Bring us a cup've hot water, gal,' she ordered, and Katie ran over to the kettle which was steaming in the embers of the fire; tipping it slightly she filled the cup as her grandmother had asked and noticed that the big black boiling pot was now bubbling away on the kettle iron. Genty crumbled up two Oxo cubes into the cup of hot water and poured it over the contents of the basin, then she put on the crust and pressed her thumb all round the edge to seal it. Taking a cloth, she placed it loosely on the top and tied it on round the rim of the basin.

'She'm ready fer the pot, gal, bring that barbed wire ring with yer.'

They walked over to the fire and Katie placed the barbed wire ring (a piece of barbed wire coiled round in a circle) into the pot and

Genty carefully lowered the basin in to sit on the ring (which kept the bottom of the basin a little way from the bottom of the pot). Then taking the kettle, she poured in a small amount of water, so that it came just below the rim of the basin. Putting the lid on she said to Old John, 'Wait til yu 'ears 'er bubblin', then swing the *saster* (kettle-iron) over a bit, will yu, man?'

Looking at Old Fred, he said, 'It's a 'ard life, baint it?'
'Not as hard as he's got up there,' replied Fred, and he called out, 'You 'ent putting that paint on upside down, are you?'
Old John shouting out, 'You've missed a bit thur.'
Fred calling out again, 'Mind you don't fall off that ladder, lad.'
They both sat rocking with laughter as the schoolmaster, sweat running down his temples, continued to slop the paint on.

A short while later Genty brewed up more tea and, as was the custom, handed Fred, the visitor, his cup first. Holding the cup up high he called out to the painter, 'I bet you're hot up there and could do with a cup of tea like we're enjoying, couldn't you? It's really lovely, it is.' And both the old timers rocked with laughter again.
'Dunna torment the dear man,' scolded Genty, and calling Little Jimmy over said, ''Ere, tek this cup over to the *Rai*, 'e looks as 'ow 'e could do with it, 'e do paint fast, dunna 'e?'

Having drunk his tea, Fred raised himself up from his chair and said, 'I'd best be sauntering home now, missus'll be wondering what's happened to me. Thank you for the tea.'
'Yur not a-stoppin' fur some food then, Fred?'
'No John, I must be getting home now,' he replied, then calling to the working schoolmaster said, 'I expect you'll be late back tonight

– I'll leave the back door unlocked for you. I bet you has a second helping of Genty's pudden' – you told me how much you liked it last year.' And with that he made his way over the plank bridge, chuckling to himself.

The painting of the sheet had been timed perfectly. The sun was now on the other side of the wagon and the schoolmaster was now standing on the ground painting the final bit on the bottom front corner. 'That's it, John, I'm finished,' he called out.
'Get yerself washed up, lad, Genty's jest a-doin' the taters an' cabbage an' she sez *hobben* 'un't a-be long,' Old John replied.

Now fully at ease with the stranger, Katie taking him by the hand led him over to her little 'accommodation'. 'Come an' see me little "nest", Mister. Granfer and Fred a-done it for me, *kushti* 'ent it? I loves it so much, have a *dik* (look) inside.'
There was very little inside, the bed across the back was neat and tidy, a few clothes hung on a string line on one side, a colourful carpet on the floor and a little stool just inside the entrance.
'It's wonderful,' he thought, 'how Gypsy people can be so happy with so little in the way of material possessions, especially now in this modern world.'
'Come an' get yer food yu two,' called out Genty, who was now putting the food out on the dish plates. She handed the 'Maister' his first and Katie handed him a fork, saying, 'Granny's done the pudden in a basin 'specially for you, Uncle – we generally 'as it done in a cloth.'
'Thur now!' commented Genty, adding, 'thur's enough fur yu t'ave a second 'elpin', my *Rai* (gentleman).'

Struggling to finish the huge dish plateful he finally succeeded, only for Genty to put another big spoonful of pudding on his plate.

'I couldn't eat any more,' he said.

'Goo on, brother, you've a-bin workin' 'ard all day – get it down yer, do yer gud an' all,' came the words from Old John as he wiped his moustache with the back of his hand.

Suddenly, Little Jimmy, who was sitting next to his sister on the other side of the fire, opposite the two men, let out a loud 'brruupt'. Katie leapt to her feet shouting, 'You dirty *baulo* (pig),' and Genty in a scolding tone shouted out, '*Yu chickli bul chavvi* (you dirty-arse child), yu should be a-*ladged*'ve yerself (ashamed of yourself). What's ever folks gooin' t'think've yer?'

'I couldn't help it, honest to God I couldn't Uncle … I feels so ashamed of meself now.'

'Don't worry yourself, lad,' said the schoolmaster with a laugh, 'we all do it.' And, still laughing, looked at the children and said, 'Do you know what a sigh is?' and Little Jimmy took a breath of air and made a sigh noise.

'That's right, now listen to this:

A sigh is but a bit of wind
that comes up from your heart
but when it goes the other way
it's known as a …'

Both Katie and Little Jimmy shouted out 'FART!'

They all laughed and Old John managed to say, 'Now thur's a thing fur a schoolmaister t'be a-teachin' children,' and he gave the man a pat on the shoulder.

Glaring at her brother, Katie said, 'He's nuthin' but a filthy *baulo*, that's what he is.'

While Genty and Katie were cleaning up after the meal, the men and Little Jimmy sat talking round the fire; Little Jimmy sat opposite the adults listening intently to their conversation of wagons and mysterious people unknown to him, all of whom appeared to be cousins to his grandfather. (Cousin, amongst Gypsy people, can mean first cousin, second cousin, third cousin once removed, and so on; or not even any relation at all.)

'Yu baint a-sin me cousin Daisy over Birkenhead lately 'as yer, brother? 'E 'unt be a-dealin' in no 'osses now I 'spect since 'e've a-bin stoppin' in that yard.'

'I saw him only a week ago,' was the reply.

''Ow's 'e a-doin', is they still in that big old wagin've theirn?'

The schoolmaster confirmed that Daisy and his wife were still living in the big wagon, and he no longer was horse dealing.

''Spect 'e's a-getting' a bit long in the tooth fur it now, baint 'e?' And both men laughed at the equestrian pun that he'd made.

'Is 'is sister still on the *durrakin* (fortune telling), did 'e say?'

'Yes, he mentioned Freda, he told me she now had a fortune telling booth on the pier at Aberystwyth, and was doing all right down there.' Then added, 'he said last time he saw her she was dripping in gold, loads of sovereigns on a chain round her neck and half sovereigns for earrings.'

Old John coughed and spat in the fire.

In a sulky voice he then said, 'They alus did like a bit've *sonakei* (gold) about 'um.' He paused for a second then added, 'but I wishes 'um well, like.'

Changing the subject rapidly the schoolmaster continued, 'My missus and I went over to Squealing Pig Common to see if anyone was stopping on there, not so long back.'

'Who wuz on thur, brother?' asked Old John, whose mind was now focused on the old stopping place called Squealing Pig Common, five miles out from Corwen.

'There were only three lots on there, John, the only ones we knew were Wisdom Price and his family. He was just finishing off a nice little barrel-top wagon that he was making. Said he'd got the bows for the roof from the barrel works down in Usk.'

'Aar, brother, they makes good bows doos them, I've a-sin 'um used on many a wagin – 'ad 'e a-painted 'er up, like?'

'He'd done a bit of scrollwork on the body, John, but he was busy making a stove from an old-fashioned conical milk churn, and he was making a good job of it as well – you must have seen a stove like it before I'd guess.'

'That I 'ave, brother, them old cone shaped churns meks a *kushti* stove, that they do. Iffn yu ever a-meks one dunna forget t'put a load've sand in the bottom, then light yer *yog* on that, otherwise yu'll a-burn the bottom out – an' the floor of yer wagin! They meks *kushti* stoves 'cause yu dunna 'ave t'cut yer *kosht* (wood) up t'small, like, yu can put long lengths in, uppards, so t'speak.'

Genty and Katie had finished their tidying up and had now taken their places round the fire. 'What's yu two a-*rokkerin* about?' asked Genty.

'The *mush* 'ere wuz jest a-sayin' that Wisdom Price 'ad a-made 'isself a stove outa a churn, over thur on Squealing Pig Common they'm *atched*.

'They meks *kushti* stoves an' all, my *Rai*,' she said.

'I've jest a-told the man that, 'ummon, an' I wuz jest about t'tell 'im whur t'find a nice bit've pipe from an' all … mek us a nice drop've *meski*, Genty will yu?' he said with a soothing tone, '*dik* 'ere, I've a-got the kettle a-boilin' ready fur yer.'

'Any old 'ow, brother,' he continued, 'yu can generally find a nice bit've pipe on an old tip somewhur, like, iffn you'm 'ard up t'buy it, like.'

'Be careful on tips, John,' the schoolmaster said quickly, 'a terrible thing happened up by us only a few days ago.'

All eyes turned towards him. 'What?' they asked.

'Well, it seems that this man found a tin box on a tip, somewhere round Chester, and it had a big padlock on it, so he took it to his pal who had a little garage and asked him to cut the padlock off – which he did with the oxyacctylene cutter – and blew them both to kingdom come. And the garage as well.'

''Ow come?' asked Old John.

'The tin box was an old Army box from the war and it was full of explosives, so be careful if you're on some old tip in the future, John, you never know what you might find.'

'*Dordi! dordi! dordi!*' came in short gasps from Genty. 'The poor dear people, I bet the man a-thought it were full of *luvva* (money), didna 'e now? Oh! my dear blessed Lord, my Gentleman, that's a sad story yu've a-told us, that it is.'

And so the conversation drifted on into the evening, and Genty brewed up yet more tea to ease their parched throats.

'I've been meaning to ask you, John, have you ever come across a "Sin Eater"?'

'Eh *dordi!* now yu've a-asked me summat, brother, that teks me right back t'when I wuz a young man, like. *Dordi*, aar, I knowed a Sin-Eater – well, I didna a-know 'im, like, I only a-met 'im, as yu might say.'

The very mention of the name Sin-Eater put Little Jimmy and Katie on the edges of their seats, mouths and eyes wide open.

'Shall I a-tell yu now?'

Everyone shouted out 'YES!'

'Well now,' Old John started, 'me and me faarthur used t'play ourn fiddles in a few *kitchimas* up an' down the borders 'ere, an' me cousin Polin used t'come with us an' all sometimes. Any old 'ow, thur's only me an' me faarthur this time, an' we'm a-playin' fur the *foki* an' the *livena* in this old *kitchima* a-called "The Sun" over thur in Lentwardine – twarn't no bar nor nuthin', beer come in big jugs. Well now, every one's enjoyin' thurselves, until this *bori* (big) farm worker *mush* a-jumps up an' we could *dik* 'as 'ow 'e's *motto* (drunk), like, an' 'e's a-hollerin' "yu two canna a-play them fiddles like Williams the Sin-Eater can". Now I *jins* that me old faarthur 'ud a-*kored* (fought) the man fur a-sayin' such a thing, but me faarthur 'ad a-weighed 'im up an' a-thought t'isself, – "*Dordi*, 'e's a *bori* (big) raw boned *mush* an' even though 'e's *motto*, I mightna a-win, like" – an' me faarthur bein' a sensible *mush*, 'e thinks t'isself agin – "We 'as a *kushti* place t'*atch* down by the bridge an' no one a-bothers yu, like,

202

an' any trouble an' we'd 'ave t'move, an' they 'uddent a-'ave us thur agin."

'So me faarthur, 'e ups an' sez, "Whur can I find this Williams the Sin-Eater, whur's 'e bide to?"

'Well now, the landlord's daughter – Flossie wuz 'er name – can see as 'ow me old faarthur's upset, an' she were a gud sort an' a-liked us, so she up an' a-tells us 'ow t'find this Williams the Sin-Eater. So with that we bids 'um all gudnight an' meks to leave, me faarthur a-brushin' by the *bori mui motto mush* (big mouth drunk man) on the way out.'

'Any old 'ow, this 'ad a-moithered me faarthur's mind all night it 'ad, an' the followin' day 'e sez t'me "Get yer coat on an' a-foller me", so I doos. Well, I'm a-follerin' me faarthur a-up an' a-down these gutters (dingles/valleys) on t'other side've Lentwardine, when all've a sudden we 'ears this fiddle music, an' mournful it wuz an' all, so we a-follers it, an' comes t'this little 'ut a-built inter the bank (hill), like. Me old faarthur 'e calls out: "Williams the Sin-Eater, I wants t'talk t'yer, come out man, come out this instant, I wants t'ear yu play that fiddle of yourn". All of a sudden this old sack, that 'e used fur the door, a flops open, an' may the dear Lord 'elp me iffn I 'ent a-tellin' yer the truth, who should a come outa that little 'ut but the littlest man as I ever did a-see – an' the hugliest 'un an' all, *dordi!* 'e were like a little elfikin 'e were, with a humpty back an' 'e were all raggity, like.'

'Well now, 'e stands thur a-lookin' at us, like, an' 'is little *mui* is all a-wrinkled up an' 'e dunna a-look very 'appy, like. Then I *diks* 'is *vasties* (hands) – *dordi!* They wuz the biggest 'ands that ever I did see – me faarthur a-called 'um "strangler's 'ands", 'e did.'

'Any old 'ow, me faarthur, 'e stands thur a-lookin' down at this little *mush* – 'cause 'e were a tall man, like – an' 'e sez, "I wants t'ear yu a-play yer fiddle, man". The little elfikin man, 'e gives us a funny sort've grin an' 'e sez "Why?" in a tiny little voice.
"Why?" sez me faarthur, "Why? 'Cause people a-sez yu'm a good player an' I, Gypsy Lock, wanst t'ear yu play that fiddle of yourn."

'The little *mush* goos inter 'is 'ut an' a-comes out with 'is old fiddle an' bow, an' 'e's a-standing thur a-lookin' at us, an' 'e baint a-sayin' a word, like. Well me old faarthur, 'e ups an' sez, "Goo on, man, a-play us summat".
"What?" says the *mush* in 'is tiny little voice.
"Give us summat a bit lively," sez me faarthur, "give us a 'ornpipe or a reel or a polka or summat".
Yu 'ent a-gooin' t'believe this, but it's true as I sits 'ere a-tellin' yer now, that little *mush*, with them great big 'ands, 'e plays that old *bosh* (fiddle)'ve 'is like me an' me faarthur 'ad never a-'eard afore. *Dordi!* Could 'e play!'
'Me an' me faarthur is so shocked that we sits down on the grass afore 'im, an' 'e's a-gooin' from one tune t'nother like Billy-o, 'e is. 'Twas wonderful t'ear, it wuz. Well eventually 'e stops 'is playin', an' me faarthur gets up an' 'e goos over t'the little *mush* an' 'e shakes 'im by the 'and – then I doos the same. *Dordi!* me *vast* (hand) wuz like a babby's t'the size've 'is, like. Any old 'ow, me faarthur a-thanks 'im fur playin' an' we turns t'goo, when all've a sudden me faarthur, 'e turns round an' sez "Wot wuz that tune we 'eard yu a-playin' as we come 'ere?"

The little *mush*, in 'is tiny voice, 'e sez, "That's very old, very very old," he sez.

"Wot's it called?" asked me faarthur.

"*Cold Blows the Wind over my True Love's Grave*," the little *mush* answers 'im.

"Will yu play it fur us?" me faarthur asks 'im.

So 'e doos – an' me faarthur, 'e gets 'im t'play it over an' over agin 'til we both larnt it, like. An' then we thanks the man and me faarthur puts 'is 'and in 'is pocket an' a-gives 'im a bit of *luvva*, like, an' meks our way back t'the wagins, whur we gets the fiddles out an' a-played that tune while it were still in our 'eads, as yu might say.'

'Aar, that's the only time as I a-come across a Sin-Eater – Williams the Sin-Eater – poor little *mush* 'e were, the sort as 'uddent a-say "boo" t'a goose. I dusn't a-think eatin' all've them sins of poor dead people 'ad a-done 'im much gud neither.'

'Do you still remember that tune, John?' enquired the schoolmaster.

'I reckons I could a-bring it t'mind, brother. Goo an' fetch me fiddle fur us, lad, an' I'll 'ave a goo at a-playin' it.'

Little Jimmy jumped up from his seat by the fire, rushed over to the wagon, and returned with the fiddle case and handed it to his grandfather.

'Me old 'ands is a bit 'maticky now, brother, but I'll 'ave a goo,' said Old John, as he tuned up the old fiddle. And then he played the old, very old tune.

'Well now, that's 'ow 'er goos,' he said as he lowered the fiddle and bow, 'my dear blessed Lord, I baint a-played that fur many a yer now, it's a-wonder I remembered it, baint it?'

All the time their grandfather had been telling his tale the children had sat motionless, uttering not a word. Suddenly Katie exploded with, 'How do them Sin-Eaters eat the sins of the poor dead people – do you know, Uncle?'

'I've never come across one, like your grandfather here has, and I've never met anyone before who had met one,' replied the schoolmaster, 'but I've read about them.'

'What's it say in them books, then?' asked Little Jimmy.

'Well lad, it says that up the borders here there used to be people known as Sin-Eaters, mostly poor old men, like your grandfather has just told us about, and when a person died the family would get a Sin-Eater to come and eat their sins.'

'But how did they eat them? I wants to know.' Katie called out excitedly.

'Well,' continued the master, 'it seems that at the graveside the parson would call out *Do we have a Sin-Eater?* and someone would call out *I am the Sin-Eater* – then he would go over to the coffin and eat a chunk of bread that had been placed on it, and then he'd take a glass of wine off the coffin and drink that. Then in a loud voice he would say, *I give easement and rest to thee, that ye walk not over the fields nor down the by-ways. And for thy peace I pawn my own soul.* And then with his head bent low, he was given some money then he would turn and walk slowly away.'

'So he ate the bread and drunk the wine as though it was the poor dead person's sins then, did he Uncle?' Little Jimmy said looking very serious.

'Yes, that sort of thing, lad, but I think it was a long time ago, but it might still happen somewhere; what do you think, John?'

'Reckon it could, brother,' and Old John gave a knowing nod of his head and a little smile.

'I must go otherwise I shan't be up early to give the sheet another coat of paint. Thank you for the meal, Genty and thank you, John for an entertaining evening – one to remember. Goodnight *chavvies*, I'll see you all in the morning.'

Fred had left the back door unlocked, as he said he would, and the schoolmaster entered the back kitchen as quietly as possible. And there blocking the entrance to the staircase was a chair, upon which was placed a bottle of Milk of Magnesia indigestion liquid and a little note saying, 'Thought you might need this'.

The following morning he was up early, but not as early as Old Fred and Mary. A huge breakfast of bacon, eggs, tomatoes and fried bread greeted him, together with his favourite, sliced and fried 'white pudding'. Mary did her usual fussing about him, patting her hair in place all the time and straightening her apron. 'Another cup of tea? More toast, dear? Doz you like me marmalade I've made? Here, let me fill that cup up for you.'

'How's your guts this morning?' asked Fred. 'What time do you think you'll finish today?'

'I want to be done by two o'clock, Fred, and leave here by about three.'

'I'll ask me lad to be with you at two o'clock then, he'll give you a hand to load up and bring you back here, then you can have a cup o'tea and a bite to eat, and be on our way – that be alright for you?'

'Perfect, Fred, you two are kindness itself,' the schoolmaster replied.

'Oh lad, you know we love having you to stay, you're welcome any time, isn't he Fred?' said Mary, patting her hair.

The second coat of paint flowed on smoothly, and having no one to 'egg him on' there were no amusing comments from Old John, who quietly sat by the fire smoking his pipe, watching the man slaving away. Just before two o'clock the painter was banging on the lids of the paint tins. The job was completed. 'That's it, John, that'll do you, how's it look?' he called out.

Old John rose from his milk bottle crate seat and slowly walked over to the wagon.

'It *diks kushti*, you've a-worked hard, brother. What do I owe yu?'

'I only want paying for the green gloss paint, John. Fred says he's given you the white lead paint and the linseed oil.'

'I canna 'ave that, brother, yu canna a-work like that fur nowt – 'ere, 'old out yer 'and,' and taking a roll of notes from his pocket he started to peel them off into the schoolmaster's hand.

'Is yu satisfied now?' he said as he pushed the painter's hand away from him.

'I don't want all that, John, really I don't.

'Listen, brother, we all enjoys yer company, yu've a-done a gud job on that cloth an' I thanks yer fur a-doin' it, an' I only 'opes yu'll a-come back soon an' see us all agin, an' when yu gits back 'ome t'that little 'ummon of yourn, yu tell 'er that John Lock thinks she's a lucky 'ummon t'ave a straight *mush* like yerself. Hey hup! 'Ere's Fred's lad a-comin'.'

' 'As this man a-told yer about the dear people as a-got 'umselves a-blowed up, lad?' Genty called over to him. 'My blessed Lord, a dear man a-found a big tin box on a tip an' 'e a-took it t'a *mush* 'e knowed t'cut the big lock offn it with 'is red-'ot cutter thing, an' they wuz a-blown t'pieces, lad, thur dear bits've bodies wuz a-blown fur miles they wuz, they thought the box wuz a-full've money but the blessed box wuz a-full've 'hexplosives', 'diny-mite', as yu might say. People's still a-findin' bits of thur dear bodies all over the place, they is. One *mush* a-found one of the dear people's fingers – an' it 'ad a ring on it an' all …. I 'uddent a-wear that, lad, 'ud yu? An' another *mush*, 'e found a heyeball on the doorstep of 'is little 'ouse, 'e did.'

Genty made the story more gory by the second; this is where stories turn into folk tales the schoolmaster thought – and who better to tell them than Gypsies?

Collected by the Rev. W. K. Clay – Hartlebury, Worcestershire, 1908

MUSKROS

'Here you is, Aunt Genty, a nice *kanni* (chicken) for you.'

It was late afternoon and Benny had called in to deliver a plump chicken for the pot.

'That's kind've yu, lad,' replied Genty.

Old John looked smilingly at Benny and said, 'Yu baint a-*chored* (stolen) that *kanni*, 'as yer?'

'Certainly not, Uncle John, we just finished doin' a farmer's barn – nice man he were an' all – and as I was leavin' he give me two of 'um, and I thought as how you'd like one. Honest to God that *kanni* is alright …'

Then with a big laugh Benny said, 'but be sure and burn the feathers!'

'Eh, *dordi*, I knowed yu'd a-*chored* it,' said Old John as he coughed and spat in the fire.

'No, no, no, Uncle John, I'm only a-jokin' with you, the *rai* (gentleman) really did give 'um to me. As I said, he's a *kushti* old *mush*, and we did him a good job an' all. He says he has a brother who's got a farm other side of Hereford, so next week we'm *jallin* down there and I reckons he'll have his barns painted an' all. To be honest with you, I'll be pleased to get out of this area, I've called near enough all of the farms now and the *muskros* (police) has been proper *bengs* (devils) to us. We've been shifted so many times I've lost count, and they've been really nasty with it an' all. I threatened to rip the head offn one of 'um but my Elsie grabbed hold of me and held me back, like, and pumped a few choice words into the *beng* of a man. It's got really bad Uncle John, I've never knowed anything like it. I'm goin' to see if this farmer down Hereford'll let us stop for a bit on his ground, like, while I works the area. I don't mind payin' the man if he'll let us pull in for a bit, then I can get on with me *booty* (work), like. It's this bein' shifted all the time that's a-doin' me head in, and see this rowin' with the *muskros* is bad for me health, 'ent it, Aunt Genty?'

Genty nodded and replied, 'That it is, lad, bad fer yer blood an' bad fer yer 'eart.'

'That's true, that's true,' he continued, 'my Elsie says them same words. Now listen, as much as I likes yer company I've got to *jall* on. My Elsie'll wonder wherever I've got to, and I bet yer life she greets me with "*muskro*'s bin and we've got t'move in the morning".'

Half way over the plank bridge Benny stopped, turned round and shouted, 'Is you goin' t'boil or roast that *kanni*, Aunt Genty?'

'Roast it,' came the reply, 'and roast *puvengris* (potatoes) an' all.'

'*Kuusshhti!*' rang out from Benny as he made his way up the little track to the road.

Shortly after Benny had left, Little Jimmy and Katie returned from playing in the wood, Nell as usual at Little Jimmy's heels.

'Yu've just missed yer Uncle Benny, 'e's brought us this fine *kanni*, *dik* 'ere,' and Genty held it in the air by one leg, the wings drooping down at right angles to its body, making it look bigger than it really was.

'Is we goin' to eat *all* that, Granny?' Little Jimmy asked as he stroked the feathers of the dead bird.

'*Owli*, lad, roast *kanni* and roaster *puvengris* fer us t'morrer, an' what's left over I'll boil up inter a nice broth fur us all.'

That evening as they all sat around the fire, Old John, taking his pipe from his mouth, remarked, 'I feels bad fur Benny an' Elsie bein' shifted by the *muskros* so much, dunna yu, my Genty?'

'I does too, my John, an' the lad works so hard an' all, don't 'e now?' Little Jimmy had been listening intently to this conversation and piped up, 'Is the policemens being bad to Uncle Benny and Aunt Elsie then, Granfer?'

'Bad baint the word fur it, my son, they's being real *bengs* t'um, they is, a-movin' 'um on an' a-movin' 'um on all the time like. Poor lad canna a-get on with 'is *booty* a-proper, like. It's alus bin "come on, it's time yu lot moved from 'ere" with the *muskros*, but never as bad as wot Benny woz a-sayin'. I feels sad in me 'eart fer 'um, that I does. We'm lucky t'bide 'ere all nice an' peaceful, like, baint we, my Genty?'

'*Owli*, my John, as I've a-said afore many times, this is our bit've 'eaven, that's wot it is, an' we'm lucky t'ave a nice kind gentleman t'let us bide whur we'm to.'

'Were the policemens bad to you and Granny when you was travelling about, Granfer?' Little Jimmy asked in a serious tone – 'I hates them policemens.'

'Dunna say that, lad,' Old John replied, 'thur's good 'uns an' thur's bad 'uns, an' without 'um whur 'ud we be? *Dordi*! we 'udent be safe in our beds now, 'ud we? Aar lad, we've bin a-told t'move on all on our lives, it's alus bin the same fur us people; but we dinna a-do too bad 'cause we was able t'get up some old lane outa the way, like, or on some old common whur we could bide fur the winter, an' then we 'ad the farms t'pull on to fur the pickin', an' up this bit a-country

– our country – everyone got t'know us, like. An' we alus tried t'keep ourselves up t'gether, all respectable as yu might say, an' we never really 'ad no bother with the *gauji foki*. An' the *muskros* got t'know that we warsn't really no bother an' all. Times 'as a-changed, an' Benny an' Elsie 'as that smart trailer an' motors baint they, an' they canna a-get up some old lane outa the way, they's on the side of the road on a layby or a bit've waste ground that's 'ard enough fer 'um t'pull on, an' a-course *foki diks* 'um all on the time an' then they complains t'the *muskros* – an' then they 'as t'do summat about it an' comes an' moves 'um on, like.

Remember that *muskro* that come to us on Castlemorton Common t'other side've Upton-on-Severn, my Genty?'
'That's when 'e went on about the *jukkals* (dogs) warn't it, my John?'
'*Owli*, it wer, gal – an' a long time agoo an' all.'
The children sensed there was a story coming and pressed their grandfather to tell them.
'Well now,' started Old John, 'we'd a-finished the work on a farm round Eve-e-shum (Evesham).'
'An' that wer the yer I got me new "gold" arm basket,' Genty butted in.
('Gold' baskets were in fact made by a basket maker called Gould from Bretforton near Evesham, who supplied travelling people with these well-made baskets.)
'That's right, my Genty, an' a good *tushni* it wer an' all, now whur woz I to?'
'You'd just finished work on a farm round Eve-e-Shum,' shouted out Little Jimmy.
'Aar, that's right; we come on up to Pershore, an' then over t'Upton-on-Severn an' then onto Castlemorton Common whur we wuz

gooin' t'bide fur a bit until we cut across t'Ledbury an' back up these parts, like.'

'Tell 'um wot 'appened on that 'ill outa Upton, my John,' Genty butted in again.

'Eh *dordi!* I'd a furgotten about that, *dordi* did yu cuss,' and Old John started to laugh.

'Warn't no laughin' matter t'me, my John, me brand new enamel boilin' pot that wer all blue inside got a-smashed an' a-chipped t'pieces on that 'ill, it did,'

'What happened?' the children shouted out almost simultaneously.

'Well I'll a-tell yu iffn yu'll bide quiet; the old mare we 'ad wuz a good 'un, an' when I sez a good 'un I means a real good 'un. She only 'ad t'see a 'ill a-comin' up and 'er put 'erself inter the collar. Well now, she's really a-puttin' some work inter gettin' up that ill, an' I'm a-runnin' up the side've the wagin with the reins in me 'ands, an' we gets t'the top an' I pulls in t'let the old mare 'ave a blow, an' meself an' all, like. I'd a-left yer Granny at the bottom of the 'ill with yer mammy in the little pushchair, that she'd *monged* (begged) offn somebody – yer mammy wuz only a little 'un then.'

'Any old 'ow, I'm a-stood thur with the mare an' she's still a-blowin' an' the road's all wet frum the sweat offn 'er. An' I'm a-waitin' an' a-waitin' fur yer Granny t'come – when all've a sudden she comes over the brow of this 'ill, an' she's a-cussin' something terrible, like.'

'I wuz an' all,' butted in Genty again, 'an' I'll a-tell yu why I wuz a-cussin' an' all. I wuz a-cussin' because one door've the kettle box 'ad a-come undone gooin' up that 'ill an' me new boilin' pot 'ad a-bounced out an' a-chipped itself t'pieces a-bouncin' down that 'ill. Twarn't even worth me while t'pick it up – it was *poggered* (broken). Thur wuz some tins've tomatoes an' stuff I picked up that wuz alright an' I piled them on yer mammy in the pushchair, but me lovely new pot wuz *poggered* good an' proper. I was real upset I wuz, it wuz brand new an' I never even got t'use it.'

'But yu got another frum Leominster 'ummon,' Old John said with a smile.

'But it warn't as good as the one that got *poggered*,' Genty replied crossly.

'No, it 'uddent 'ud bin 'ud it, yu alus blamed me fur not closin' the kettle box properly, an' it wuz yu that put the stuff in thur,' Old John coughed and spat in the fire, and he and Genty fell silent.

Little Jimmy and Katie looked at each other and started to laugh. This was the first time that they'd seen their grandparents argue and they found it really amusing. The laughing of the children made Old John and Genty laugh, and Old John continued his story.

'What I wuz a-gooin' t'tell yu – afore this 'ummon a-butted in on me story – wuz what 'appened on Castlemorton Common. Well now, when we gets t'this old common we *diks* that thur's others on thur an' all – I thought thur might 'ave bin 'cause it wer a reglar stoppin' place fur me cousin Fred an' 'is missus Dolly an' thur *chavvies*. I cuddna mek out who t'others wuz until we pulls over by 'um; turned out t'be Eli Smith an' 'is missus an' kids. Never recognised who they wuz until we sees 'um, 'cause they 'ad a differcnt wagin. Eli 'ad 'ad a *chop* (exchange) for this 'un down Gloucester way, an' 'is missus warn't too pleased about it neither.'

'Any old 'ow, it wuz nice t'see 'um all agin an' they says they've bided thur fur nearly two weeks. *Kushti*, I thinks, we'll 'ave us a couple'll weeks 'ere an' all. Well now, we'd only bin thur a couple'll a days an' who turns up early the next mornin'?'

'The policeman,' shouted out Little Jimmy.

'*Owli*, the *muskro* on 'is old bike. Well now, 'e pushes 'is old bike over t'us, like, 'cause 'e canna a-ride like 'cause the ground's all bumpified. *Mornin' Mr Policeman, Sir* I sez, all polite, like, an' 'e's a-leanin' on the 'andlebars of 'is old bike, an' 'e smiles an' sez, *mawnin* back t'us. Then 'e sez *'Ow long 'ave you bin 'ere?* Well 'e knowed 'ow long we'd all a-bin thur now didna 'e, it wer 'is patch warn't it? But 'e asks any old 'ow.'

'Fred and Eli sez, *We've only bin 'ere a few days, Sir.* They wuz a-shoutin' this out t'the *muskro* 'cause the *jukkals* is a-barking like billy-o, *dordi!* They wuz a-mekin' a noise I can tell yu. I think Fred 'ad about 'alf a dozen an' Eli 'ad a few an' all. We only 'ad one an' 'e warn't no bother at all, wuz 'e, my Genty?'

'He warn't no bother at all, my John, a dear little *juk* 'e were, we called 'im Billy, didna we?'

'Aar we did, 'e used t'ride on the footboard've the wagin when we wuz a-travellin', an' this one day, over by Presteigne warn't it, he jumped off right in front've a motor car an' a-got 'isself a-kilt (killed), didna 'e? We wuz upset, warn't we, gal?'

'We wuz, my John, that we wuz.'

'Any old 'ow, as I say, all the *jukkals* is a-barkin' an' yu couldna a-hear yerself speak hardly, an' the *muskro* 'as t'shout an' all.'

'You've got some nice dogs thur,' 'e sez. An' Fred ups an' sez, 'Yes Sir, we breeds 'um all ourself, that we do Sir,' an' Eli *pens* (says) much the same.

'I'm a-stood t'one side an' I reckons I knows what's a-comin' – an' I was right an' all.'

'What was it?' Katie said impatiently.

'Well, the *muskro* 'e ups an' sez *you've got a lot of 'um, baint you?* an' 'e's a-countin' 'um. Fred an' Eli sez, *yes, Sir. Well,* sez the *muskro, I'll be round in the mornin' to see the dog licences you've got between you.* An' with that 'e gives us a smile an' sez *mawnin' t'you all,* pushes 'is old bike t'the track, mounts up – an' is gone.'

'An' so wuz we the followin' mornin' – 'cause none've us 'ad no licences, now did we?'

'He wasn't a real bad policeman, was he Granfer?' Little Jimmy said thoughtfully.

'*Kekka,* lad,' replied Old John, ''e wuz one've the old sort, 'e didna a-want no hollerin' an' a-screamin', now did 'e? No, 'e didna, 'e used 'is 'ead an' a-done 'is duty in a peacified sorta way, like, an' all the time I reckons 'e wuz a-laughin' t'isself. But they warn't all like 'im, thur wuz some real *waffedi* (bad) 'uns an' all, an' my blessed Lord, a-listenin' t'our Benny they'm gettin' wusser.'

'Tell 'um about Claudy Loveridge, my John,' Genty said with a chuckle, as she handed him a dish of tea.

'Oh my dear blessed Lord, that wer a long time agoo an' all, warn't it now? Claudy Loveridge! *Dordi!* Now thur wuz a man who didna a-like *muskros,* no 'e didna, 'e warn't never polite t'um an' never ever tried t' "moody 'um on", like. 'E didna like 'um at all, not one've 'um. We warn't thur at the time that I'm a-gooin' t'tell yu about, but this story 'as gone from Traveller to Traveller right up an' down this bit've country.'

'By all accounts what 'appened wuz old Claudy an' 'is missus Violet – but everyone called 'er Blackbird – is a-stoppin' up this little lane down by Tewksbury; they 'ad a pretty little square "flap wagin", didna they, my Genty?'

'They did, my John, a pretty 'un it wer, but I dusn't a-like they flap wagins, I likes a door an' windows t'close at night.'

(Flap wagons, more commonly known as 'open lots' were made without a door and windows, the front being covered with two fitted canvas sheets.)

'Any old 'ow,' Old John continued, 'they'd a-bin up this old lane fur a while an' the local *muskro* 'as a-bin t'um t'shift a few times an' Claudy 'as a-told 'im t'buzz off an' leave 'um alone, like. Well this one mornin' the *muskros* arrives in force an' thur's a sergeant with 'um an' all, a-shoutin' 'is mouth off. Claudy was a-sat thur cross-legged by 'is bit of *yog* – never got up fer 'um 'e never, an' 'e a-tells 'um 'e baint a-gooin' t'shift, I'm a-bad with me bronchials 'e tells 'um, goo away an' catch some thieves an' robbers if yu can an' a-leave us poor people alone. Goo on, buzz off, 'e tells 'um.'

'Well now, this sergeant 'e steps for'ard an' sez *How dare you speak to your superior like that?* Claudy, 'e looks up at him, an' 'e sez, *My superior! My superior? I'll a-tell yu summat, I could put me 'oss in the shafts this very minute, but I baint a-gooin' to – an' I could think t'meself I think I'll goo t'Gloucester, 'alf way thur I could a-change me mind an' think no, I thinks I'll goo t'Worcester – but yu canna a-do that, yu 'as t'do what you'm told now, dusn't yu? This suit a-clothes I've a-got on is mine baint it? But that suit a-clothes you'm a-wearin' baint yorn now, is it? So 'ow in this dear Lord's world can you be my superior, constable?* 'E knowed 'e wuz a sergeant but called 'im constable t'annoy 'im, like.'

'*Doordi!* he told him, didn't he Granfer?' Little Jimmy shouted out excitedly. 'Did they let 'um stay where they was to?'

218

'*Kekka*, lad, this sergeant 'e orders 'is men t'pull the wagin off the grass verge an' on t'the road. Claudy an' Violet knowed as they'd 'ave t'shift that mornin' an' luckily Violet 'ad a-packed all the china an' bits an' pieces, otherwise they'd a-bin smashed t'pieces 'uddent they? No, Claudy 'e didna a-like the *muskros* one little bit, an' only did they things t'annoy 'um, like. Mind you, 'e made it 'ard on 'isself, 'e an' old Violet was a-chivvied about in that area after that, an' they moved back up to Worcester – t'pastures green as yu might say. An' now I'll a-tell yu summat funny afore yu *jalls t'woodrus*, 'cause I reckons it's a-gettin' that time' an' we've 'ad enough talk of *muskros*, baint we?'

'Years agoo, afore we come 'ere, we wuz a-stoppin' this side a Chester in a place that's knowed as Humpy Bridges lane. We 'ad us a bit a good company up that old lane an' all, some've the Taylors an' some've the Prices wuz *atchin* thur, an' we all got on fine t'gether, like. Any old 'ow, thur was this *kitchima* not so far off, called The Headless Woman, an' on the front've it wuz a big sign "NO GIPSIES SERVED". We'd a-tried t'get a pint of *livena* thur, but as soon as we walked in they *diked* who we wuz an' said *Get out, we dunna serve you people 'ere*. One've Mushy Taylor's lads went in on 'is own, all smart 'e wuz, with a collar an' tie on, but as soon as 'e got close t'the bar they twigged what 'e wer an' a-told 'im t'get out.'
'How did they know, Granfer?' asked Katie.
'They smelt 'im, gal – we all smells smoky from a-bein' round the old *yog* we dusn't a-smell it 'cause we'm used t'it, but the *gaujos* does. Well now, this one day I'm a-sittin' 'avin' a smoke an' a chat with me old pal Stranger Price, when up pulls this smart little motor an' who should stick 'is 'ead outa the winder but another old *mush* we

knowed a-called Rowland Griffiths. 'E an' 'is lot 'ad bin in bricks fur a long time, an' 'e'd a-done well with 'isself, like.'

'Any old 'ow, Rolly gets outa the motor an' a-comes an' sits with us round the *yog*, an' 'e sez, "I've just a-had a bit a-sport in the 'Eadless 'Ummon".
"You got served!" we sez.
"I did," 'e sez, "an' I 'ad a bit've sport an' all."
Now yu 'udden't a-tekin' Rolly fur a Gypsy man, he wuz all blondy-'eaded an' 'ad rosy cheeks an' a-course 'e never smelt smokified 'cause 'e lived in a 'ouse, an' unlike us 'e'd bin t'school an' 'e could read an' write, like.
"What 'appened?" we *putches* (asks) him.
"Well," 'e sez, "I seed that big new sign a-put up on the front of the public, so in I *jalls*. They serves me as cordial as yer like an' I pays fur me pint, and I'm a-stood thur at the bar a-drinkin' it, an' I looks up an' blow me, thur's another sign a-starin' me in the face – NO GIPSIES SERVED. I calls the barman over an' I sez *Could you put me up twelve bottles've brown ale, twelve bottles've Vimto an' twelve packets've crisps – oh! an' you better put a bottle've Bells whisky in the cardboard box an' all, I'm 'avin' a little party tonight. "*

"Well, the man gets all this a-packed in the box an' puts it on the bar beside me, an' I can *dik* 'im a-lookin' out how much it all comes to, so I ups an' sez 'Excuse me barman, I've not got my specticals with me an' I was wondering what that sign sez?'
'Oh,' he sez, 'NO GIPSIES SERVED.'

'Oh! deary, deary me,' I sez, 'I'm so sorry to 'ave a-come in 'ere.'
'Why?' he sez.

'I'm a Gypsy,' I sez, an' I turns around t'goo out.

'Hang on a minute,' the man sez. 'Pay for this and we won't say any more about it.'

I turns round to 'im an' I sez 'I am an 'onourable man, sir, an' I dusn't like t'do nothin' that 'ent right – so I'll bid yu good day.' An' with that I walks out a-chucklin' t'meself."

'He had him, Granfer, didn't he?' laughed Little Jimmy, and Katie, with a puzzled look exclaimed, 'Did he buy the beer and stuff for the party somewhere else then?'

A Sunday Visit and the Ghost Story

The bells of the village church were ringing, calling people to worship, as Old John leant against the five-barred gate that led on to the little lane with grass growing in the middle. Taking his pipe from his pocket he filled it, lit up, and puffed contentedly.

He'd mooched off on his own this morning, going through the wood, along the edge of the field to the five-barred gate on which he was now leaning. Opposite was 'his' copse which over the years had supplied him with materials for his clothes-pegs, flowers, skewers and baskets. He opened the gate and slowly sauntered down the little lane. It was July now, the weather had not been that warm, but at least it was dry.

'Thank the dear Lord we enna 'ad too much wet weather,' he thought, 'I cuddna a-do with us all a-cooped up in the tent fur too long. *Chavvies* 'as bin with us fur three months now, or thurabouts, the dear little lambs, they baint no bother – but I likes a bit a-time t'meself.'

The children had settled down well to the daily routine of Old John and Genty's life, and were now respectful and helpful. Occasionally they squabbled and there were tears, but Genty soon sorted that out.

Although he was walking slowly, Old John suddenly stopped, coughing alarmingly and spat in the hedge.

'*Dordi*, my breathin's getting' wosser, must be 'cause I'm well over seventy an' slowin' down a bit,' he thought.

He sauntered on, and just before he came to the little ford a wagtail flew up from the water and landed on the road before him; it ran, paused and wagged its tail rapidly.

'*Kushti sarla* (good morning) little friend, we'll 'ave visitors t'day then, eh?' Old John said quietly to it. The bird again ran, paused, and wagged its tail a few more times then flew back to its safe haven on the edge of the ford.

'We shall 'ave some visitors shortly,' shouted Old John as he made his way over the plank bridge and walked towards the fire.

'How do you know that, Granfer?' Little Jimmy exclaimed in amazement.

'Yes, how do you know, Granfer?' joined in Katie.

'The wagtail's just a-told me,' answered Old John.

The children looked at each other in disbelief – but pursued the matter no further.

'He's alus coming out with funny things, 'ent he, Jimmy?' Katie whispered to her brother, who nodded his head in agreement.

Genty, standing by the table outside the tent, had heard Old John's remarks and smiled to herself. It was Sunday, she thought, and Sundays are always visiting days for Gypsy people. But the wagtail is never wrong with his knowledge of forthcoming visitors.

'Wonder whosoever will a-come an' see us?' she called to Old John, who had now taken his seat by the fire.

'Dunna know, 'ummon, but these *chavvies* 'ad a-better get 'umselves a-tidied up a bit smartish. Come 'ere Jimmy lad, an' let me tie that bit a-silk around yer neck a bit tidy, like.'

Little Jimmy, doing as he was told, walked over to his grandfather, who proceeded to untie the badly folded scarf, then placed it on his right thigh and folded it properly. Then, putting it back round Little Jimmy's neck, tied it in a perfect square knot.

'That looks better, me lad,' he said with a satisfied smile, 'put them ends in yer shirt now.'

Before Old John could utter another word, Katie was skipping over to them, singing, 'Look at me, look at me, in me new best pinner.'

'Eh, *dordi!* Yu *diks* a proper little *rauni* (you look a proper little lady) in that, me gal. Yer Aunt Sylvie meks 'um *kushti*, don't she now?'

Maurice and his wife Sylvie had visited a few weeks ago, and to Katie's pleasure Aunt Sylvie had given her the pretty 'pinner' that she'd made especially for her.

'You only wear that for best now, Katie gal,' she said. 'Took me a long time to make it, it did.'

Katie loved her best 'pinner', made of cotton material with a rose motif, dark blue pockets with a basket of flowers embroidered on each, and a dark blue frill all round the edge. Katie had skipped back to her granny, who was trying to tie a piece of ribbon in her hair.

'Keep yerself still, gal, an' 'old yer 'ead up,' Genty said crossly.

'Sorry, Granny,' Katie replied, 'but I 'as to keep lookin' at me pinner. *Dordi!* it's pretty, 'ent it?'

Suddenly a call of 'hoy, hoy' came from the direction of the gate into the field.

'There yu is,' Old John exclaimed, 'that dear little *chiriklo* (bird) is never wrong, never wrong, I tells yu.'

Little Nell began frantically barking and Little Jimmy, without being asked, ran over and tied her up under the wagon. Another call of 'hoy, hoy' sounded, as three people came into view.

'Well my blessed Lord, it's our Mary-Ann and Zacky (Zachariah) I do declare, my John, an' the young fella must be thur lad Robert.'

Genty was waving wildly, bubbling over with excitement, as they approached the little plank bridge over the brook.

Standing beside her grandfather, Katie began to giggle and whispered '*Dordi* Granfer, don't she walk funny, I never seen anything like it.'

'*Atch yer mui, rakli* (stop your mouth, girl),' Old John reprimanded, 'you'll upset the dear 'ummon.'

Mary-Ann did indeed walk strangely; with every step her little plump body swayed alarmingly from side to side, in her right hand she carried a walking stick and on her left arm a very colourful shopping bag. She was Genty's younger sister, by two years; her face was round and fresh – unlike Genty's, whose was weather-beaten and now deeply lined. Her hair was permed, covered by a large silk scarf tied under her chin. She wore a dark blue two-piece and round her neck a large gold chain suspended on which was a two-pound gold piece in a fancy mount. Following behind Mary-Ann came her husband Zacky and their son Robert, who held his father's arm, helping him along the pathway.

Joining his sister, Little Jimmy declared, 'They'm smartly dressed 'ent they, Katie? *Dik* at the old *mush*'s suit.'

Zacky, a small rotund man, dark of complexion with well-groomed short grey hair and moustache, was dressed in a light blue three-piece suit. The waistcoat, which stuck out over his portly stomach, sported a large gold watch chain with a gold sovereign fob attached. Robert, unlike his parents, was tall, but had his father's dark complexion and dark flashing eyes. With Zacky's failing eyesight Robert had taken over the carpet hawking business completely and was dressed appropriately for his calling; white shirt with tie, dark trousers and black polished shoes – smart and every inch a business man. Moving down from Staffordshire to Worcestershire in the 1920s, Zacky's parents had settled near Kidderminster and that is where he'd met and married Mary-Ann, who, having the same surname, was a distant cousin.

Kidderminster, a carpet-manufacturing town, soon gave him his occupation as 'Carpet Hawker'. Birmingham, only twenty miles north, supplied linoleum. With these two commodities Zacky had flourished and now owned a brick-built bungalow, on a nice piece of ground, to the rear of which was a smart yard with large buildings for storage. It was here that Robert and his wife Coralena lived in their trailer caravan, to the side of which stood their wooden day room and cookshed.

'I'm a-comin', I'm a-comin',' Mary-Ann squawked out as she precariously put one foot on the plank bridge.

'Oh my blessed Lord, do take care, my sister,' called out Genty as she mounted the bridge and, taking her sister's hand, led her over. Robert, going first, led his father over. The two sisters hugged each other, and Genty, overwhelmed with joy, mopped her eyes with the corner of her pinner. Looking at Old John, with a squinty stare,

Mary-Ann shouted out, 'And how's you, my John? Every time I sees you, you looks wosser!'

They all laughed, and Old John walked over to greet Zacky and Robert.

'My brother, it's *kushti* to *dik* yu (good to see you).'

And Zacky replied, 'And you too, my brother – no mind to her, you *diks* well to me, but me old *yoks* 'ent as *kushti* as they used to be.'

And they all laughed again; Old John started to cough and spat into the fire.

Hand outstretched, Robert approached Old John, and shook his hand vigorously. 'Nice to see you again, Uncle John, me mam and dad have been moitherin' me for weeks now to bring them over to see you. We haven't seen you for years now, have we?'

'That yu 'aven't, lad, but it's good t'see yu all now – with the exception've that old witch over thur,' and he threw a glance at Mary-Ann.

They all laughed again and Old John coughed and spat in the fire.

All this time Little Jimmy and Katie had been standing quietly, watching and listening.

'Come 'ere you two,' Genty called to them, and they slowly walked over to their grandmother.

'You baint never sin our Addy's *chavvies*, 'as yer, my sister? This is Little Jimmy an' this is Katie – say hello t'yer Aunt Mary-Ann an' yer Uncle Zacky an' Uncle Robert.'

The children, on their best behaviour and overwhelmed by these well-dressed people, went to each one and shook their hands.

'Eh, *dordi!* They'm well behaved and respectful *chavvies*, 'ent they, my sister?' Mary-Ann exclaimed.

'We 'as to be otherwise we gets a smack,' piped up Katie, and they all laughed, and again Old John coughed and spat in the fire.

'Now make haste, you two, an' bring them two chairs from the tent, lad, fer me brother an' sister t'sit on, an' Katie, yu goo t'the wagin an' bring Robert a cushion.'

And with that Genty placed an upturned bucket by the fire as a seat for Robert – 'Wait fer the cushion, my son, yu dunna want t'get yer *bulengris* (trousers) dirty.'

Robert looked a little embarrassed and managed to stop himself saying, 'I've got a dozen pairs at home, Aunt.'

Mary-Ann handed over the colourful shopping bag to Genty, saying, 'There's a bit of *hobben* in there, my sister, as you didn't know we was a-comin' so I made us all some sandwiches and got a few pork pies and pickles for us all. I knowed you'd have plenty of *floppy* (tea) a-brewin'.'

And with that she threw a glance at the teapot in the embers of the fire.

'When you'm seated my sister, I'll brew up,' Genty replied quietly. Little Jimmy had placed a chair by his grandfather for Zacky, and Katie put the cushion on the bucket for Robert and the three men sat quietly discussing 'men's things'.

'Bring that chair over 'ere fur yer Aunt Mary-Ann,' Genty called out to Little Jimmy, and he placed it by the cupboard table for her to sit on. She lowered herself down onto the seat with a loud groan, saying, 'Oh my dear sister, me legs 'as a-got wosser lately, I've a-bin under two doctors now, and they can't a-help me. Me dear old head is so bad sometimes as I can't a-sleep. They pills don't a-help me, my sister, some nights I 'as the pain so bad that I cries out to the dear Lord.'

Shouting to her husband she said, "Ent that right, my Zacky, I cries out to the dear Lord to help me with the pain I gets in me head?' Looking up, Zacky, with a loud sigh, shouted back, 'Yes.'

And Robert, looking at Genty, said, 'Doctors can't find out what's the matter with me mam – they say she's a medical mystery,' and he gave a little chuckle.

'Honest to God, my sister, them words is true that our Robert just a-spoke – they says I'm a medical mystery, if they had the pain I has to suffer they'd get 'umselves a-sorted out, wouldn't they?' and Mary-Ann, head bowed, fell silent for a few moments. Genty took the opportunity to call Katie, and prepared to make tea.

'*Jall* up in the *vardo* (go up in the wagon) an' bring three've they pretty cups outa me china cupboard, gal, an' be very careful with 'um, like.'

Returning with the cups, Katie placed them carefully on the cupboard table, then from the cupboard took the two tea dishes and her and Little Jimmy's cups.

Standing to the side of Mary-Ann she studied the appearance of her great-aunt, who had now removed the big silk headscarf from her head. Katie's big dark eyes took it all in. 'Her hair looks funny,' she thought, 'I likes me granny's scraped back and done in a bun better, and her face looks all paleyfied with all the powder she's put on.' And she gave a little sniff and could smell it. 'I likes her earrings, though.' Big, heavy gold earrings dangled from the old lady's ear lobes – 'I hopes I gets a pair like that when I'm older,' she thought.

Genty had made the tea and poured it out. "Ow many sugars does yu two take?' she called across to Zacky and Robert. 'I knows yu likes yorn sweet, my sister,' and Mary-Ann nodded appreciatively. Picking up a cup for Mary-Ann, Katie handed it carefully to her.

'You'm a dear sweet child,' she said as she took the cup from her, 'I likes yer pinner, gal.'

Katie beamed and replied, 'Me Aunt Sylvie made it for me. Pretty 'ent it, it's only for best.'

'So it should be, gal, the dear 'ummon a-took some time to mek that, take mind gal, and don't a-get it dirty like.'

'I won't,' she said, 'I loves it!'

'Take they two cups over t'yer uncles now gal, an' try not t'spill 'um,' Genty asked.

'What about Granfer?' came the reply.

'They 'as thern afore yer Granfer t'day, gal, 'cause they'm visitors, so be respectful an' 'and 'um over politely, like, then tek yer Granfer 'is.'

They all sat drinking their tea, Mary-Ann moaning about relations and people in general.

'She'm a spiteful woman, my sister,' … 'our Alfie said he'd tear his liver out,' … 'she still goos out with 'er basket, but I knows how she gets 'er *luvva*, wicked, wicked, that's what 'er is,' … 'and yer knows our Willy's 'ummon, don't yer, 'er's the sneakiest 'ummon I ever knowed, I sez t'er t'other day, I sez you'm lower than a snake's belly, you is, and our Willy 'ent much better since 'e 'ad 'er, my sister. I udden't a-give 'er a drip off the end of me nose – no I udden't!'

Genty sat quietly nodding at her sister, then noticed that Katie and Little Jimmy were standing a few paces away listening intently.

'Tek that pinner off now, gal, an' yu two goo an' play somewhur fer a bit,' she hurriedly said, 'yer ears 'ent old enough fur this sort've talk.'

Taking a cigarette from her lips – the end of which was covered in bright red lipstick – Mary-Ann asked Genty where her shopping bag was.

'I put it on the table in the tent,' came the reply.

''Ere now, you two *chavvies jall* and a-look in that bag of mine and you'll find a bag of sweeties I's a-brought for ya.'

The children were gone in a flash, and Mary-Ann chuckled to herself, then, turning to Genty, in a serious manner, said, 'Tell us about yer gal, my sister.'

'Come on up in the wagin, sister, I dusn't want my John t'ear nothin' – 'e gets quickly upset as yer knows.' And with that Genty led the way to the private interior of her living-wagon. Turning round to the swaying form she enquired, 'You'll a-manage the steps, won't yu?'

'Been a long time since I used steps, my sister, but I'll manage if you gives us a pull-up like,' and again old Mary-Ann gave a little chuckle.

The three men, sitting around the fire, were engaged in deep conversation, and Robert had just asked his Uncle John if he had any horses now.

'*Kekka*, lad, bin a fair time since we 'ad 'um, the old mare wer near enough thirty, Farmer got a knacker man from over thur in Cullmington t'come an' put the dear thing down. I nearly ended up a-*korin* (fighting) the *mush*, he'd got a chain around 'er neck an' wuz a-winchin' 'er up any old 'ow, an' I shouts fur 'im t'stop an' drag 'er up all dignified, like. She wer a *kushti* old *grasni* (mare), never jibbed on a 'ill, never put a foot wrong, 'er didn't. An' me daughter's little coloured 'oss I sold when 'er runned off with that low-life *mush*,' and he spat in the fire, dropped his head and went quiet.

She wer a kushti old grasni, never jibbed on a 'ill, never put a foot wrong 'er didn't.

Like most Gypsy people Zacky was over-sentimental and knew of Old John's grief; with a quick intake of air, he exploded with 'my brother, you listen to this now, it'll mek you laugh, *mush*.'
Old John raised his head, 'It'd better be a good 'un, brother.'
'It is an' all, my John, you just sit thur and smoke that *swiggler* and a-listen t'this.'
Taking another intake of air he started the story.

'Me lad Robert 'ere takes me out a-callin' with him sometimes, just for the ride, so to speak. Well now, t'other week we was down Pershore way, and we've a-cut up this little lane from the main road, and the little lane brings you onto the other Eve-e-sham (Evesham) road by the Berkley Arms public. You'll know where I'm to, won't you?'

Old John nodded and Zacky continued.

'Well my brother, we'm driving up the lane and Robert says "*dik akai* (look here), dad, 'ere's one of them Stankoviches" – you remembers they foreign travellers, always wears them big black *stadis* (hats), don't you, *mush*?'

Old John replied '*Owli*, nice people an' all.'

'Pull up, I sez to Robert and he does. I winds the window down and shouts: "How yer doin', *mush*?" and he stops his walkin' and comes over t'ave a *rokker*, like. Well it turns out to be Old Johnny's lad, very civil lad too. I enquires after his father and he says he's away buyin' motors. You remembers, brother, they deals in them big motors and loves them American jobs.'

Old John, fully recovered now, and taking the story in with enthusiasm answered: '*Owli, owli*, carry on, *mush*.'

'Well, we'm a-*rokkerin* away, and I asks how business is and he replies "could be better", like we all does, then he says: "Listen to this, uncle. We had a man come to our place few weeks ago to buy a motor and I'm stood there listening to me dad telling the man how perfect it was. Well, the man wants to take it out for a test drive, don't he, and me old dad, looking all hurt, says, 'Sir, that motor is perfect, it's as perfect as can be, Sir, there is no need for you to bother your head about that, as I say, Sir, it's perfect.'

So the man he ups and pays me dad, gets in the motor and off he goes. 'Bout half hour he's back a-hollerin' and a-screaming. The bloody thing had broke down, at the bottom of the lane, and he'd come back for his money, hadn't he, and he's saying 'you said it was perfect, you did.' Well, me old dad, he stands there stroking his big 'tash and then he says to the man: 'Do you know why I've got this big 'tash, Sir?' And the man, he replies, 'No, why?'

'I've got this big 'tash, Sir,' he says, 'so's you cannot call me a bare-faced liar!' "

'*Dooordi!* that's a good 'un, that is,' Old John managed to say between laughing, coughing and spitting. 'Did 'e give 'im 'is money back, brother?'

'My John, I never asked the lad, I was too busy laughing meself,' Zacky replied.

'And I never asked him neither, Uncle John, 'cause I was doubled up an' all,' said Robert.

'Man, I shall have to remember that 'un if I's a-*rokkerin* any *hokabins* (lies),' and Old John gave his moustache a wipe on both sides with the top of his index finger. Just then they heard the cackling voice of Mary-Ann, 'I's a-comin', I's a-comin',' she called out, swaying from side to side, picking her way slowly over the grass to her chair by the cupboard table.

'Is yu three ready fur some *hobben*?' Genty called, as she disappeared into the tent to get the food that her sister had so thoughtfully brought. Old John, placing the top of his thumb and index finger in his mouth, gave a loud whistle – long, high, finishing with a short low pitch – for the children to return from their playing in the wood.

'We give Nell one of they toffees Aunt Mary-Ann. *Dordi!* it was comical to watch her tryin' to eat it, she got it stuck on her teeth and her mouth was goin' twenty to the dozen, wasn't it, Katie?'

'It were an' all, Jimmy, I laughed so much me tummy started to hurt.'

'Mine hurt more than yours, though,' he replied.

Genty was now busy handing out the sandwiches, pork pie and pickled onions, and Old John had swung the kettle over a few flames to boil for more tea.

'Bring yer chair over t'the fire, Mary-Ann,' he called to her.

'I'll bide where I'm to, thank you John,' she replied. 'I doesn't want t'get all smokified, thank you.'

'She'm a proper *rauni* (lady), she is, 'ent she now?' uttered Zacky, and he smiled and winked at Old John.

Although the children had munched their way through a bag of sweets they were soon devouring the salmon and lettuce sandwiches, chunks of pork pie and crunching on pickled onions. The salmon sandwiches were definitely a favourite – a real treat for them both.

'These sandwiches is posh, 'ent they, Katie?' Little Jimmy said to his sister, who, with a full mouth replied, 'I loves them.'

Genty saw this, and threw Katie a stern stare and pointed to her mouth.

Zacky had caught these words, and looking at Little Jimmy he said, 'Posh grub, eh! – I'll tell you what, my lad, that salmon took some landing. I had it on the hook, a-fighting with it for near on two hours, afore I landed it.'

Amazed, Little Jimmy replied, 'Did you, uncle Zacky?'

'*Kekka* lad, I'm only a-joking you, it comes out of a tin.'

Little Jimmy let out a long 'naaar – you'm as bad as me Granfer, you is.'

The meal was finished, tea had been drunk, and the dishes and cups washed. Genty and Mary-Ann remained seated by the cupboard table, the children joining the three menfolk sitting opposite them by the fireside, quietly taking in the conversation. Looking across at them, quietly sitting there, Robert in his soft-spoken voice said, 'You two is so well behaved – 'ent they, dad?' And Zacky replied, '*Owli*, I wish you'd a-bin as good as they when you was that age … I reckon I give you too much rein, my son, but you've a-turned out *kushti*,' and he gave his son a thump on the arm.

'By the looks of you, you two must like this old life,' Robert continued, 'what's you been getting up to since you've been here?' Katie, bubbling over with Robert's compliments, was the first to answer.

'Well now, uncle Robert,' she replied in a very grown-up manner, 'Granny's bin a-teachin' me to cook – and I does a lot of it meself now, and I polishes all the brass and copper in the wagon for Granny, and I helps her with the groceries when we goes to town on Thursday, and I cleans out me own little wagon, and I helps Granny with the washin' …' She stopped to think, ' … and me and me brother plays in the brook, and we plays in the woods with Nell – we has our own little secret hidey hole there, don't we Jimmy?'

Little Jimmy, eager to get in on the conversation, quickly said, 'Yes, it's very secret, only we know where it is, nobody in the whole world could ever find it.'

Eager to show off his most precious possession, he proudly removed his catapult from under his shirt and pulled it over his head.

'There now, dad, he's a proper Gypsy boy a-carrying it like that, isn't he now?' declared Robert. 'Let's have a *dik* at it, lad,' and Little Jimmy passed it to him.

'It's a good 'un and all, I can see your Granfer made it; I'd know his cattys anywhere. You 'ent lost it, Uncle John.'

'I still 'as a goo, my son,' Old John replied with a smile.

'Any good with it yet?' Robert continued.

'Naar uncle, I keep practisin' and practisin' but I only hits the tin now and again.'

'Which hand do you hold it in?'

And Little Jimmy held up his right hand.

'Why don't you try holding it in the other hand, to see if it suits you better?'

'My blessed Lord,' Old John exclaimed, 'I never a-thought t'tell 'im that. Goo an' 'ave a goo now, my son.'

And Little Jimmy disappeared to his practice area behind the tent.

'Granfer plays his fiddle for us some nights, but not as much 'cause his fingers is 'maticky, and Granny does a little dance, tippity tap, tippity tap she goes on the board that we keeps on the back of the wagon – and they tells us stories. I loves the stories, honest to God I does,' Katie blurted out excitedly.

Zacky, well known as a good story teller, looking at the excited Katie, said, 'Stories, stories is it? Do you want to hear a good 'un?'

'Will you tell us one, Uncle Zacky?'

'I will, my gal, *jall* and get yer brother and I'll tell you a very strange story.'

As Katie got up from the fire a loud PING came from the back of the tent, and the joyous sound of Little Jimmy shouting, 'I hit it, I hit it.'

'*Mandi jins* (I know) what my Zacky is a-goin' to *pooker the chavvies* (tell the children), my sister – and it's a good 'un and all. You 'ent a-heard him tell this 'un, sister. *Dordi!* it's a good 'un,' Mary-Ann rocked backwards and forwards with glee. The children took their places opposite the three men, and Zacky commenced his tale, saying, 'I dusn't want no interruptions now, you understands?' And the children nodded attentively. And Zacky began.

'Now years and years and years ago we used to get all over this bit of country, and all over Wales there, hawking the carpets and lino, like. We used to pay a farmer *mush* to stop on one of his nice clean fields, and from there we'd call the area, like, and then we'd move on to another area. Well, this one day we'm calling round Oswestry, and I thinks to meself I could do with a pint of beer – 'cause it was a hot day. So I *jall* into this little *kitchima*, and who should be sitting thur a-drinkin' his *livena* and a-smokin' his pipe, but Seth Wood. You remembers him, don't you John? You know, he that had old Jim Roberts' gal, Kitty.'

'I 'ent a-sin that man since I was a *chavvi*,' Old John replied, 'but I *jins* who yu means, *mush*.'

'Well now, I hadn't a-seen him meself for years and years. "What's you doing over this bit of country?" I asks him.
"My brother," he says, "I'm over here a-seeing me sister who's bad with her health; she's in a little house just up the street there," he says.
Now none of that breed ever had wagons or trailers like me, they was tent and barn people, and they all went into 'bricks', as you might say – but nice people an' all. Well we has us a few beers and we'm *rokkerin* away, a-catchin' up on bits of news and people that we knows, and his old granny comes up in the conversation.

"You never knew me old granny Saiforella, did you, brother?" he says, "she was a proper old *chovihani* (witch), 'er was."

"I never knowed her," I replied, "but people used to call her 'Taw', didn't they?"

"They did, brother," he says, "that was a nickname that she got 'cause she used to say 'taw' after everything she said."

'What's it mean, Uncle Zacky?' ever-inquisitive Katie asked.

'Gal,' he replied, 'I'm afraid I don't know.'

'I knows the meaning,' Old John said, taking his pipe from his mouth, 'they only uses that word in that part've Wales, and it sort've means "quiet, now – sshh".'

'My John, you's a walking encyclopaedia, that you is,' Zacky said with a little laugh. 'Now where in the blessed world was I?'

'You was in the Public talking to the *mush* about his old granny called Taw,' the children shouted out.

'There you is, see, I lost where I was to, and I told yer not to interrupt me.'

"Well, brother," he says, "me old granny used to get about by herself, all over the mountains she'd go a-visitin' people, doin' her magic and a-takin' money from the poor old *gaujos*. Night time she'd get her head down where she could, and she had one special place that she'd stop at when she was in them parts. It was a little cottage at Llanuwchllyn (Chlan-you-ch-lin) down the far end of Bala Lake. Old Evan Evans and his old missus run the place as a lodgin' house and that's where she'd accommodate herself for the night."

"Old Mrs Evans was always knitting socks and her old man used to take them over the mountains and sell 'um to the navvies that was working on the dam at Lake Vyrnwy. He'd get the money and straight away go into the public house and spend it on beer, and get hisself *motto* (drunk). These navvies was a nice lot, and they used to have a whip-round and get him a bit of *luvva* to take back to his old woman."

"Well man, the story I'm a-goin' t'tell you now," Seth says to me, "is a story that me old grandmother told us boys. Oh man, it was a long, long time ago I'm a-thinkin'."

'Now Seth, he puts on this funny croaky voice to imitate his old granny, he does, as though she's a-tellin' the story – you follows me now, don't you?' Zacky said to the children.
'We does, Uncle Zacky,' they said, 'the old witchy woman is tellin' the story now.'
'You got it, she's a-talkin' now.'
And Zacky put on a croaky voice, and the children started to giggle.
'Hush now! otherwise you'll spoil it, and this is a story that you're goin' to like. And don't forget the old 'ummon is a-talkin' to Seth and his brothers. No doubt they was all in some old house huddled round the fire with just a candle a-beamin' – and it would a-bin in the winter time.'

Putting on the old croaky voice Zacky started the story:
'Pay attention boys, and listen to what I'm a-tellin' you; years ago I put up at Evan Evans' for me bed for the night, and I rolls meself up in the blanket and I gets t'*sutti* (sleep). Well boys, I 'aden't a-bin asleep for long when I'm awoke from me slumber by this horrible scream, taw.'

Zacky let out a blood-curdling scream and the children shrieked in horror – then he continued in the croaky voice:

'I gets up sorely a-*trashed* (frightened) and I pulls the doorway curtain back and I knocks on the Evans' bedroom door, a-callin' on 'um t'tell me what it was, taw.'

"Go back to bed, Saiforella," they says to me, it won't harm you."

'So I gets back to me *woodrus* (bed) and I gets meself to *sutti* when all of a sudden I'm a-woken up again by this horrible scream, but louder this time, taw.'

Zacky let out his blood-curdling scream again, and Katie whispered to Little Jimmy, 'I'm scared, 'ent you?' 'Naar,' came the reply.

And Zacky continued in the croaky voice:

'Well now boys, I gets up again and knocks on the Evans' door and pleads to them to tell me what it was. And again they says, "Go back to bed, Saiforella, it won't harm you". So boys, I gets back into *woodrus*, and although I'm sorely *trashed* (frightened) I'm very tired as I'd walked across the mountain that day. I pulls the blanket right over me head this time, and I gets back t'*sutti*. *Mi-Duvvel!* (my God), I hadn't a-bin asleep for long when I'm woke up again by this horrible scream, taw.'

Again Zacky let out the blood-curdling scream, then continued in the old croaky voice:

'Well boys, by now I's had enough, so I goes to the bedroom door and knocks on it real hard and demands to know what that horrible scream is. I demands that old Evan he gets hisself up and a-tells me. Well boys, he gets hisself up and he opens the door, and he says to me, "Please go back to bed, Saiforella, nothing will harm you". But I's had enough of it boys, and I tells him I shall a-curse him if he don't a-tell me what it was, taw. Old Evan he looks at me, all strangely, and he says, "Saiforella, if you gives me your promise never t'tell another living soul, I'll a-tell you." So I takes an oath and promises him. And *chavvies*, he tells me a story that fair put the hairs on me head straight up, terrible! terrible! it was to hear, taw.'

'Boys, I goes back into that room and I gets me wallets (bags), and I goes out into the night and I walks on till I comes to a dear rowan tree (mountain ash) and I lies meself down under it and I knows I'm safe. And that's where I slept all safe under the dear Lord's sky, taw.'

Zacky, back to his normal voice said, 'What do you think of that, then?'

Little Jimmy and Katie, sat motionless, big dark eyes staring at Uncle Zacky. Suddenly Katie, coming slowly round from this long weird tale said, 'But what was that terrible scream, Uncle Zacky?'

'Them's the same words that I said to Seth when he told me the story in the Public,' came the reply, 'and do you know what he told me?'

'What, Uncle Zacky?' asked Katie.

'He said, "Them's the same words that I asked me old grandmother Saiforella when she'd a-finished the story. And do you know what she told me?"

"No," I answers him.

"Well, she said, 'Boys, you knows as how I never 'as bin known to tell a lie, taw?' – Well I has to think about that, but to please her I agrees. 'And I never tells anybody anythin' that anybody 'as ever told me, taw?' – Well I has to think about that an' all, but I agrees with her. Then she ups and says, 'And when I promises anybody anythin', I never breaks me promise, now do I, taw?' – Well I has to think about that as well, but to humour her I agrees. 'Well,' she says, 'I promised Evan Evans never t'tell nobody what he a-told me …' and she shouts out, 'AND I CARN'T A-TELL YER,' and burst out laughing."

Genty, Mary-Ann, Robert and Old John had grasped the story and were rolling about with laughter. Little Jimmy and Katie sat motionless, with an expression of bewilderment on their faces. At last, Old John, after spitting in the fire, said, 'Oh my brother, what a good 'un, an' yu told it well, brother. They Woods 'as some good tales now, don't they?'

'Arr they does, John, and they loves a-tellin' 'um. You should have seen Seth after he'd finished tellin' me; tears was a-rollin' down his cheeks, and he thumped the table with his fist so hard that the beer spilt outa me glass. All the people in the Public was a-laughin' with us an' all.'

'Dad, I think we ought to get on now, Coralena will be wondering what's happened to us,' Robert said after looking at his watch.

''Ave another cup've tea afore yu goos, look kettle is almost a-boilin' now,' and Genty picked up the teapot from the embers.

'Just a quick one then, Aunt,' Robert replied, as he handed a cigarette to Old John.

'*Kekka*, lad, they boughten *tuvlers* (cigarettes) baint a no *kushti* fur me old chest.'

Just then, Katie, looking very serious, turned to uncle Zacky and said, 'I wants to know what that scream was, I don't understand why you was all laughing so much.' Little Jimmy, acting the little man, poked his sister with his finger and said, 'I knows what it was but you'm too young to know, and I shan't tell you.' Katie pounced on him and they started to squabble.

'Hey! Hey! Hey!' shouted Genty.

Mary-Ann started to laugh, 'The dear blesseds, they'm only children after all, 'ent they?'

The last cup of tea was finished and they all walked up the little pathway to the lane where Robert had parked his van.

'Have you got a boarded floor in the kitchen tent, Aunt?' he said.

'We 'ave that, lad,' she replied.

Opening the back doors of the van, there revealed rolls of carpets and a big pile of rugs. Taking out two colourful rugs Robert handed then to Genty, saying, 'Here you are, Aunt, they'll go nice on the floor.'

'Oh! my blessed Lord, lad, they'm too good fer the likes of we – but I thanks yu kindly, my Robert.'

Zacky had witnessed this, and laughingly shouted out, 'My blessed Saviour, the way my boy gives they carpets away we shall never have no money.'

Old John quickly replied, 'Go on with yu, my brother, we 'eard tell that Mary-Ann 'ere walks the way she do 'cause of they two bags've sovereigns she carries under 'er arms, 'eld with a rope around 'er neck.'

'Sure enough, sure enough,' Zacky laughed.

Lots of hugs and kisses and shaking of hands followed, and Genty, eyes watering, gave the final wave goodbye as the van disappeared round the bend of the little lane with grass growing in the middle.

That evening, Katie remarked, 'I still wants to know what that scream was.'

Zachariah Solomon Boswell died a few years later; the inside of his coffin was lined with best Kidderminster carpet. He was dressed in his brown hawker's dust-coat and held in his hands his old carpet knife. A fitting tribute for a well-known and much loved old carpet hawker.

The Ancients and the Blood-Red Beads

'An' that's 'ow it wer when I wuz a *chavvi* – no bigger than yu two,' Old John had just finished telling the children how he lived when he was about their age. Taking a small brand from the fire he re-lit his pipe, coughed and spat in the fire.

'Does anybody still live in them tents now, Granfer?' Little Jimmy asked.

'The only 'uns I knows to is old Obie (Obediah) Lovell an' 'is missus Black Britty (Britannia). They'm really old people, an' when I sez old, I means really old, I 'eard that they'm still alive though.'

'Older than you, Granny?' Katie remarked seriously.

'*Owli*, gal – much, much older than me,' and Old John looked at Genty and they both laughed.

'Will you take us to see them, Granfer? We'd like to see them old people and the tent, wouldn't we Katie?'

Katie nodded to her brother, then, looking at her grandfather, she said, 'Yes, we would, is they near by, Granfer?'

'*Kekka*, gal, they'm miles away over in Wales thur, at the bottom of the Dinas Mawddwy (mow-th-wee) – this side, not t'other. They've a-bin thur as long as we can remember, baint they my Genty?'

'They 'as too, my John, they never moved agin after a-comin' over that mountain, did they? Farmer never a-minded 'um, they's quietified people like, no bother as yu might say.'

Little Jimmy, concerned as to the welfare of these really, really old people, asked, 'But if they'm that old does they have anyone to help them, like we helps you?'

'One've thur sons, Moses, 'bout our age, baint 'e my Genty? Lives in a little 'ouse few miles away, and 'is son – what's 'is name, gal? – works fur the Forestry, don't 'e?'

'Owen,' came the reply from Genty.

'Aar, Owen, that's it, nice lad too. Well 'e lives in the same village as 'is mam an' dad an' 'e keeps his *yoks* on 'um. Teks 'um loads've firewood that 'e gets from the sawmill an' a bit of *hobben* fur 'is old granny t'boil up, like. 'E told our Willy, yers agoo, that they wuz all a-worried 'bout 'um, an' they wanted 'um t'come down an' live in the 'ouse, but they 'uddent a-shift, no they 'uddent.'

Pictures of this ancient couple were conjuring up in Little Jimmy's mind, and he again asked, 'Can we go and see them? If it's miles away Uncle Maurice would take us in his car, wouldn't he?'

'I s'pose 'e 'ud lad, if yu asked 'im kindly, like,' replied Old John, with a smile.

A few days later, Maurice and Sylvie called in on their way back from Hereford. Little Jimmy couldn't wait to ask Uncle Maurice if he'd take them over to Dinas Mawddwy to see this ancient couple and the tent in which they lived.

'Will you, Uncle Maurice – please?' came a little please from Little Jimmy, echoed by Katie.

'*Dordi!* – it's a fair drive over there, and to be honest with you, I'm not over-keen sitting with them two. *Dordi!* You said they was bad enough when you seen them years ago, didn't you Uncle John?' Maurice said in a non-committal sort of way.

Old John, seeing the disappointment on the children's faces, quickly replied, 'Aar, they was a-getting' a bit the worst for wear, warn't they, the dear people but me an' Genty 'ud like t'visit 'um an' all; my dear Lord, I reckons it'll be the last time we'd a-see 'um. I'd a-put the petrol in, lad.'

Looking at the two little faces, Maurice gave a smile and said, 'I could wait in the motor, couldn't I while you goes and sees them? You wouldn't want to bide there long, would you, Uncle John?'
'No we 'uddent, my son, we 'uddent a-stay too long, an' we 'uddent 'ave no tea nor nothin' – just t-see 'um, like.'

Maurice smiled at the children, nodded his head and said, 'What about Saturday? Sunday we'm goin' over to Sylvie's mam and dad's, that's right 'ent it my Sylvie?'
'Yes,' she replied, 'but you can go on your own into Wales, I don't want no smokified people and no old smokified tents!'

All was settled. 'I'll pick you up about eight o'clock Saturday morning then, and I don't want no hanging about 'cause it's a tidy old run. I knows a little café by Welshpool where we can have a bit of breakfast, like.'
Then, looking Uncle John and Aunt Genty up and down, with face beaming, he said, 'They even serves old Gypsies like you!'
They all roared with laughter as Maurice and Sylvie made their way over the plank bridge, Maurice calling out: 'Don't forget to wind up that old watch of yours – I don't want no hanging about.'

By the time Old John emerged from the wagon early on Saturday morning Little Jimmy had the fire going and the kettle almost boiling. Katie was up too; she had washed herself and combed her hair in readiness for her grandmother to plait it in the long pigtail that trailed down her back. She had put out the tea dishes and her and Little Jimmy's cups and the teapot was ready, with tea, awaiting the boiling water.

'Eh *dordi!* Yu two is eager, baint yu?' Old John called out.

'We're so excited, Granfer.' came the reply.

Genty was now up and about, busying herself in the kitchen tent. Taking her cross-over arm basket she put in a loaf of bread, large piece of cheese, and a few onions together with a large and small knife.

'I think I'll a-tek 'um this cabbage an' they broth bones I *monged* (begged) offn the butcher, my John,' she called out, 'they lives on broth, don't they? Katie gal, run over an' get they bones outa the meat safe.'

Returning with the bones, Katie asked, 'Do they only live on broth, Granny – and nuthin' else?'

'More or less, gal, they 'as a big old *kavvi* (pot) that sits in the embers an' whatever *hobben* they 'as brought 'um Old Britty a-chucks it in an' a-boils it up. Moses a-told us few yer back that 'e'd never knowed it t'be empty.'

And with that Genty took a clean tea cloth and placed it over the food in the basket.

'Is yu lot ready?' Old John shouted out as he came down the steps of the wagon. He was dressed in his navy blue serge suit, black velour Trilby hat and had round his neck a colourful Paisley scarf.

'*Jall* an' put yer best pinner on, gal, I'll a-put me best black 'un on an' all,' Genty said to Katie, as she hurriedly made her way to the wagon. Little Jimmy, having nothing special to wear was quietly standing by the fire, silently watching and waiting. Old John's eyes looked him up and down. "As yer chucked yer washin' water out, lad?'

'Oh! No! Granfer, I forgot,' came the reply.

Little Jimmy often 'forgot' to empty the washing bowl and swish it in the brook, and this was one occasion when Old John was pleased that he had forgotten.

'Whur's yer comb to, lad?' asked Old John, and little Jimmy handed the comb to his grandfather who, placing it in the soapy water combed it through the boy's hair a few times, then repeated the process, and finally taking his index and middle fingers like a pair of scissors he pressed in a big wave on one side of Little Jimmy's head.

Nell was tied up, the fire was made safe by piling ash over a smouldering log and the little party made their way to the junction of the village road at the end of the little lane with grass growing in the centre, to wait for Cousin Maurice. The clock in the church tower rang out eight o'clock, and a few minutes later Maurice's car appeared round the bend in the road.

'I knowed we 'uddent 'ave to wait too long fur yu, *mush*,' Old John said with a smile, as he took the front passenger seat, Genty and the two children taking the back seat.

'I don't want no trouble from you two now, 'cause we got us a long day ahead,' Maurice said as he turned his head round to look at Little Jimmy and Katie.

'We'll be really good, Uncle Maurice, honest to God we will, won't we Katie?' Little Jimmy replied, and Katie squealed out, 'We're so excited.'

The other side of Welshpool Maurice pulled in to a little roadside café. 'Here we are then, so you all want bacon sandwiches and tea? The young *rauni* (lady) *koms* us *foki* (likes us people), she's *kushti dikin* (good-looking) an' all,' and he winked his eye at Old John. 'I always comes here when I'm calling this way, and the place is proper clean, Aunt Genty.'

Genty nodded her approval, as the colourful little party entered the café and seated themselves at a large table by the window. Seated a short distance from them were two young couples, and Genty, with her back to them, heard the word 'Gyppos'.

'Tek no mind t'them *dinili gaujies* (foolish people),' she softly said to the two children, 'they baint worth a-botherin' about. I've a-cussed an' a-wished 'um *vasavo bokt* (bad luck) in me *sherro* (head).'

Katie and Little Jimmy giggled with pleasure.

'Haven't seen you for a while,' the pretty young woman said as she came over to the table and smiled at Maurice. 'You've brought me some custom this morning, I see.'

'These are me relations, love,' he replied. 'Can we have five bacon sandwiches and five cups of tea at your convenience, please, and will you give the bacon a bit longer in the pan, we all likes it done well, like?'

'Well done it'll be, sir,' she replied with a little laugh. Then, turning to Katie said, 'I love your black hair with that long plait, sweetie.'

'Me granny says it's as black as the tip of a raven's wing, don't you Granny?'

Genty smiled and patted Katie on the head, then turning to the woman said, 'That's what we people calls Gypsy hair, lady,' and she threw a glance at the two couples on the other table, and smiled at them.

Sandwiches and tea were devoured with relish and the little group was ready to go. Old John, putting his hand in his trouser pocket, pulled out a wad of pound notes to pay for their breakfast. Seeing this, Maurice quickly said, 'I'll get this, Uncle John, you said you'd get the petrol,' and went over to the counter to pay.

Nearing the door Old John turned, and graciously said, 'Thank you kindly, dear lady.' She gave him a wave of her hand, calling out, 'Come again soon.'

'Pretty country, baint it?' Old John observed from his front seat, 'not much longer now, *chavvies*. We baint a-bin up this part've the country fur a long, long time, 'as we my Genty?'

'We baint that, my John,' came the reply.

Leaning forward in his seat he stared out of the windscreen. 'I knows whur we'm to, lad, 'ave no fear, we'm almost thur. Goo steady along 'ere, lad, an' pull on the verge just up thur by that long copse.'

Maurice drove the car onto the verge, parked and turned the ignition off, and they all piled out.

'Where are they *atched* to then, Uncle John?' he enquired.

'They'm up the end've this long copse, lad,' and he pointed to a small track that led through it. A short distance up which was a large pile of off-cut timber, that Owen delivered now and again from his job at the Forestry saw mill.

'You said they had a wagon, Uncle John, how the devil did they get it through here?' and Maurice pointed to the overhanging branches that formed a tunnel-like appearance.

'Twarn't all a-growed over like 'tis now when they pulled up 'ere – yu could get a wagin through thur easy like. They've a-bin 'ere long as I can remember, sort've took root so t'speak,' and Old John gave a little chuckle.

Removing the cabbage and broth bones from the basket Genty handed the cabbage to Little Jimmy, and the bones to Katie. ''Ere, yu can carry these,' she said, me an' yer granfer 'ull get an armful of that *kosht* (wood) an' a-tek it up t'the poor dear people.

'I'll bide here and wait for you, you won't be too long will you now?' called out Maurice as they all disappeared up the track.

'Don't a-worry yerself, lad,' replied Old John, as he stooped to pick up a pile of the pine, fir and larch off-cuts of timber. 'Thur's a lot've resin on this *kosht*, my Genty, mind yu dunna get all stickified.'

With a pile of wood under their arms, Old John and Genty led the way up the track; turning round to the children Genty said, 'I dusn't want yu two t'be frightened when you *diks* 'um. They'm very, very old people, an' you'd a-never a-sin anybody like 'um afore, an' I reckons yu never will again.'

At the end of the track through the overgrown copse was a clearing, and there stood an old straight-sided wagon, slightly leaning to one side, wheels sunk well down into the earth, the broken door hung on one hinge and the two top windows were open with raggedy curtains hanging from them. To the side of the wagon was a large round beehive-style rod tent, some ten feet in diameter, the outer covering of old canvas sheets black with age. On the top of the tent, where the framework of thick hazel rods stuck out, was an old upturned blackened tin bath which acted as a cowl to stop, to a certain extent, the rain going in through the smoke hole, through which a thin plume was rising. A blackened hessian sack, which served as the door flap, was pulled back and held in place by a long off-cut of timber. The interior looked black and intimidating.

'Hoy, hoy, is yu thur, Obie my brother?' called out Old John as he put down the off-cuts of timber, and Genty did the same.

A muffled groan came from the darkness of the tent, and then a figure appeared in the doorway. Bent almost double stood the oldest, wildest person imaginable. Katie held on to her grandmother's hand and squeezed it for reassurance.

'*Dordi!* it's the *beng* (devil) 'isself,' she whispered.

With watery glazed eyes the old man stood blinking vacantly at the little group before him. His woodsmoke-stained grey hair hung almost to his shoulders partly covered by a huge greasy tweed cap. A large grey nicotine-stained moustache filled most of his wrinkled mahogany coloured face, with high cheekbones protruding and the cheeks sunken in. A once colourful scarf was wrapped haphazardly round his neck, and the dark navy blue suit he wore was speckled with wood ash, greasy and well wood-smoked. From the left lapel of the jacket dangled an old military medal, the ribbon from which it hung greasy and well smoked with age.

A low husky Welsh voice, almost unintelligible, came from the lips of the old bent figure.

'Whosoever is it that's a-come a-botherin' us poor people today?'

Taking a few steps forwards and holding out his hand, Old John replied, ''Tis me, John Lock an' me missus Genty, an' the grandchildren a-come t'see yu Obie, yu remembers us, don't yer? We baint a-sin yu an' yer old 'ummon fur some yers now.'

'John Lock! John Lock! Gentleman John's lad is it now? *Mi-Duvvel* (my God), I'm 'appy t'see yu brother,' and the old bent figure of Obie held out a thin claw-like hand to shake Old John's.

'Come on in our "liberty" (dwelling), all on yer now, you're most welcome, mind yer don't a-trip over that *kosht*.'

A few long lengths of off-cut wood that fed the fire in the middle of the tent protruded out of the doorway.

'Britty's a-*sutti* (asleep) in 'ere,' the low, husky voice said, as Obie turned and led the way into the gloom of the tent, where, with a groan, he took his usual position round the fire, sitting cross-legged, his back bent over so much that his head almost touched his knees.

Old John led the way in, followed by Genty holding Katie's hand, and lastly Little Jimmy. A sweet sickly smell greeted their nostrils as they entered and squatted down round the smouldering embers of the fire. Through the cloudy smoke at the dome of the tent, came a strange silky light from the smoke hole, and with light coming in from the doorway the children – eyes now adjusting to the gloom – could now make out the interior of Obie and Britty's home. The long, thick hazel rods that made the framework of the tent were now the colour of ebony; whilst brown and grey ex-Army blankets, now a dark smoky colour, covered the framework and over those were old canvas sheets, now turned black by the elements. To the left-hand side of the doorway was a pile of firewood consisting of small dry twigs and larger pieces of off-cuts from the saw mill.

On the right-hand side stood a low table with pots, bowls, plates and dishes on it, one corner encrusted with wax and the stub end of a candle. By the side of the low table stood a large wicker laundry basket, on top of which was placed an old black and greasy cast-iron hoop-handled frying pan and an old bucket containing water, with wood ash floating on the surface. The rear of the tent was taken up with large hessian sacks filled with straw, strewn over with piles of old Welsh blankets, which served as the ancient couple's bed.

Raising his head slightly Obie shouted with all his feeble might, 'Britty! Britty! people's 'ere t'see us.' From the piles of blankets came a movement and a high-pitched moan. Katie held on to her grandmother's hand tightly. The blankets slowly raised and the children's eyes opened wider as the form of old Black Britty slowly emerged.

'Oh my dear blessed Lord,' Katie whispered, as old Black Britty moved herself into a sitting position. She sat there for a few moments, seeming to be half conscious, her old misty pale blue eyes staring at the people sitting round the fire. Then, with a strange high-pitched voice she asked, 'Who is these people a-sat round me fire, Obie man?'

'Why, 'tis John an' Genty Lock an' their dear little grandchildren a-come to *dik* us, woman,' replied Obie, shouting the words.

'Who is they, man?' she repeated.

And Obie shouted out the words again.

'John Lock? What, Genlemun's lad?'

'*Owah* (yes)!' shouted Obie.

Slowly from the gloom Black Britty slid closer to the fire, peering at them all sitting round the smouldering embers. The light from the smoke hole now revealed her appearance, and Katie again squeezed her grandmother's hand. Black Britty was indeed black, her wrinkled toothless thin face overpowered by a huge nose, was the colour of the big black pot that stood on the edge of the smouldering embers of the fire. Her grey hair, now an ochre colour from the smoke of the fire, fell in two unkempt long plaits down the front of her black blouse, and her long black greasy skirt was burnt with holes from the sparks of the pine, fir and larch wood that they burnt. The only colour on Black Britty was the dark blood-red beads around her neck, and the long dangling conical-shaped gold earrings that were now catching the light from the smoke hole and doorway.

'I's pleased t'see yu dear people, that I is, yu's John 'ent you?' the strange high-pitched voice echoed out. 'Man, we 'ent a-sin yu fur many a year, 'as we now?' Then her misty pale blue eyes focused on Genty. 'My sister, I's pleased t'see yu as well.' Slowly her eyes moved to Little Jimmy and Katie. 'These *chavvies* carn't a-be yourn, can they now?' she said and pointed a long black finger at them.

Genty replied quickly, 'They'm our grandchildren, my sister.'

'They *diks* too *kushti* fur me old *yoks* (they look too good for my old eyes) – they'm a-getting' too much *kushti hobben* (good food) for me liken, but that 'un's a *kushti dikin kauli Romany rakli* (good looking black Gypsy girl).'

Katie squeezed her grandmother's hand and whispered, '*Dordi!* she don't want to eat me, does she Granny?'

Genty let out a little laugh and shouted out to Britty, 'I's brought some bits've *hobben* fur yu, sister,' and with that she produced the broth bones and cabbage. Black Britty's long claw-like hands reached out to take them, old worn silver rings glinting on her black fingers. 'I thanks yus, my sister, they'm lovely; Obie man, *dik* what the dear people 'as a-brought us.'

Obie's head raised slightly and he said, '*Owah.*'

'I'll a-put these in the pot this very minute, indeed I will – give us that *choori* (knife) offa the table, sister,' she screeched out to Genty as she pulled the big heavy pot towards her and removed the lid.

Taking the broth bones from the newspaper in which they were wrapped, she threw them into the pot, adding them to the simmering contents. Then with the knife she cut the root end from the cabbage, cut it in half and then proceeded to cut it up in chunks, and that too went into the pot.

'I'd a-thought she'd wash that cabbage first,' thought Katie, 'I bet there's some slugs in that.'

'Put us some *pani* (water) in thur, my sister, will yu?' Black Britty asked Genty in her screeching voice, 'outa the bucket behind yu, use that cup on the table, my sister.'

Doing as she was asked, Genty scooped out a cup full of wood ash-covered water from the bucket and poured it into the pot. Black Britty gave the contents a stir with the knife and said, 'Another two cups'll do, my sister,' and again stirred the contents; then with a screeching laugh said, 'Stir with a knife and yu stir up strife they says, don't they? We poor people's 'ad strife all on our lives, 'ent we? A bit more 'ent a-goin' t'urt us now, 'tis it?' She then replaced the lid and pushed the heavy pot into the fire embers, causing a cloud of ash to rise and cover the seated group.

'I'll mek yu dear people a drop of *mutterimangri* (tea) now,' she said as she leant over to reach for the old black kettle that was steaming on the edge of the fire.

'I carn't drink none, Granny,' Katie whispered.

'None've us will, gal,' Genty whispered back. 'My sister,' she shouted to Black Britty, 'dunna yu put yerself out now, we couldna a-drink a drop, we'm full up, we all stopped at a dear little café not so far from 'ere.'

And Old John shouted out, 'Dunna a-bother yerself, sister – 'ere, 'ave some've this baccer,' and with that he handed his tin to her.

Reaching into her old greasy black skirt pocket she produced a little short-stemmed clay pipe, now burnt a dark brown colour, which she proceeded to half fill with the tobacco. Then with her rough black old fingers she picked up a tiny ember from the fire and put it on top of the tobacco. Placing the little stem between her gums she started to puff and a cloud of strong smoke filled the already smoky air.

'Pass that tin to Obie, sister,' Old John shouted out.

Obie's head raised slightly at the mention of his name, and the offer of tobacco. He too smoked a clay pipe, which he took from the top pocket of his old jacket. Following the same method as Black Britty he half filled the bowl of the pipe, then raked through the hot embers with his old black index finger to find just the right sized piece to fit on the top of the tobacco.

Little Jimmy had watched all this in amazement. '*Dordi!*' he whispered to his grandfather, 'their fingers must be as hard as iron.'

'They is, lad – 'arder than mine, that's fur sure.' Old John whispered back.

The ancient couple sat quietly smoking their pipes; the smoky air made Old John cough and he got up from his place by the fire and went outside to spit. On re-entering he remarked to Obie, 'That old wagin've yorn 'as a-sin better days, brother, yu dunna a-use it now I minds.'

'We 'ent bin in it fur years now,' Obie replied, 'we got too old t'get up into it. Me boy Mosey (Moses) an' 'is lad a-helped me t'put this up,' and he waved his hand in a circle, his index finger pointing to the interior of the tent.

Trying to have a conversation with Black Britty was almost impossible; needing to shout every word, and then repeat it, was exhausting and Genty had now given up.

'I thinks it's time we all *jalled* (went) on, sister,' she finally said.

'What's that?' screeched Black Britty.

Shouting at the top of her voice Genty repeated the statement. Raising her right hand up high, the ancient woman screeched, 'Wait! Wait!' – and her misty blue eyes focused on Katie.

'I's bin a-*dikin* at you, *rakli*, an' I likes what I sees. I never 'ad no girl childs, only man childs, an' the womenfolk they 'ad woz never t'me liken, an' thur *chavvies* warn't t'me liken, nor thur *chavvies* warn't either. Me an' me man thur 'ent a-got much longer on this dear earth, that we 'en't.' She paused to take breath, then removed the old dark blood-red beads from around her neck and passed them to Katie, saying, 'I wants yu t'ave these t'remember me by – 'ent no one else I'd a-want t'give 'em to, yu'll never be bad with yer throat when yer wears them. Eh *dordi!* you'm a pretty Romany *rakli*, that you is.'

Holding the heavy beads in her hand, Katie smiled at the old woman and said, 'Thank you, Aunt.'

Genty gave her a nudge and whispered, 'Shout it to her.'

With all her might Katie shouted out the 'thank you'.

'*Dordi!* gal,' Genty said with a chuckle, 'yer uncle Maurice'll 'ear that down thur on the road.'

Black Britty let out a screeching laugh, 'I knows me *poori kans* is *nafli* (old ears are ill) but they 'ent that *nafli*, gal. Now yu wear them beads with pride an' never be ashamed've what yu is, always be proud've what yu is – an' remember me, old Black Britty, my pretty *rakli*.'

They all got up from their positions round the fire, with the exception of Black Britty. 'I shall bide whur I'm to, me old legs is bad t'day,' the strange high-pitched voice screeched out, 'but I wishes yu all a safe journey and I thanks yu for a-comin' t'see us.' A sudden impulse came over Katie and she bent down and kissed the black wrinkled cheek of the ancient woman, whose final words were, 'You'm a dear pretty *rakli*, that you is.'

The doubled-up form of Obie followed them out into the bright daylight and he stood motionless for a few moments, blinking rapidly as his watery old eyes adjusted to the light. Then, in his low husky voice, he said, looking at Little Jimmy, 'Them words me woman spoke is true – so true, that's what they is. I 'ent got much t'give, but I wants t'give yu somethin', my *chavo* (boy) t'remember me by. *Jall* up in the *vardo* (wagon) an' in the cupboard on the left, by the side've the fireplace, yu'll find me old trout 'andled knife. Mind 'ow yu goes a-getting' up thur, the steps is a-*poggered* (broken).

Old John walked over to the wagon with little Jimmy and he gave him a leg-up. 'Mind that footboard, lad, 'tis as ripe as a pear.' Little Jimmy cautiously stepped into the old wagon and looked at its sorrowful appearance. The roof had let in water, the old range stove had rusted and fallen apart, the whole of the wagon was slowly rotting away.

Opening the cupboard door Little Jimmy peered inside and there amid old tins and cracked cups he found the knife, the blade of which was red with rust, but the handle was a well carved trout's head, the eyes and scales having been burnt on with some pointed iron object, more than likely the red hot pointed tang end of a small file.

'Me cousin Uriah made that fer me, yu remembers 'im now don't yu John? 'E wuz over Portmeirion thur fer years a-mekin 'is baskets an' a-sellin' 'um t'the *gauji foki* 'an' a-earnin' 'isself some *kushti luvva* (good money). God rest 'is soul, man,' and Obie's head appeared to drop even lower. Then the husky voice said, 'Give the *chavo* a penny, my brother, an' 'e can give it t'me – fur 'tis bad luck t'give a *choori* without a copper bein' given back.'

Little Jimmy handed the penny to Obie and he said, 'That *choori* 'as a-earnt me some *luvva* in its time an' I 'opes it does the same fur yu, my lad.'

'Thank you, Uncle Obie,' replied Little Jimmy, 'it looks like a real fish, don't it? Me and Granfer will clean the blade up when we gets home.'

With a little laugh Obie replied, 'Mind yu doesn't a-cut yer fingers off.'

They all shook hands and made to leave, Obie calling out to them, 'Watch out fur them *prastermangros* (policemen), *mandi shuns* they'm the *beng's baulos* (I hear they are the devil's pigs) over thur in England.'

Turning round they saw the doubled-up form of Obie disappearing into the darkness of the tent.

'I reckons we shanna a-see they two again, Genty gal, they'm nearin' the end, baint they?' Old John said in a sorrowful tone, as they started to slowly walk down the track through the copse to the main road.

'The dear people,' replied Genty, 'they's got 'earts've gold, baint they, an' t'give the *chavvies* them things wuz kind, warn't it?'

Katie and Little Jimmy were walking in front of their grandparents excitedly examining the wonderful gifts the ancient couple had given them.

'I don't want to put these beads round me neck until I've washed 'um, Granny, they'm all greasy and dirty – but I loves 'um,' Katie called back to her grandmother, who, turning to Old John said, 'That gal is a-turnin' out t'be a good 'un, baint she now?'

Arriving back at the car they found Cousin Maurice stretched out asleep by the side of the hedge. Old John put his index finger to his lips and made a 'sshhussh' noise, then crept over to the sleeping Maurice and in a Welsh-sounding voice shouted out, 'Wake up, you vagrant, this is the police, you are under arrest.'

Maurice sat bolt upright, blinking at Old John towering above him. '*Dordi!* Uncle John, you frit me to death – you said you wouldn't be long and I got all sleepified a-waitin' for you.'

They were all laughing and Little Jimmy and Katie were squealing with delight. 'He got you, Uncle Maurice, he got you good and proper, didn't he?'

'I'm hungry,' came the reply from Maurice.

'So's we, lad, let's get gooin' an' yu find us a nice clean little place t'*atch* an' we can 'ave the bread an' cheese I've a-brought in me basket,' Genty said as she and the two children clambered into the back seat of the car.

'I'm dying to know how you got on, Uncle John,' asked Maurice, as he reversed the car into the trackway and out onto the road.

'I'll a-tell yu in a minute, lad, jest a-goo a bit steady down 'ere, I noticed a nice little place t'pull in when we was a-comin' up 'ere – steady now – 'ere, 'ere, pull in 'ere, *mush.*'

Maurice pulled into a layby with a wide grass verge flanked by a rocky hillside with a little stream trickling down. They all piled out, Katie running towards the cool mountain stream, 'I wants to wash me beads, and me face and hands,' she shouted out.

By the time she returned Genty had bread, cheese and onion prepared and they all sat on the grass to enjoy their simple meal. Katie had hung her beautiful blood-red beads on the wing mirror of Maurice's car to dry, and turning round to look at them he said, ' They'm really old beads, 'ent they Aunt Genty? *Dordi!* The one in the middle is as big as a pigeon's egg.'

'Old Britty said they wuz 'er granny's, and she 'ad 'um a-give t'er when she wer no bigger than our Katie 'ere. So in my reckonin' the old ' ummon must 'ave a-'ad 'um round 'er neck fer nigh on over eighty yer – or thereabouts,' replied Genty.

'*Dordi*, you'm a lucky gal to have them, Katie – see, it pays to be polite to people, now don't it, and it helps if you'm pretty an' all,' and Maurice gave Katie a big wink of his eye, to which she blushed and said, 'Naaar.'

Feeling a little left out, Little Jimmy held his trout head handled knife in the air and called out, 'Look what Uncle Obie give ME, Uncle Maurice,' and he handed the knife to him.

'I never seen a handle like that, boy,' he said, 'I've seen peg knives with 'osses 'eads and boot handles, but never a fish's head.'

'It's a trout's head, Uncle Obie said so,' Little Jimmy responded.

After carefully examining the carved head, Maurice looked over to Old John, 'It's a good 'un, 'ent it Uncle John? Do you reckon the blade'll come up clean, like?'

'Aar, it's a good 'un an' all, reckon it'll clean up alright – push it in the ground a few times, lad, an' get a bit've rust offa it.'

Maurice pushed the blade down into the earth a couple of times, and sure enough a lot of the rust had come off. Handing it back to Little Jimmy he said, 'Your Granfer's always right, when you gets home he'll fettle it up for you – be like new it will, like.'

The return journey home was full of questions from Cousin Maurice; Katie, now proudly wearing her heavy blood-red beads, leaning over Maurice's shoulder giving him the answer to most of them. 'They only lives on broth outa a big black pot, that Aunt Britty keeps a-bubblin' away all the time, Granny says it's never been emptied all the years they've had it, don't you Granny? And I've never sin anything like it, Uncle Maurice, she cut up the cabbage and chucked it in that old pot and never a-washed a bit of it – slugs an' all went in, honest to God they did.'

'Where do they get a drop of *pani* (water) from, Uncle John?'

'Thur's a little spring just behind the old wagin of thern, old Obie dug it out when they fust *atched* thur, banged in some old iron sheets t'stop the sides a-cavin' in, like, an' sorta made 'isself a little *pani-hev* (well).'

'The old wagon's in a bad shape, then.'

'*Owli*, lad, it's *poggered*, good an' proper, they baint a-bin up in it fur years now, they lives an' sleeps in the tent, like.'

'Had the wagon bin a good 'un in its time, Uncle John?'

'Aar, lad, it 'adna a-bin a bad 'un, straight-sided 'un, with a lantern roof, big back wheels on 'er so she'd a-rolled alright, built up thur in Bilston, t'other side've Wolverhampton way. Proper made 'un, man called Woodhouse used t'mek 'um, 'ad a few men a-workin' fur 'im an' all, like.'

'I remembers when they *chopped* (exchanged) fur the old wagin an' all. They wuz over thur by Denbigh an' some've old Longsnout Taylor's breed 'ad a-crept outa Cheshire over them parts an' they wuz all *atched* together on this old common, like. Any old 'ow, Black Britty, she took a-likin' t'the wagin, man called Minnow Taylor an' 'is 'ummon an' *chavvies* 'ad it. 'E wuz only a little *mush*, no more thun a bit over five foot 'igh, as yu might say. Well now, Minnow 'e 'as this big Irish draught 'oss t'pull the wagin, mustabin near on 17 'ands 'igh; 'e 'ad t'get on a chair t'put the collar on t'animal, an' 'e'd a-got it offn Daisy Lee – 'e used t'goo over t'Ireland an' a-buy 'um an' bring 'um back, like. Nice civil man 'e is too.'

'Any old 'ow, Minnow is a-getting' a bit fed up with this big wagin an' 'oss, so when Obie asks 'im t'ave a *chop* 'e jumps at the chance, don't 'e? Now Obie and Black Britty, they 'ad a nice little barrel-top wagin, not painted up good it warn't, but light an' sound it wer, an' the 'oss they 'ad wuz as quiet as a babby, yu could a-driven it with two bits a-cotton thread fer reins, yu could. So they 'as a *chop*, and Minnow 'e draws a bit've *luvva* an' all. That never a-bothered Obie 'cause old Black Britty a-took plenty of *luvva* from the *gaujies* that she wove 'er spells on a-*durrakin* (fortune telling) 'um.'

'Any old 'ow, they 'as this big wagin an' 'oss fur a while an' they travels on, an' gets down Dolgellau (Doll-geth-lye) way, whur they finds 'umselves in a bit a-bother, like, over old Britty a-tekin' a *bori putsi* of *luvva* (big pocket of money) offn some *dinili gauji* who she'd a-worked 'er spells on – an' the 'ummon 'ad complained t'the *muskros*. Well, they 'as t'shift in a bit've a hurry, like, an' Obie yokes up the big 'oss an' is 'eadin' fur Machynlleth (Mac-kun-thleth). BUT – the old *dinilo*, 'e teks the left fork outa Dolgellau 'stead've the right 'un. Why 'e did this we shall never know – 'e knowed that country like the back of 'is 'and, 'e did.'

''E said 'e wuz a-worried t'death the *muskros* was a-chasin' 'im, an' 'is mind warn't proper on the job, like. Old Britty, she'd a-got 'erself hid away under the bedplace in the wagin an' a-closed the two slidin' doors an' all. An' thur she remained fur all that terrible journey as Obie 'ad up an' over that mountain. Obie a-told me that the brake blocks wuz a-worn almost t'the metal, an' the dragshoe wer a-worn as thin as a fag paper. That big 'oss 'ad a-brought 'um up an' over an' down that mountain, whur at the bottom they pulled up that old track – whur we've bin t'day – an' never moved agin. Moses was with 'is dad that day, 'e wuz the only one at 'ome then, an' said 'e'd never bin so *trashed* (afraid) in all 'is life.'

'That's some story, Uncle John,' Maurice said as he looked over and smiled. 'What happened to the big 'oss?'
'Well, I'll a-tell yu, the man who owned that ground they'm on never a-minded 'um bein' thur. Seems 'e wuz a decent sort, an' Obie sold 'im the big 'oss – an' never overcharged 'im neither 'cause 'e didna a-want t'nark it fur 'um bidin' thur, did 'e? Before the old *mush* died 'e told 'is son t'let 'um bide whur they wuz to, an' they've a-bin thur as long as I can remember, that they 'ave.'
'Good 'un, Uncle John, you can tell 'um, carn't you? We're almost home now, *chavvies* is asleep, 'ent they Aunt Genty?'
'They is, lad, an' fur some time too,' she replied.
'Pity, they'd a-liked that 'un, Uncle John.'

'Aar, 'spect they 'ud, lad, no doubt I'll 'ave t'tell it over agin one night to 'um.'

Maurice was now turning up the little lane with grass growing in the centre.

'Here we are then, home safe and sound,' and he parked on the verge by the five-barred gate and switched the engine off. They all piled out, and Genty asked, 'Is yu comin' in fur some tea and *hobben*, lad?'

'Aunt Genty, I'd love to, but I'd better get back, my Sylvie'll wonder what in the world's 'appened to me – bin a long day, 'ent it?'

'Tas that, lad, but we thanks yu kindly, an' I knows these two baint a-gooin' t'forget it, is yu?'

'No we won't, Granny,' echoed Little Jimmy and Katie.

'Thank you, Uncle Maurice,' said Katie.

Little Jimmy held out his hand and shook Maurice's and said, 'Thank you, Uncle Maurice – you'm a good driver, 'ent you?'

And Old John held out his hand, shook Maurice's vigorously and said: 'We thanks yu, lad, I knows yu'm a modern man with modern ways, but yu've a-made us old 'uns 'appy a-seein' them old people, an' I reckons it's fur the last time.'

And so it was. Towards the middle of January 1962, Moses's son Owen found old Obie and Black Britty dead in the tent. They lay side by side on the straw-filled sacks, Black Britty's right hand across Obie's chest and his left one holding it.

Obediah and Britannia were buried together in a small churchyard in a little village not far from Dinas Mawddwy. After the funeral

Moses got permission from the farmer to burn the old wagon and tent.

Somewhere in the wood, where Little Jimmy and Katie played, is the trout head handle knife. Little Jimmy lost it, and though they all searched for it time and time again, it was never found. Fifty years have now passed and Katie still wears the blood-red beads with pride – and has always remembered Black Britty's words – 'Be proud of what you is.'

CHAPTER 6

A TRAILER FOR ADDY

''Op pickin' marnins' Old John called them; the grass was dewy and woodsmoke hung low in the misty air, autumn was on its way, summer coming to an end. And also coming to an end was the children's time living with their grandparents. Five months had passed since Sylvie had picked up their two little bags in the doorway of the caravan and led the children away to happier times.

A short while after the departure of the children Addy had managed to compose herself. She wiped her eyes, picked up a small bag that contained a few clothes and photographs of the children (her only possessions) and walked out of the rough caravan, vowing never to return. She had gone straight to her doctor who, the previous week, had advised her to do so, and was driven to a Home in Birmingham for treatment.

At six o'clock that evening Sylvie phoned the public telephone box as arranged – there was no reply. Both she and Maurice were worried. The following day Sylvie's mother drove over to see them to say that she had received a message from Addy. 'I'm being looked after but I don't want you to know where I am. Don't worry about me, I'll be alright, give my love to the children, I'll phone again,' was all she would say.

After four months in Birmingham she was transferred to a smaller Home not far from the city of Worcester, and it was from there, almost a week ago, that Addy had telephoned Sylvie's mother and father. 'The doctor says I can go home, I'll phone again next week,' was the short message … but Addy had no home to go back to.

The appearance of Cousin Maurice deceived people as to his real self, especially in his daily 'business' life of scrap dealing, in which he was successful and had prospered. Putting on a hard face he would buy for the price he wanted to pay, even at three factories that he collected scrap waste from and had a contract with, the owners liking his 'no beating about the bush, pay there-and-then' method. Underneath this hard faced 'businessman' was a different personality; a gentle, caring, fun-loving Maurice, who, now a grown man, cared very much about the welfare of his Cousin Addy. The day after Addy's phone call he had got permission from the owner of the small yard on the outskirts of Shrewsbury, where he and Sylvie lived, to have another trailer (caravan) by the side of their own – and this would be the home that Addy and the children would share.

The following evening, after the long-awaited message, Maurice and Sylvie drove over to see Uncle John and Aunt Genty. With 'eye talk' Maurice asked Old John to send the children away to play in the wood.

'I'm putting the cards on the table, Uncle John. I'm buying a trailer for me cousin and the *chavvies*, and having it next to ours in the yard, so that's why we've come to see you, so as I can tell you, like.'

All went quiet as Old John re-lit his pipe with a brand from the fire, coughed and spat into it. Maurice and Genty's eyes met and she gave him a smile. 'My dear blessed Lord, 'e's a gud lad, that 'e is,' she thought to herself.

Looking into the flames of the fire, Old John spoke.

'I canna let yer doo that, lad.'

All went quiet again, then Maurice asked, 'Why, Uncle John?'

''Cause I'm a'goin' t'buy it, that's why! My dear blessed Lord, all've them yers ago I tuk an oath, an' on them two dear little *chavvies'* lives, every day've them yers I've a-regretted it – that I 'ave, so 'elp me.'

Silence fell once again, then Old John turned his head towards Genty and said, 'Tek these two dear people inter the wagin, gal, an' a-give 'um the *luvva.'*

Maurice protested, but to no avail. Old John had said his piece. It was his way of trying to recompense all those years of banishment he had served on his only child.

When they returned to the fireside they found Old John with his head bowed in deep thought.

'I'll a-mek some more tea, my John,' Genty hesitatingly said.

'Arr, in a minit, gal,' he solemnly replied.

Raising his head he looked in turn at the three seated figures. 'We should a-gone an' a-got our gal back, my dear Lord we should a-done, but we's only a scrap've a family, baint we? Yu lad' – and he pointed a finger at Maurice – 'wuz only a young feller, I knows yu was a-fit, like yu is now, but yu 'uddent a-bin fit enough t'tek on that mongrel breed, neither 'ud our Benny or our Robert in 'is nice suit've clothes, neither 'ud the others on us an' we 'uddent a-slept easy in our beds, 'ud we? We brought our gal up right, dinna we, my Genty? Broke our 'earts, that it did. When I swore that oath I wuz a-livin' up t'the blood've me faarthers, that I wuz, but now – an' may the dear blessed Lord 'ear this – I teks that terrible oath back, with all me 'eart an' soul, I does.'

All eyes were looking into the flickering flames of the fire as Old John delivered these powerful sentences in a strong, slow, but gentle voice. Sylvie broke the silence that followed. 'I'll help Aunt Genty make the tea, Uncle John,' she said as she got up from her seat by the fire and put her hand on the old man's shoulder for a few seconds, and gently gave it a pat, then walked over to the table cupboard to arrange the dishes and cups.

Still looking into the flickering flames Maurice quietly addressed his Uncle John, who was now sitting with his head again bowed.
'I'm off to Chester tomorrow, Uncle John, to look at a nice clean trailer I've heard about. I know you don't know about them, but this is a Vickers Lunedale 18-footer, oak-lined living area and formichael (Formica) kitchen. One of the Florences has it, Albi's lad, you remember Albi, don't you? But I'm sure you don't know his lad. Anyhow, he's the sort of *mush* to have a deal with. The *luvva* Aunt Genty has given us is more than enough – I'll bring back what's left over.'

Old John, with head still bowed, replied, 'Dunna bother, what's left over get Sylvie t'buy some bits an' pieces t'fit it up nice, an' iffa yu wants any more, ask me lad. I knows money canna buy love, but I wants it right fur 'um, like.'

The time for the deal to buy the trailer took time, more time than Maurice had bargained for. He and Sylvie had arrived at the bit of wasteland at Howarden, not far from the airfield on the outskirts of Chester, at midday, where Albi's lad and his wife and children were stopping, together with two other members of the same family. 'The trailer's at me uncle's place in Connah's Quay,' Maurice was informed, 'foller me,' Albi's lad said as he jumped in the cab of his Bedford J-type lorry and made his way over the bumpy wasteland to the road. Albi's brother, with the nickname of Conky, owing to his large nose, had bought several years ago a house with a piece of rough ground attached, just outside Connah's Quay; and it was on this rough land that he allowed other Gypsy families to stay, for which they paid a small rent.

The Vickers trailer was all that Maurice and Sylvie had hoped for and stood shining in the tarmacked yard by the side of Conky's house. Maurice and Sylvie made no comment, their faces expressionless. Their arrival had spread like wildfire to the families that were encamped on the rough ground and now a large number had congregated in Conky's yard to help Albi's lad in the selling of the trailer. Maurice and Sylvie were on their own. The air was filled with excitement, and shouts of 'You won't find a cleaner trailer than that' … 'You could tow that at a 'undred miles an 'our an' it'd still be thur without a sway nor nothin'.' Maurice made no comment.

One young Traveller lad was now getting a little over-excited, his voice ringing out above the others. Standing quietly in the crowd was Old Temperance Lee – known by the nickname of Temper, an apt name as she could show it very quickly – matriarch of her family and kinswoman to Old John. Although no more than five feet tall, and in the winter of her years, she stood erect with dignity and grace. Either side of her mahogany-coloured face, now weather-worn and lined, hung long neat plaits. Gold half sovereign earrings dangled from her ear lobes, her head covered in a silk Paisley scarf knotted Gypsy-style at the back.

'Give us a bit o' room,' she called out in a high croaky voice as she pushed her way through the Travellers. 'I wants t'ave a word with that *bora mui* (big mouth) young man.'

All went quiet and all eyes were on the youth as the old lady approached him. 'You, boy, is nuffin' but a 'indrination (hindrance) to these two dear men 'ere who's a-tryin' t'ave a peaceyful deal over that pretty tin can thur, keep yer *bora nok* (big nose) outa it, boy, an' all on yer leave 'um alone so's they can 'ave a *kushti* bit o' business a-tween the both've 'um.'

Everyone laughed, the youth turned and walked away. Albi's lad opened the door of the trailer and Maurice followed him inside to conduct the deal in private, leaving Sylvie to talk with Old Temperance.

'They'm taking a long time, 'ent they, Aunt?'

Sylvie had just finished the sentence when the door of the trailer opened and out stepped Albi's lad and Maurice, both men now smiling. The deal had been done, and Maurice was now the new owner of the Vickers trailer.

'Afore yer 'itches up an' *jalls on* I wants yer both t'come an' 'ave a bit've bread an' meat an' a drop've *mutramangri* (tea) with me,' Old Temperance said, as she looked at Maurice and Sylvie with piercing dark eyes.

'We'd like that, Aunt,' Maurice replied, then turning, he said goodbye to Albi's lad and shook his hand. 'I 'opes yer cousin 'as

luck with the trailer, mush, an' good luck t'yu both an' all,' Albi's
lad called out as he made his way over to his motor. 'Hey! an' don't
forget t'buy them two *chavvies* something nice with that bit of luck
money I gived yu.'
'Sylvie'll find them something,' called back Maurice, as he and Sylvie
followed Old Temperance in the direction of the encampment on
the rough land.

Six modern trailers were spaced haphazardly over the ground, four
of which were occupied by members of Old Temperance's large
family. 'That's me 'abitulation (habitation),' Old Temperance
croaked as she pointed a finger to a small Bowtop wagon with a
cottage tent pitched alongside, which were standing in a corner near
a hedge, well away from the modern trailers.
'I likes it over 'ere away from t'others, all I wants is a bit o' peace,
the *chavvies* does me old *sherro* (head) in now,' Old Temperance
declared as she led the way into the square-framed tent that served,
as did Old John and Genty's, as her kitchen and day room.

The warm and cosy interior was a delight to the eyes, and consisted of a boarded floor, partly covered by a well worn colourful carpet. The walls were hung with cotton curtain material with a large roses motif; there was a small table and two chairs, a large wooden box and the crowning glory, a cast iron range, known as the 'Bungalow Belle'. As the name implied these large ranges were made for houses and never used in horse-drawn living wagons, being far too big and heavy. But here in the tent, just inside the doorway, on the left-hand side, the old range stood proud, throbbing out heat.

'You two *besh* (sit) on them chairs,' Old Temperance commanded as she moved the kettle over from the oven side of the range to sit on the ring above the fire box. She then proceeded to cut large slices of white crusty bread, spreading butter thickly on them. From the wooden box she lifted out a crock dish containing a cooked hock of bacon and within a few seconds had cut slices from it, which with her fingers, she put on the bread and butter.

'There you is then, get that *morrow* (bread) an' *mass* (meat) down yer,' she croaked out, 'kittle's a-boilin', I'll a-mek the tea.'

Maurice's eyes were on the old range; dealing in scrap iron he was weighing up the value of it. With a smile and a twinkle in his eye he looked at the old lady and jokingly said, 'That old stove's heavy, 'ent it, Aunt?'

'That it is, my son, tuk two've me grandsons t'get it in 'ere … an' they'm big lads an' all,' she replied.

'I'd give you a few bob for it, Aunt,' Maurice said, knowing full well that Old Temperance wouldn't sell it. Her piercing dark eyes flashed at Maurice, who was having trouble to hold back a laugh.

'My dear blessed Lord, young man, I couldn't a-part with that, the Lord h'allmighty I couldn't, that 'ere stove is like a hovercoat t'me in the winter, no, never in this wide world would I a-part with it, that's a hinsultation (insult) you's *a-rokkered* (spoken) t'*mandi* (me), that it is.'

Maurice and Sylvie burst out laughing.

'He's only jokin' you, Aunt,' Sylvie at last managed to say, and Maurice coughed out, 'Sorry, Aunt.'

The old lady's face broke into a smile, and with a little chuckle she said, 'There now, I reckons a bit of that close bred t'ya old *dinilo* (fool) John Lock 'as a-rubbed off onta ya.' And they all burst into laughter again.

The journey back to the yard was uneventful, the Vickers trailer towed well, and Maurice and Sylvie drove into the yard just before dusk, which was well-timed because the electrical plug for the trailer lights was broken.

Early the following morning Maurice and Sylvie drove down to see Uncle John and Aunt Genty to tell them the good news about the trailer.

'Wot's it like, gal?' asked Genty, 'it's a clean 'un, is it?'

'It's a good 'un, Aunt, clean as a new pin, an' my Maurice here got it for the price he wanted to pay.'

'I knowed yu 'ud, lad,' remarked Old John with a smile, then coughed and spat in the fire.

'There's more *luvva* left over, Uncle John,' Maurice quietly said. 'Is it alright if we get some blankets an' stuff with it? Sylvie and me's decided to buy a pretty china tea set.'

Old John looked up from the fire and nodded his head. 'Yu two do 'as yer likes – fit it up nice like an' iffn yu wants any more yu jest a-let me know.'

'We don't need any more, Uncle John,' replied Maurice, 'tonight we'll go over to Sylvie's mam and dad an' use their phone. I'll phone Barry an' get him to bring some blankets over, an' some cans an' bowls an' see what china he's got. He gived me his number when we saw him at the last Stow Fair.'

(Barry, affectionately known as Barry the Blanketman, was a young man who lived on the outskirts of Birmingham and supplied the travelling fraternity of the surrounding counties with his wares of Welsh blankets, water jacks [cans], bowls and china.)

Suddenly Old John uttered, '*Kekka rokker, chavvies* is *vellin* (don't speak, children are coming).' Within a few minutes Old John had sent them away to play in the wood again.

'What's they up to, Jimmy? They's acting all slyified – summat's going on, what do you think it is?'

'I don't know, Katie,' replied Little Jimmy with a puzzled look, 'but they's up to summat, that's for sure.'

With the children out of earshot, Maurice continued.

'We know Addy's down Worcester way 'cause she let on to Sylvie's mam 'n' dad.' (Maurice now using Addy's name in front of his Uncle John – and Old John now calling her 'our gal' instead of ''er-what-baint-with-us-no-more').

'Well, Uncle John, Benny an' Elsie is pulled in down Bromyard – an' that'll be on our way to Worcester so we thought we'd go an' see them, tell them what's happened, an' see if they'll give us summat to go in the trailer.' Maurice took a breath, 'aaan' then we thought after Worcester we'd go up to Kidder (Kidderminster) an' see Robert an' see if he'll *dell* (give) us some nice rugs. An' then from Kidder we can *jall* back Bridgnorth way, like.'

'*D-o-o-o-rdi!*' exclaimed Old John in a loud voice, 'yu's a-got it all worked out, boy, baint yer?'

'*Owli,* Uncle john, when we gets goin' we don't mess about, like – all we want now is the phone call from Addy … an' Bob's yer uncle! We'll be on our way.'

'Will yu tek the *chavvies* with yer when yer goos, lad?' asked Genty.

'We think it best too, Aunt, we'll call in an' pick 'um up early, like. I reckon it'll be in the next few days, so make sure they has a good scrub-up every morning,' Maurice ending the sentence with a laugh.

Sylvie, giving him a sharp slap on his arm, 'Thur's a thing to say, man, Aunt Genty always has 'um tidy, don't yer, Aunt?'

'I doos me best, gal,' came the reply.

Maurice looked seriously at the old couple. 'You'll tell the *chavvies* after we've gone, will you?'

Genty lifted her eyes from the fire, looked at Maurice, and said, 'We will, lad.'

With his gaze still in the flames of the fire all Old John said, in a sad tone, was, 'Aar. We shall miss 'um, lad.'

'I know you will, Uncle,' replied Sylvie and she put her arm round the old man's shoulder and gave it a soft squeeze, 'but it 'ent as though you're never going to see 'um again, is it now?'

Genty gave a little smile. Old John, head bowed, remained silent.

Not long after Maurice and Sylvie had departed, Old John stirred himself from his milk bottle crate seat by the fire and stood erect. 'Best t'tell the *chavvies* now, gal,' he said in a solemn voice. Then, putting the tip of his thumb and index finger in his mouth, he gave the high-low *joter* call (signal whistle).

That evening Maurice and Sylvie drove over to see Sylvie's parents to discuss the 'plan' and to telephone Barry the Blanketman.

'When Addy phones tell her we'll pick her up the following morning, don't tell her about the trailer, an' don't tell her we'm bringin' the *chavvies*,' Maurice instructed.

'As soon as I get the phone call I'll come straight over and tell you, lad, whatever time of the day or night it is,' replied Sylvie's father.

By luck, Barry was not away on one of his rambles round the counties selling his wares, and he answered the telephone to hear Maurice's urgent-sounding voice.

'This is a bit urgent, *mush*,' he repeated several times.

'I'll be there about midday tomorrow, will that suit you?'

'*Kushti*,' Maurice said as he replaced the receiver.

The following day, punctually at midday Barry drove his van into the small yard; and that evening, when he sorted out the one and five pound notes, he was glad that he had made the effort to do so. Maurice and Sylvie had bought from him a pile of Welsh blankets, a pair of galvanized 'Bishop of Lowestoft' water jacks ('Katie'll have them shining – she's been polishin' Aunt Genty's can all summer,' Sylvie had said with a smile), and three different size bowls, all with the remainder of the money for the trailer. With their own money they had purchased a pretty bone china tea service which Sylvie arranged in the glass-fronted china cabinet in the trailer.

Her mother and father donated a chromed kettle, together with numerous pots and pans. Whilst Sylvie's sisters came over with cutlery, cups and saucers, plates and dishes for everyday use, and a novel little push-along hoover with a long thin handle and a dustpan and brush. Also stopping in the small yard was Eliza Taylor and her husband Aaron, known as 'Walleye' owing to one of his eyes being a much lighter colour than the other – as is to be found occasionally with horses. They lived in a trailer that had belonged to Maurice and Sylvie, and had bought it from them when they took possession of the new 'Siddal'.

Eliza was a close relative of Maurice and, of course, wanted to 'get in' on the action.

"Ere you is, dear people,' she called out at the door of their trailer. In her arms were six silky and lacy cushions. "Ere you is, put these in the trailer for the dear gal an' them two dear *chavvies*, you'll know 'um anyway, they was yourn, an' was in the trailer when we a-bought it from yer.'

Acts of kindness abounded. All was ready. Maurice and Sylvie now awaited the phone call and the visit from Sylvie's father.

Returning home, a little disheartened by the money he had obtained from his weigh-in of scrap, Maurice's spirits were lifted by Sylvie's news. 'Me dad's bin over, Addy's phoned, we can go tomorrow. I know exactly where she's to.'

It was now a week to the day since the first phone call. They had worked hard for a new home for Addy and the children.

Early the next morning Maurice filled the petrol tank of the Ford Consul to the brim and they were off, heading south. An air of both sadness and gladness hung over the encampment of Old John and Genty, even little Nell seemed to perceive it, as an emotional goodbye was said.

'*Dordi!* Just *dik* at you lot, youm only goin' to be a few miles apart, anybody 'ud think you was never goin' to see each other again in the whole wide world,' Maurice's voice rang out in the chill September air. 'I'll bring you and yer mammy back here in a few days to see 'um.' Then looking at Old John, said, 'Is that all right with you, Uncle John?'

'*Owli*, lad, I'd like that, I'd like that an' all.'

Heading south on the main road, Leominster was soon reached. Maurice then followed the road east to Bromyard, where a few miles further on in the direction of Worcester he pulled up on a layby where Benny and Elsie had parked their trailer. They had been there for over two weeks and, to their relief, so far, no officer of the law had been to move them on.

Benny appeared in the doorway of the trailer and Maurice shouted to him, 'We heard you was here.'

'Aar, an' we've heard what youm on, *mush*, come on in all on yer,' shouted back Benny. Although having little access to telephones, news spread fast within the Travelling community. Tea was made and handed round by an over-emotional Elise who, with tearful eyes, looked at Sylvie, 'An' you says youm goin' to get our Addy now, God love her, my sister it's wonderful what you an' Maurice is a-doin' for her an' these two little 'uns, God love 'um, honest to God it is.'

'Have you got anythin' you want to give to Addy, my sister?' enquired Sylvie.

'Got anythin'? Why, the dear gal shall have this.' And Elsie picked up a large porcelain figurine of a boy leading a camel, and handed it to Sylvie.

'Are you sure you want to part with that, my sister?'

'Sure I'm sure,' came the reply from Elsie, 'you tell her it comed from us an' God bless the dear gal – my Benny'll find me another, won't yu, man?'

Looking a bit crestfallen Benny nodded his head. With the figurine wrapped in a towel and placed gently in the boot – together with two rabbits caught by Benny – they headed on in the direction of Worcester.

As was expected a very emotional event occurred at the Home on the outskirts of Worcester. While Addy and the children hugged and cried, Maurice and Sylvie spoke with 'the man in charge', said 'thank you, Sir' and shook his hand. Sylvie, adding, 'She'll be alright now, Sir, she'll be back with her own people.'

With Addy and the children in the back seat, Maurice drove on, heading north for Stourport-on-Severn near Kidderminster to call on Cousin Robert, the carpet hawker, and his wife Coralena, who lived in a trailer in the yard of his father and mother's bungalow – his mother, Mary-Ann, being a sister to Maurice's Aunt Genty. As Maurice drove into the yard Coralena appeared in the doorway of the small kitchen shed that stood to the side of their trailer. Wearing a wide frilled-edged pinner, with hands on her hips, she gave a big smile, 'Well you lot has timed that just perfect, we've been expecting you, I've got some food on and kettle's boilin' for *floppy* (tea).'

The 'jungle telegraph' had indeed been working overtime, aided, of course, by the telephone. Settled Gypsy people who were wealthy enough to have a telephone could phone other settled Gypsies in an area and a message could then quickly be delivered. Cousin

Robert's parents Zacky and Mary-Ann had a telephone in their bungalow and so did Sylvie's mother and father who, it appeared, could not keep a secret!

Coralena had never met Addy or Little Jimmy and Katie and made a big fuss over them, Robert not having seen his cousin Addy since she was a little girl. Tea, food, happiness and laughter were the agenda for the next hour or so, when Maurice suddenly said, 'What's the time?'

Robert was a 'time man' and wore a wristwatch. Looking at it he said, 'It's after four now.'

'Eh, *Dordi!* We got to *jall on*, we want to get back before dark an' get this little family settled in, we thanks yu both for your hospitality, but honest, we got to get on,' said Maurice as he stood up and shook Robert warmly by the hand.

'Can't you wait for me mam 'n' dad to come back? They'll be upset if they miss seeing you all. As I told you, me dad's had this bit of business in Brum (Birmingham) to see to, they shouldn't be much longer.'

'Sorry, old mate,' replied Maurice and he beckoned Robert to follow him out into the yard.

'Honest, *mush*, we really must go. Addy knows we've got her a trailer, but we've not told her what it's like. Sylvie's sisters is waiting in it now … we wants it all to be a surprise, like.'

'I understand, cousin, and I'll explain to me mam and dad,' Robert said knowingly. 'Come on over to the shed and I'll sort a couple of nice rugs out for our cousin Addy.'

The rugs were hurriedly put in the boot of the car, then Maurice called into the trailer, 'All aboard, we're going.'

From Kidderminster the journey continued north to Bridgnorth and from there the homeward stretch to the small yard on the outskirts of Shrewsbury. In the front of the car Maurice and Sylvie were smiling to themselves. Since the reunion with their mother it seemed that Little Jimmy and Katie had never stopped talking. Bubbling over with excitement they were telling their mother all that had happened over the last five months. With her children either side of her, Addy sat quietly and was happy.

Tooting the horn of the Ford Consul vigorously Maurice drove into the yard and parked by the side of the Siddal trailer, which obscured the view of the Vickers Lunedale. Taking Addy by the hand, Sylvie led the way round the Siddal. The door of the Vickers flew open and a chorus of voices rang out, 'Welcome to your new home.' Addy burst into tears, Sylvie's arms were round her and she held her close. Little Jimmy and Katie, looking at the beautiful shining trailer, squealed with delight, 'Is it our'n, is it our'n?'
'Come on in,' called out Sylvie's youngest sister. With Sylvie's arm still round her Addy stood sobbing in the kitchen end of her beautiful new home. Looking round she saw the pile of Welsh blankets, sheets and pillows with frilly cases piled up on the end bench seat (that pulled out into a bed). The bone china tea set displayed in the china cabinet, and as she looked to her left the shiny chrome kettle with its black wooden handle sitting proudly on the gas stove surrounded by a set of enamel pots. All she could manage to say, amidst sobs, was, 'Thank you, it's *kushti*, oh my dear Lord, it's *kushti*.'

Sylvie's three sisters were seated on the bench seat (that also pulled out into a bed) opposite the Cortier coal burning stove and moved along to allow Addy to sit with them just as Maurice appeared in the doorway.

'Hey, hey, hey, 'ere you is, Addy. These is from your Cousin Robert,' and he rolled out on the carpet the two pretty rugs. 'An' there's something else, gal,' he said as he disappeared out of the door, returning with the large porcelain boy leading the camel figurine. 'This is from Benny an' Elsie … *dordi!* I was *trashed* (frightened) it 'ud get *poggered* (broken) on the way home, but here it is, gal, all safe an' sound.'

'Put it on there, Maurice,' Sylvie instructed as she pointed her finger to the top of the drawer unit opposite to where Addy was seated. 'An' don't you two go a-playin' with it, it's very precious,' she added as she pointed her finger at Little Jimmy and Katie, who were bouncing about next to the pile of bedding on the end bench seat. 'Is you goin' to make us a cup of tea in your new home, Addy?' Sylvie continued, 'kettle's full of *pani* all ready for yer an' thur's matches in that top drawer.'

A little unsteadily, Addy walked over to the gas stove, lit one of the front burners and placed the kettle over it. Then, turning to face the sisters, she wiped her eyes and said, 'I don't know how to thank you.'

'We 'ent done much, my sister,' responded Sylvie, 'it's yer mammy an' daddy you really got to thank, they's the ones who's *pestered the luvva* (paid the money) for the trailer fur you an' the *chavvies.*'

'Me mammy and daddy? Oh, my dear blessed Lord, me mammy an' daddy, me mammy an' daddy,' and Addy again burst into floods of tears.

Sylvie took charge of the tea-making and called the menfolk in, then handed round piles of sandwiches that her sisters had prepared earlier. Addy drank tea, but she could eat nothing, she was just too overwhelmed to do so.

A little later the menfolk were ordered out of the trailer and Sylvie and her sisters helped Addy to make up the beds. The far bed for Addy and Katie, and Little Jimmy's bed opposite the Cortier stove. The sisters then hugged Addy and the children, said goodnight, and departed, followed by Sylvie who turned in the doorway and said, 'I almost forget, sister, *dik* in that drawer there, there's something for you.'

Opening the drawer, Addy saw a beautiful pinner deep frilled all round with two embroidered horseshoe-shaped pockets.

'I made it 'specially for you, my sister, you put that round you tomorrow an' you'll feel like a Gypsy gal again.'

Addy's eyes welled with tears; she smiled but could not speak. Just then Maurice poked his head round the corner of the door.

'Hey, hey, hey, there's somethin' else an' all, thur's two *shushies* (rabbits) out here for you that Benny sent, bin a long time since you've eat a *shushi* I'm expecting.'

Addy nodded her head and gave a little laugh.

'That's more like it, gal, I 'ent heard that laugh in many a year … I likes to hear it,' and with that Maurice's head disappeared from the doorway.

'I loves to eat *shushi*, mammy,' Katie said as she hung with her arms round her mother's waist.

'I knows how to catch 'um,' added Little Jimmy, acting the 'little man' again.

It was a long time before Addy could finally sleep that night. For hours she sat on the edge of the bed wrapped in a new blanket, smelling the woolly newness of it. She was thirty years of age, but her features and stature appeared much, much older.

CHAPTER 7

FLY AWAY WAGTAIL

Early the following morning Maurice and Sylvie drove quietly out of the yard.

'Woman, I feels a bit *poggered* t'*sarla* (not so good this morning),' Maurice said as he puffed on a thinly rolled cigarette, 'but we has to go and see Uncle John an' Aunt Genty an' tell 'um, don't we?' Yesterday had been a long, stressful and emotional day and Maurice knew that the old couple would be frantically waiting for the news.

Old John and Genty were standing together by the fire as Maurice and Sylvie crossed the narrow plank bridge over the little brook. 'You two looks tired this morning,' Genty said as they came closer. ''Ow did it go, is they all alright?' asked Old John. '*Vel* an' *besh akai* (come and sit here) an' a-tell us, we baint 'ad much *sutti* (sleep) all *rarti* (night) a-worryin'.

'It was a long day, Uncle John, wasn't it, Sylvie?'

'It was, man,' came the reply, 'but everythin' went *kushti* an' they'm all alright, they loves the trailer.'

The next half hour was spent with Maurice and Sylvie relating the day's happenings, with the old couple sitting quietly gazing into the fire. Suddenly Genty raised her head and looked hard at Maurice and Sylvie. ''Ow do our gal look now arter all on these yers? Tell us now, I knows she's a-changed, baint she?'

It was Sylvie who replied to Genty's question.

'Well, Aunt,' she slowly said, 'ten years is a long time, 'ent it, an' Addy's had it a bit rough, as you knows.' She paused, then quietly said, 'She don't look like the gal we knowed all on them years ago.' 'Oh my dear blessed Lord, I knowed it in me 'eart, I said she'd a-changed, dinna I, my John? Oh my dear blessed gal – but she'll be alright now, won't she?'

'As I told the man yesterday, she's back with her own breed now, an' she'll be alright,' Sylvie said, 'shall we bring 'um over tomorrow?' With tears in her eyes Genty nodded and said, 'yes'. Still gazing into the fire, and not looking up, Old John uttered, 'Aar, we'd like that, we'd like that an' all.'

Then he coughed violently and spat in the fire. No one noticed that there were faint traces of blood in the saliva.

Whilst Maurice and Sylvie were away Eliza had walked over from her trailer, on the opposite side of the yard, to see how Addy was settling in.

''Ow is yer this morning, sister? Is there anythin' you'm short of?' she called out as she approached the open door of the trailer.

'Come on up, Eliza,' Addy called back, 'I'm just making a drop of tea, I was coming over later to thank you for the cushions.'

As Eliza entered the trailer Addy continued, 'Eh, *dordi!* they'm the *kushliest* cushions, 'ent they?'

'They was Sylvie's, she left 'em in the trailer when my Aaron bought it offn 'em, they'm pretty, 'ent they? Maurice and Sylvie likes good stuff, like we all doos,' – and Eliza let out a little laugh.

The two women sat chattering and drinking tea when suddenly Eliza said, 'When you feels like it, sister, I want you t'come out callin' with me, if you wants to, that is.'

Eliza was a good caller (selling door-to-door) and earned good money doing so, and she also knew that Addy would now have to earn money to keep herself and her two children. Unlike Addy, she had fair skin and fair hair like her mother who was not born a Gypsy. She was in her middle thirties and had two children, a boy and a girl, who Little Jimmy and Katie had palled up with this morning and they were now all happily playing together.

'I was thinking last night what was to become of me, my sister,' Addy said with eyes staring at the floor. 'I used to go out callin' with me mammy, an' I liked it, but I 'ent got me *tushni* (basket) no more, nor nothin' to put in it.'

'Don't you worry about no old *tushni*, I don't use one no more, I goes out with a shoppin' bag an' I can soon find one for you, they's better to use than a basket an' them slinky-eyed *muskros* don't twig what you'm about so much. And, my sister, me an' my Aaron's got a van load've swag (cheap articles to sell) that we gets from the swag shop in Burn-in-um (Birmingham).'

'What sort of swag?' enquired Addy.

'All small stuff, my sister, stuff that'll fit in me shoppin' bag. We's got scrubbin' brushes, dear little mops, tea cloths, them springy pegs that the *gaujis* now likes to clip their bit've washin' on the line, all stuff like that … an' they'm *kushti covvels* to *bikkin* (good things to sell) an' all. When I knocks on the *gaujis' wudders* (doors) you can be sure most of 'em'll buy summat. And, my sister, me an' my Aaron don't go out every day neither, an' you can come out with us whenever you feels like it, you can do one side've the street an' me the other, an' my Aaron'll be waiting' round the corner with the van for us t'fill up the bags again. We gets all over the place, an' that 'ud do you good an' all … an' sometimes I finds an old *juvvel* (woman) to do a bit've *durrakin* (fortune telling) with,' and again Eliza let out a little laugh.

Maurice and Sylvie arrived home just as Eliza was leaving Addy's trailer and she beckoned them over.

'I've just been askin' Addy if she'd like to go out callin' with me an' my Aaron, when she feels like it, so to speak.'

'What's she say?' asked Sylvie.

'She says she wants to,' replied Eliza.

Ever protective, Maurice quickly said, 'How's this goin' to work then? Do you want me to chuck some *luvva* in for the swag?'

'No, I don't, man,' Eliza answered, 'me an' my Aaron'll work summat out. Dear Lord, the stuff don't cost us a lot anyoldhow, don't you worry yer head about nuthin', my old cousin – you leave it to me, I'll see that Addy an' them dear *chavvies* has *morrow* an' *mass* (bread and meat) for their *muis* (mouths).'

Ending the sentence with a little laugh, Eliza made her way back to her trailer. She always ended what she was saying with a little laugh. She was a good person with a heart of gold.

'Is you lot ready?' Sylvie's voice rang out clear in the morning air as she knocked on the trailer door, opened it and looked inside.

Little Jimmy and Katie were sitting on the end seat watching their mother fussing with her hair in the mirror above the stove place.

'I can't get it right, Sylvie, I can't get it right, an' I wants to look me best for mammy an' daddy.'

'I brushed it for mammy, like I do's granny's, but I only made it worser,' piped up Katie.

Sylvie soon had the situation under control, and with the sound of Maurice revving the engine of the Ford Consul they trooped out of the trailer.

'*Dordi!* You lot *diks kushti*,' he said as Addy and the two children got in the back seat. Both Addy and Katie were wearing the pinners that Sylvie had painstakingly made for them, Little Jimmy had combed his hair with soapy water and pressed in a big wave with his fingers (as his grandfather had taught him).

After driving through the village Maurice turned left and drove slowly up the narrow lane with grass growing in the centre. Just before the ford he pulled up on the verge and switched off the engine and the little group clambered out of the car. Taking Little Jimmy and Katie by the hand, Addy looked at Maurice and Sylvie. 'I feels all trembly and sickified,' she said.

Words cannot describe the emotional reunion of Addy and Old John and Genty. But what can be said is that after hugging his daughter and kissing her on the forehead, Old John turned and slowly walked away in the direction of the wood.

'Where's you going, Granfer, can I come with you?' called out Little Jimmy.

'Let him bide, lad,' was all Genty softly said. Leaning against an old oak tree Old John cried, like he'd never cried before.

It was now the middle of September. The summer school holiday was over and the children in the yard were back at school, including Little Jimmy and Katie, at first much to their displeasure. Little Jimmy was now eleven, but Addy told the headmaster that he was ten so that both children could at least go to the same school together for a while.

Seven little Gypsy children walked fifty yards down a rough track to the main road five mornings a week to wait for the school bus. They encountered very little bullying by the other school children, there was safety in numbers, they were always smartly turned out and their appearance was '*Gaujified*'. Little Jimmy had worn a knotted scarf round his neck all the time he had been with his grandparents and was upset when Addy had said, 'You can take that *diklo* (neckscarf) offa your neck, you 'ent goin' to no school in that.' To which he had replied, 'Me granfer wears one.'

'So he might, lad,' had been the reply, 'but you 'ent goin' to school in one to be called Gyppo all day long, you can wear it when you comes home an' when we goes to see your granny and granfer. Just take a *dik* round this yard, there's only Old Marty that wears one, none of the other *mushes* does, your Uncle Maurice 'ent worn one since he was your age – he even puts a tie on sometimes, don't he? Times has changed an' is changin' more an' more an' I wants you two to do well at school, that I do. Look at you and your sister now. Since you've been with your granny and granfer you've both changed so much – you'm both so sensible an' lovable,' and she threw her arms round Little Jimmy and planted loads of kisses on his cheeks. Letting out a yell he managed to break free and scurried away. He looked at himself as being 'the man' of the family, and being planted with kisses was certainly something he did not like.

The following week, after the emotional reunion, Maurice collected his Aunt Genty and Uncle John and brought them back to see Addy and the children and their new home. They both sat happily in the trailer drinking tea and nodding approval at the lovely interior.

Genty's eyes fell on the pair of galvanized water jacks that stood by the side of the gas stove, now shining with many hours of polishing with Brasso metal polish.

'You've polished them up nicely, gal,' she said as she looked at Addy. A wail came from Katie. 'I've done 'em, Granny, like I used to do yourn, I've polished and polished 'em till me dear little hand almost dropped off.'

Everyone laughed. Old John started coughing and he went outside to spit. 'My chest is a-getting' wosser,' he thought to himself.

Every Saturday that followed, Maurice and Sylvie drove Addy and the children down to see Old John and Genty, sometimes leaving them there and picking them up again on Sunday evening. The weather in October and November was mild and sunny with very little rain and Addy was happy re-living the life of her younger days. Little Jimmy again slept in the kitchen tent, Katie in her bed in the accommodation, with her mother sleeping on a thin mattress that Maurice had acquired from somewhere, which was placed lengthways on the floor.

After their return on the Sunday evening, Addy washed Little Jimmy and Katie's hair and insisted they 'scrub up' well. 'I don't want you two goin' to school smellin' of smoke,' she would say. 'I had enough of being called stinky Gyppo when I went to school.'

True to their word, Eliza and Aaron took Addy calling with them, which she enjoyed, and by which she now had a means of supporting herself. They would leave the yard after the children had gone to school, and return early afternoon before the children returned home, which enabled the women time to prepare food for the main meal of the day, which was eaten any time between four and five o'clock.

Towards the end of November Old John complained that his breathing was worse, and of pains in his chest. 'We'd better goo an' see the *drab-mush* (doctor), my John,' Genty had worriedly said.
'Stop yer fussin', 'ummon, I'll be alright,' had been his reply.
But Old John was not alright. For several weeks he had eaten very little, which was unusual as he was a man who loved his food. The last Friday of the month saw a sharp decline in his health and late in the afternoon he said to Genty, 'I reckons we'll goo an' a-see the *drab-mush* on Monday, gal, I feels real bad in meself. I'll goo up in the wagin an' 'ave a little rest.'

When Maurice, Sylvie, Addy, Little Jimmy and Katie arrived, as usual, on the Saturday morning there was no smoke drifting upwards from the stick fire – and there was no one sitting round it. Genty appeared in the doorway of the wagon and beckoned them over. Sylvie instinctively knew that all was not well and ordered Little Jimmy and Katie to go and wait in the tent. As they entered the wagon Genty tearfully whispered, 'He's a-gooin'.'
Trying so hard to control her emotions, so as not to upset her father, Addy held the old man's hand and, with tears rolling down her cheeks, softly said, 'I'm sorry, daddy.'
Old John's eyes opened, and then closed for the last time.

While the womenfolk and Little Jimmy and Katie huddled together, now outwardly showing their grief, Maurice walked up to the farmhouse. Farmer Hughes and his wife were greatly saddened to hear the words spoken by him.

'Leave everything to me, I'll telephone the doctor and undertaker straight away,' then thoughtfully added, 'would you like us to help with the paperwork for you?'

'I'd appreciate that very much, Sir,' Maurice replied.

'Is there anything else you would like us to do, Maurice?' enquired the farmer.

'Well, Sir, as I was walking up here I was thinking, an' I wondered if you'd let our Benny and Elsie pull their trailer into your field by the road for a few days, like, until the funeral's over, that is?'

'Of course, Maurice,' came the reply, 'anything else?'

'Well, Sir, after we've buried me Uncle John would you object to us burning the wagon? It's our way, you know.'

Farmer Hughes smiled kindly at Maurice. He knew of the custom and was pleased that it was to be observed. 'I have no objection, Maurice – John would have wanted it, wouldn't he?'

'He would, Sir, he was old-fashioned like that, an' me Aunt Genty would want it an' all,' replied Maurice in a soft-spoken voice, his head slightly bowed, eyes staring at the floor.

'There's just one thing,' continued Farmer Hughes, 'I'd like you to pull the wagon down by the brook before setting it ablaze, it will be safer there. I'd not like to see the old wood going up in flames too.'

'Of course, Sir,' answered Maurice, 'an' I thanks you for your kindness to us; we'll take me Aunt Genty an' the little dog back with us to our place when they've been for me Uncle John, an' tomorrow me missus an' the others will come over an' do out the tent ready for me Uncle comin' back.'

Farmer Hughes also knew of the custom of the deceased person being brought back by the undertaker, to lie in state in an open coffin, watched over continuously until the day of the funeral.

The following afternoon saw Sylvie and her sisters busily removing everything from the tent. Lastly they removed the pretty cotton print material from the walls and replaced it with white bed sheets, to which they pinned, here and there, sprigs of green rosemary (rosemary for remembrance). Then Sylvie removed, at Genty's request, a few articles from the wagon.

Two days before the funeral the undertaker and his men brought Old John back to the little encampment. They transferred the coffin from the hearse onto a four-wheeled bier and carefully four of them pushed it down the track from the farmyard, a fifth man carrying a pair of trestles on which to place the open coffin in the tent. Mr and Mrs Hughes, Maurice and Sylvie, Benny and Elsie had arranged everything perfectly, and Farmer Hughes had cleared the farmyard for the parking of vehicles, knowing that there would be no room to park in the little lane. Maurice brought Genty, Addy and the children back the same afternoon; Sylvie and her sisters following in another car, Sylvie bringing with her several boxes of candles, for a candle would be alight at the head of the coffin until the undertakers came again on the day of the funeral.

Mrs Hughes had obtained a quantity of folding chairs and these were placed in the tent round the open coffin, and this is where the womenfolk sat day and night with Old John, Sylvie replacing the candle as it burnt low. Heaps of firewood had been gathered by Maurice and Benny who, with the other menfolk, sat day and night round a large fire where Sylvie's sisters made continuous tea and prepared simple food. There was a lot of coming and going, but for Genty, Addy, Sylvie, Elsie, Benny and Maurice there was no sleep. Little Jimmy and Katie, overwhelmed and exhausted, were bedded down in Benny and Elsie's trailer.

Old John had been dressed in his dark suit by the undertaker and when he and his men arrived on the morning of the funeral, Maurice put Old John's pipe and round tobacco tin in one of the jacket pockets and his catapult in the other. He then put in the old man's fiddle and bow and the undertaker secured the lid and gently lifted the coffin onto the four-wheeled bier. Solemnly the little group followed the undertakers up the track to the farmyard where a number of distant relations and other travelling folk had parked their vehicles and were there waiting to join the cortège.

A large white flowered cross was placed on the coffin before being put in the motor hearse to slowly drive the short distance to the church, the mourners following on foot. Nearly everyone was dressed in black; a few of the older men wearing long black overcoats and black Trilby hats. People carried their floral tributes in the form of circular wreaths and bunches of flowers. (There were none of the elaborate wreaths beautifully made to depict 'the vacant chair', 'gateway to heaven', 'a wheel with a broken spoke' and in the form of cherished possessions of the deceased person, that are to be seen at present-day funerals.)

Several villagers, including old Fred Lloyd and his wife Mary, were waiting at the church. Genty, almost collapsing with grief, graciously nodded her head towards the old couple. Fred removed his tweed cap and, with his face full of sorrow, nodded back. Two different cultures today joined into one by deep sadness and grief.

After a short service in the church the burial took place and after the clergyman had given his address and sprinkled earth into the grave the mourners slowly did the same, some of the older people dropping in a few silver coins. Then everyone walked back to the farmhouse where, in the large kitchen, Mrs Hughes had kindly laid on tea and cakes for the forty or so mourners (a little different to the funerals of today which are attended by hundreds of people).

Maurice, Benny and a few other men left the farmhouse ahead of the others and walked back to the little encampment where they pulled the wagon and the little accommodation that Katie had slept in all summer, down near the brook. Then they dismantled the cottage tent and put it in the wagon. The odd bits of furniture that had been used in the tent were smashed up and placed in the little accommodation, then two bales of straw were cut open and sprinkled inside the two vehicles, with tractor fuel poured on it. By the time all this was completed the group of mourners had arrived. Maurice and Benny approached their Aunt Genty, who was supported either side by Sylvie and Addy.
'It's all ready, Aunt,' Maurice said in a strong voice. Hardly able to speak, she whispered, '*Yog* (burn) it now, boys, *yog* it now.'

After a few days, Maurice drove his lorry down the track to where the little encampment had been and which his Aunt Genty had referred to as 'our own little bit've 'eaven'. He loaded all the ironwork from the burnt vehicles into the back of the lorry, then carefully raked through the dead embers collecting every small nut and bolt and all the harness buckles; these he threw into the brook.

The following day he drove into the scrap yard and 'weighed in' the ironwork … the money went towards buying a small trailer for his Aunt Genty, which he parked alongside the trailer of Addy and the children.

So ended the old Romany lifestyle, which is now nostalgically referred to as 'Waggon-time'.

Fifty years have passed. None of the family ever visited the *atchin tan* again – where once the sweet smell of woodsmoke had drifted lazily in the air. No longer is the wagtail to be seen by the brook that crosses the little lane with grass growing in the centre, then slowly meanders on westwards through unspoilt country – where history meets mystery.

THE END

EPILOGUE

Genty was never fully happy living in the little trailer in the yard. She died the following spring. In Katie's words, 'Me granny never took to the trailer, it was a shame warn't it to burn the wagon but me granny wanted it done 'cause she knew that me Granfer would have wanted it that way. She was happy to be with us, of course, but I can see now that she really missed me Granfer an' her old fashioned way of life. She asked me to go an' pick her some primroses one afternoon an' she put them in a cup of water by her bed, an' the following morning she had gone. She'd gone all peaceful in her sleep, mammy told us. I think she died of a broken heart, honest to God, I do.'

Addy supported herself, her mother and her children by going out 'calling' with Eliza and Aaron; and she also did something that as a young girl she said she wouldn't do – she told fortunes. If Eliza could find a gullible *gauji* woman she would tell her anything and pocket the money. Addy would not do this: 'I wants to help the poor dear *gauji juvvals* who's got the same bit of trouble as what I had,' she told Eliza. She saw both her children married and leave home. A few years later she was taken seriously ill and died in hospital. She was in her mid-forties.

Wolverhampton Jimmy also died in hospital. A prison hospital.

After Addy's funeral Maurice and Sylvie left the yard near Shrewsbury and moved to a yard in Gloucestershire.

Benny and Elsie kept travelling until the end of the Sixties. Constant harassment from councils and police forced them to move onto a Council-run Traveller site.

Robert and Coralena are buried in the same churchyard as Robert's mother and father. Their son, and his son, owns a large carpet warehouse in a small Worcestershire town.

Old Fred Lloyd mourned the passing of his old friends. He, his wife Mary and their 'lad' are buried in the village churchyard, not far from the grave of Old John and Genty.

Farmer Hughes and his wife passed away almost two decades ago. Their grandson now runs the farm. Unlike his grandfather and grandmother he has 'no time for Gypsies' – 'Gyppos' is the word he is wont to use. It is a pity that he didn't 'study to know, know to understand and understand to judge' as his grandparents had done.

Little Jimmy (who I must now call Jim) – Katie still calls him Little Jimmy – did well at school, as did Katie. After he left school he went out 'calling' for scrap iron with his Uncle Maurice, saved enough money to buy a truck, passed the driving test and went 'out' on his own. He married at the age of twenty-one, having earned enough money to buy a new trailer and a decent clean lorry. His father-in-law was a 'tarmac man' who taught Jim the job. He then started on his own, and – as the old saying goes – never looked back.

At the age of eighteen Katie married a Gypsy boy who came from a long 'settled down' family in north Wales. They moved into a little house near Wrexham, and Katie loved it. 'I took to this old *kenner* (house) like a little *shushi* (rabbit) in a *poove* (field),' she said. She has a good man, a good marriage and is happy.

Little Nell, the rough-coated terrier again became Little Jimmy's dog and followed him everywhere. Old Marty produced a small barrel and filled it with straw, which became her 'dog box'. She lived to a good age and was buried under a thorn bush up the track from the yard near Shrewsbury. The track is still there – but the yard is no more. The Council, in its 'wisdom', issued its closure notice and moved the Gypsies out.

During the autumn of 2008 I visited the old *atchin tan* of Old John and Genty Lock, where that one summer in 1961 had made such a difference to the lives of Little Jimmy and Katie.

I drove up the 'borders' from Hereford in the direction of Shrewsbury and, somewhere between Ludlow and Church Stretton, I turned up a small lane which passes through a pretty little village, in the centre of which stands the old church. I parked up and entered the churchyard, and there in a peaceful corner is the grave of John and Genty Lock. The headstone of granite has a carved fiddle and bow on the top, and below their names part of a verse from Housman's *A Shropshire Lad*, Farmer Hughes having requested that he be allowed to have the headstone erected and pay for it himself, as a final act of friendship to the old couple. (As Farmer Hughes was attracted to the Romany lifestyle it is feasible to presume that he had seen the gravestone of Herbert Lock, a second cousin of Old John. The gravestone depicts a fiddle and bow carved on top with an inscription in *Romanes*, and is situated in a small country churchyard not far from Knighton.) The final line of Housman's verse should read 'and cannot come again' – on Old John and Genty's gravestone it reads 'and ne'er shall see again'.

I stood quietly for a few moments then placed a small bunch of flowers that I'd brought for Genty, amongst the array of faded plastic ones. Opening my tobacco pouch, I took a palm full and sprinkled it by the headstone for Old John.

Remembering the information Little Jimmy had given me, I looked to my right, and a short distance away stood a simple wooden oak cross, with a brass name plate which read 'Adaline Lock' and the dates. A few faded plastic flowers lay beneath it. Walking back to the grave of Old John and Genty, I took a single flower from the bunch and then placed it at the base of the cross.

I'd paid my respects; returning to my motor I drove on through the village, and there on a bend is a tiny lane with grass growing in the centre. A short way up this lane is a small ford, and just before it, a strip of grass verge where I parked. There in the hedge was the five-barred gate. I'd not been here since I was eighteen years of age, over fifty years ago, but I'd found it easily. Opening the gate I followed the little path along the edge of the brook, then stopped and looked across to the clearing in front of the wood. The old oak tree, that the meat safe was once nailed to, stood proud. All was quiet except for the bleating of sheep.

The wooden plank bridge was no longer there, so I could not cross the brook – all I could do was stand, look, and remember that day when the old wagon and tent were set ablaze. That was the end of an era, I thought … long gone.

Feeling rather sad I drove the four-and-a-half hour journey home. That evening I opened a bottle of my favourite Australian red wine and drank to all the people depicted in this book.

The following morning I received a telephone call from Katie informing me that she was a grandmother, and her daughter had called the baby Genty. 'That's wonderful,' I thought. 'Little Jimmy's first grandson is named John, and now Katie's grand-daughter is named Genty – the memory lives on.'

The 'old days' in this book have, of course, gone forever. Like all society, Romany people have had to alter their lifestyle, sometimes for the good, sometimes for the not so good. But they have survived the changes over the generations, and will continue to do so.

Verse from 'A Shropshire Lad': *Those Blue Remembered Hills*

What are those blue remembered hills,

What spires, what farms are those?

That is the Land of Lost Content,

I see it shining plain,

The happy highways where I went,

And cannot come again.

E. Housman

APPENDIX

AND OTHER NOTES OF INTEREST

OLD JOHN AND GENTY'S SQUARE-BOW WAGON was built sometime in the 1940s by Mr George Cox of Hereford, who was the last apprentice of H. Jones & Sons – wheelwrights and wagon builders of Blue School Street, Hereford.

In 1924 Mr Cox set up business in Widemarsh Street and built living wagons both for Showmen and Gypsies. He employed about half a dozen men, together with a carver, Mr Gertnor, and a painter, Mr Wood, who spent almost all his working life with the firm.

The 1940s saw the firm building Square-Bowtops for Gypsy people. These vehicles were light in weight and were sometimes built on four-wheel drays that were supplied by the customers themselves (Evesham drays were popular, particularly drays built in Pinvin, a small village on the outskirts of Evesham).

Mr Cox also built Square-Bows from the wheels up, as was Old John and Genty's. In 1998 Mr George Cox died at the age of 103.

ROD AND BLANKET TENTS, commonly referred to in the south of England as 'Benders'. These were the tents which, as a young boy, Old John and his family lived in and travelled with before changing to the horse-drawn wagon. The simple bowed construction made from bent rods of hazel, ash or willow, comprised a ridge-pole, approximately six feet long, with five sets of holes drilled through, ten side rods about seven feet long and three to five longer back rods. It was an easy structure to erect. The thick ends of the side rods were inserted into holes in the ground (made with the kettle iron, on an outward angle), they were then bent over and the thin ends fitted into the ridge-pole holes on both sides. In a semi-circle the back rods were inserted into holes in the ground and bent over and through the side rods – this formed a rigid framework which was then covered with woollen blankets which were secured with blackthorn pins, small skewers or even horse-shoe nails.

By 1900 Old John's family was using 'felts' to cover the tents, which were obsolete paper mill conveyor belt felts approximately eight feet wide and twenty-eight feet long. One of these when cut up would cover a single tent. They were obtained from a paper mill in Flint, north Wales.

From the single tent there came adaptations. Two tents could be erected (open ends facing each other), leaving a space between them which then had long rods (known as leaners) put round to form a conical shape. This, when partly covered, acted as a chimney (to a certain extent) to draw the smoke from the central fire.

A large circular tent, known as a 'baulk' or 'beehive' was also used. This is the style as used by Obie and Black Britty described in the story 'The Ancients and the Blood-Red Beads'.

A single tent, comprising rods, ridge-pole and covering, together with other goods, was transported on a pack donkey in the following manner: The coverings, either woollen blankets or felts, were folded and placed on the back of the donkey. Next a 'pocket' (an elongated sack sewn at both ends with a long slit in the middle, which when closed was secured by buttons). Bed blankets were folded and placed in the pocket then other articles were placed in and the pocket 'buttoned up'. This was then put over the tent covering to hang part way down either side of the donkey. This was then securely girthed around the donkey. Tent rods (thick ends facing forwards), ridge-pole and other items were secured by cords passing between the girth and the pocket.

Old John's father and mother moved from a tent to a living-wagon very early in the 1900s. The pack donkeys were sold and a horse was bought to pull the wagon which had been built by Jones of Hereford and was a small 'Ledge' type, Old John and his two elder brothers still continuing to sleep in tents. The tent rods were too long to carry on the cratch of the wagon so were transported by making two bundles tied at each end; these were slid between the kettle box and back springs on either side to rest on the back axle. The thin ends of the rods were then tied to the underside of the cratch.

BLACKTHORN PINS, used for pinning covering to the tent framework. These were rined (taking the bark off) either with a knife or a strong thumb nail. After allowing them to dry for a short while they were impregnated with fat by quickly frying them in the frying-pan. Some of the older women used blackthorn pins for pinning their hair.

STOPPING PLACE NAMES. A lot of the old stopping places, which had been used for generations, had strange names known only to

Gypsies who camped there. Butchers' Broom Lane was so named because 'butchers' broom' grew in the hedgerows. Humpy Bridges is an old stone packhorse bridge of three arches – hence 'humpy bridges'. Crabby Apple Common had crab-apple trees growing on it. Dead Rai's Corner was named way back in the past; a Lord of the Manor had fallen from his horse and died from his injuries. This grassy corner was reputed to be haunted; travelling people being superstitious encamped a little way up the lane from the corner. Blasted Oak Lane, named because an oak tree had been struck by lightning. These names are but a few of the many that were used by travelling people of the border country.

GRINDING BARROWS. Various types of grinding machines were used by English and Welsh Gypsies. The earliest type was a single-treadle machine which was light enough to be carried on the back by the aid of shoulder straps; this was known as the 'Creel'.

A much larger and heavier version of the 'Creel' was the 'Kick-up' barrow. This, like the 'creel', was a single-treadle, the large driving-wheel serving also as a road-wheel. To operate the machine it was tipped backwards onto the handles, which allowed the wheel to lift from the ground; the driving-belt could then be slipped onto the wheel and operated by the foot treadle. The name 'kick-up' coming from the operation of tipping the barrow backwards onto the handles.

The 'Two-wheel' barrow, as described in the story 'Billy Smith and his Grinding Barrow' was operated by the grinder sitting on a board seat that went across the two pushing handles, his feet operating two treadles that drove the independent drive-wheel. A leather belt went round this wheel which went back to the pulley-wheel in the centre of the spindle which held a grindstone either end.

In the 'early days' both the 'kick-up' and 'two-wheel' grinding barrows were made by village carpenters/wheelwrights – also by a few coach-building firms. The living-wagon builders Dunton & Sons of Reading in Berkshire, made a fine example of a 'two-wheel' barrow, of exceptional quality, before they closed down in the early 1920s.

The 'latter days' saw travelling men making their own barrows. Most were made with wheels from invalid carriages or by using bicycle wheels. These barrows showed much individuality; being heavily chamfered and painted with masses of brass bed knobs fitted round the top edges. Some were even sign written by the owner declaring the occupation: 'NIFES AND SISSORS SHAPENED'. Small tool boxes were fitted to the barrows and some had a tiny anvil and a small vice.

The 'Bicycle grinding machine' had only one grindstone which was fitted into a fork-shaped iron bracket fitted to the crossbar and lower bar just a few inches back from the handlebars. The pulley-wheel for the drive-belt being on the left hand side of the grindstone spindle; this belt went into the channel of a drive wheel fitted to the spokes of the back wheel. To operate, a stand was lowered which raised the back wheel from the ground by a few inches.

KETTLE IRONS. Also called a kettle prop, kettle crane, kettle stick and by the Romany name *kavvi saster*. These come in different shapes and sizes, some being a round iron bar bent at a right angle, roughly three feet six inches to four feet from the pointed end, the arm extending about nine inches, with a hook on the end to hold a kettle or pot over the fire.

A much nicer looking kettle-iron was shaped in a graceful curve (like a shepherd's crook), with the end tapering down to a small hook. An ideal size was four feet long, allowing the kettle-iron to be firmly placed in the ground to hold a heavy pot or a bucket of washing. Seven-eighths of an inch iron round bar was the usual thickness.

In the 'rod tent' days the kettle-iron was used for making holes in the ground for the rods to go into; and was also a handy tool for prising a hawthorn 'stump' for the fire from a farmer's hedge.

Some old style Gypsy people always removed the kettle-iron from the ground when not in use, saying it was 'bad luck' to leave it there; why this was so is probably that the kettle-iron would be cold if the people had to move in a hurry.

When the kettle-iron was inserted into the ground by the side of the fire, a good method for raising and lowering it was to pull it backwards and forwards, making a slot. To raise a pot from the fire the iron was pulled backwards and a piece of stick placed in the slot, and to lower the pot the stick was pulled out.

An iron-rod tripod with a chain and hook hanging down from the top was also used by many travelling people. These 'chitty-irons' were not used by Old John and Genty or any of their people, being looked down upon as '*kekka kushti kovvels*' – things which are of no use to us.

FIRESIDE ETIQUETTE. Passing between a person and the fire is considered very bad mannered. Little Jimmy and Katie soon learnt this from the scolding tongue of their grandmother: 'Get outa yer granfer's face, yu brazen child.' Handing a cup of tea to a person with hand over the top is considered bad mannered; it should always be handed by holding the handle. When sitting round someone's fire it is considered bad mannered to poke it or put more sticks on it. Never throw any bread into the fire; it is unlucky to do so. 'Burn bread, live to want.' Keep dogs away from the fire when food is being cooked and eaten.

KETTLES AND COOKING POTS. An old favourite with travelling people was a copper kettle with the knob on the lid in the shape of an acorn; these boiled the water quickly. Cast iron kettles were also popular but were heavy. Vitreous enamel kettles were much lighter in weight than the cast iron ones, boiled water quicker, but the enamel could get chipped if roughly treated.

After the Second World War thick aluminium kettles could be bought from 'surplus stores'. These had a large flat bottom which enabled them to boil quickly; they were light in weight for transportation and if they got knocked only a dent would appear. Many travelling men fitted a small linked thin chain to the knob of the lid and the handle of the kettle which saved the lid from getting lost when on the move.

Cast iron pots with a cast iron lid and swinging pail handle were known as Dutch ovens. Stews could be made in them, bread could be baked in them, and for roasting meat or birds they were excellent. A favourite method for 'roast' potatoes was to remove the meat when cooked, then put more fat in the pot, put back over the fire without the lid being replaced and get it really hot, then put in par-boiled potatoes and stir them around until golden, crispy and crunchy.

Two foundries that manufactured Dutch ovens and other cast iron ware that were favoured by Welsh and Border travelling people were Archibald Kenrick of West Bromwich, founded in 1791, which finished manufacturing in the 1950s and in Bilston the foundry of Thomas Holcroft, which ended manufacture in 1969.

The black vitreous enamel pots with pale blue insides and a swinging pail handle – called 'boilers' by travelling people – came in different sizes and were either round or oval in shape. The handle on the lid bore a brass plate with the name 'Judgeware'. They were manufactured by Ernest Stevens Ltd, Cradley Heath. All these industries were in the same area on the outskirts of Birmingham.

Genty didn't clean the outside of her Dutch oven or her cast iron hoop-handled frying pan, but she did clean the outside of her 'Judgeware boilers'. This she did with a damp cloth dipped in wood ash from the fire.

WATER CONTAINERS, known as 'water jacks', held approximately three gallons and were made in copper, galvanised iron, and later, stainless steel. Old John and Genty's 'jack' was made by Mellor & Sons of Oldham, Lancashire, who supplied sundries for living-wagons for Showpeople and Gypsies. In 1926 a galvanized 'jack' with three brass bands retailed at 24 shillings (£1.20).

Also in Lancashire, tinsmith Leonard Turner of Preston Brook near Warrington made cans for canal boat people but also made, in the 1950s and early 1960s, a few 'jacks' of good quality for local Gypsy families. Bishop of Lowestoft in Suffolk made galvanized 'jacks' which had a turned wooden handle.

In Elgin, Scotland, William Murdoch made heavy duty stainless 'jacks' and also novelty miniature ones with a slot in the lid which served as a money box. Superior quality 'jacks' were made by Brailsford Bros. of Barnsley, south Yorkshire.

B&K Llewellyn, tinsmiths of Darlington, County Durham, made excellent quality stainless 'jacks'. When they retired their equipment was donated to Beamish Museum. The south of England saw the work of master tinsmith Derek Matthews of Tonbridge in Kent, known to travelling people by the name 'Staybright' owing to his glistening stainless steelware. He made his last two pairs of 'jacks' in 1991 for John Partington Smith of Sevenoaks Weald. These 'jacks' display what a master tinsmith he was, made of high quality stainless steel, with two brass bands on the body and one brass band on the neck. The side handle, carrying handle and lid handle all having applied brass; the name plate of brass, bearing the initials J.P.S. – tin smithing at its finest.

One firm still selling stainless steel 'jacks' and other related ware is P.J. Stainless Steel, Bilston, in the West Midlands.

FOOD HAMPERS AND CUPBOARD TABLES. A large rectangular wicker laundry basket, the lid of which was hinged by leather straps, served many travelling women as a food and china container; this could be placed on the ground by the cooking fire and transported on the cratch at the rear of the wagon. The food hamper was never used to sit on, and if anyone ever attempted to do so a cry of 'git yer dirty *bul* (bottom) offn me *hobben* (food)' would ring out.

A two-doored cupboard on legs was very popular, which would contain food and china, the top covered in check oilcloth serving as a table. This, like the hamper, could be placed near the cooking fire and also could be carried on the cratch when on the move. The kettle box, also called pan box and by some old fashioned travelling people the 'victual' box, was situated below the rear of the living-wagon between the two rear springs, and could also be used for storing food, although designed originally to hold cooking pots, axle grease and grease-cap spanner.

WASHING FIRE. Being settled in one place gave Old John and Genty the opportunity to have a separate fire for doing the laundry. When continually on the move this was not always possible. Genty, like most Gypsy women, was particular in the way she did her washing. Male and female garments were not washed together, neither were they hung to dry together; men's garments were put on a line (most times on bushes) over here and women's over there, with undergarments being hidden in blouses or skirts. Household items – tea cloths, etc. – were separately washed in the bowl used for washing the crockery and utensils, never with the laundry.

WELSH BLANKETS, called 'Carnthens' by Welsh people have been made across Wales since the 1700s, mostly in the north and west Wales areas. Two different pieces of cloth were woven together to form a double cloth which made them ideal as bed blankets. Several mills near Carmarthen produced heavily fringed blankets which could be bought direct from the mill or at Carmarthen Market. The largest mill in Carmarthenshire at Pentre-cwrt closed in 1981, but Rock Mill, Capel Dewi and several other mills are still in business. Old Welsh blankets are now to be seen in antique shops and are very collectable.

CLAY TOBACCO SMOKING PIPES. As will be seen in the story 'The Ancients and the Blood-Red Beads' Obie and Black Britty smoked short stem clay pipes known as 'cutties' – this word coming from 'cut down' (to shorten). Long stem pipes were broken off a few inches from the bowl which made them less likely to be broken. When short stem pipes were manufactured they too were called Cutties – the name carrying on.

Clay pipes smoked by Welsh Border Gypsies were made in the little town of Broseley in Shropshire, famous for its pipes since the 17th century. Established in the 1830s, the Southorne family made smoking pipes of a high quality with clay being transported from Devon and Cornwall. The 1880s saw Rowland Smitherman establish the Crown Pipe Works, which was taken over by the Southorne family at the end of the 1920s. The firm closed in 1957 after the death of the owner, Harry Southorne.

Amongst travelling people a favourite pipe bowl was in the shape of a horse's hoof. If time and expense could be spared a pipe would be put in a jar containing black beer or, better still, rum and left to soak for as long as possible. This made the pipe smoke well! After much smoking the clay pipes would turn a dark brown/black colour, being impregnated with nicotine.

Travelling people were always being 'called on' by religious groups attempting to save the souls of the 'poor Gypsies'. Catholic priests were welcomed by most, and if a Catholic Bible could be obtained it was of a great benefit. The pages of Catholic Bibles were of a very thin paper – which was ideal for rolling cigarettes in. When the cigarette was rolled the edge of the paper would be bitten between the teeth which made a jagged edge, then it was licked with the tongue and the small saw blade points would adhere to the paper. To keep tobacco moist a slice of apple or a bit of cabbage leaf was put in the baccy tin.

WOMEN'S PINAFORES, called 'pinners' or 'pinnies' were made with two large front pockets in the shape of a horseshoe, with a diagonal slot opening. Some of these pockets had an opening inside which led to long inner pockets. These inner pockets were known as *'monging putsies'* (begging pockets). When 'calling' houses it was customary for Gypsy women to try a little begging: "Ave yu got a few woollies for the babby, lady?' If successful these begged articles were put in the pocket, then through the slot and into the inner pocket, and if lucky the woman would appear larger as the day wore on.

HAWKING BASKETS. Arm baskets were used for 'calling' houses (selling door-to-door). Mostly used were of a rectangular shape, as used by tradesmen (bakers' delivery men, etc.). Genty's basket was of the type known as a 'cross-over' arm basket. This was of an oval shape with loops inserted around the top edge of the basket in a cross-over pattern. These loops allowed more goods to be placed and displayed in the basket, but were ideal when selling flowers. An added bonus was that they were very decorative. A long leather strap was attached to the handle which, when the basket was on the arm, could be put over the head and some of the weight carried on the shoulder. A basket containing several gross of clothes-pegs was heavy.

PEDLAR'S CERTIFICATE. Due to the 1881 Pedlars and Hawkers Act people who sold small wares from door to door were obliged to have a Pedlar's Certificate, which was obtained from a Police Station and lasted for one year. The person's name, age, height and a facial description were on the certificate, which in 1961 cost five shillings (25p). When out 'calling the houses', Genty was sometimes stopped by a policeman and asked to produce her Pedlar's Certificate. With a twinkle in her eye and a big smile she would say 'Don't be so silly, my dear Sir, I baint be a-riding no bicycle!' Then she'd burst out laughing and produce her certificate.

MEN'S NECKSCARVES were of silk, a yard square in size, and were called '*dicklos*' in the Romani language. They came in different colours and patterns. Popular was a dark navy blue, maroon or yellow, all with white spots of different sizes; these were known as 'snowstorm' *dicklos*.

Old John favoured a dark navy 'snowstorm', but also sometimes wore a *dicklo* of bright red or one of a colourful Paisley pattern, which he tied round the neck in a square knot, the two ends being wrapped around his braces.

Another method was to hold both ends of the folded scarf in front of the neck, cross the ends over at the back of the neck and tie a square knot in front. Two methods could be used for folding scarves; the simplest was to fold the scarf corner to corner, then from the pointed end fold in about 1½ inches at a time. The other method was to lie the scarf out in a square, then fold one pointed end to the centre, then the same with the other end and fold in from both sides.

Some of the nicest silk dicklos were made at a silk factory at Leek in Staffordshire.

DOUBLE-BUCKLE BELTS. These belts were fashionable in the 1950s and 1960s. They were made by taking two horse-shoe buckles from old harness; these were then sewed to the two ends of a leather belt, leaving a space of some four or five inches in between where a loose strap could be inserted, the centre of which sometimes having ornamentation on it.

OLD JOHN'S BOOTS were of the make known as 'Beaver' boots. They were of thick brown leather with a heavy sole and high laced. Occasionally he would waterproof them by applying a coat of 'neatsfoot' oil. This he obtained from his old pal Fred Lloyd (who in turn had obtained several cans of it from the closed down little harness-making shop in the village before it was demolished).

WHIPS. Most favoured by horse-dealing Gypsy men were dealers' whips made by G. Holland, 126 Haggerston Road, Hackney Road, London E2. They were whalebone lined and silver mounted.

OLD JOHN'S FIDDLE. Like many other Gypsy fiddle players of the borders and Wales, Old John mostly played his fiddle with only three strings. The top string was not needed as most of the tunes could be played on just three strings.

TO GET RID OF MOLES, Old John's 'secret' method was to dig out a piece of turf to expose the mole run; into the run he would place a sprig of gorse, then replace the turf. The mole would come along the run, prick itself on the gorse, and bleed to death, moles being haemophiliacs.

TO GET RID OF WARTS, Genty's method was to take a black slug and rub it over the wart, then she would impale the slug on a thorn of a hawthorn hedge, thorn bush or blackthorn, and as the slug died the wart would disappear.

HEARTH BRUSHES. These brushes were a good 'seller' to cottagers of the Borders. They were made from straight grained hazel, about fourteen inches in length and about three-quarters of an inch in thickness. With a sharp peg-knife both ends were rounded off. Then from about four inches from the top the bark was shaved off by the same method as shaving hazel for clothes-pegs (knife held firmly in right hand against right knee, left hand pulling stick against blade). With the bark removed long thin slivers were shaved down to about three-quarters of an inch of the bottom, then they were bent over and securely bound with string just below the bottom of the rounded end of the stick – which then formed a brush head. To finish the brush the bottom of the bark handle was cut in a circle and the odd jagged edges of bark cleaned off. Sometimes a hole would be burnt through the top of the handle and a piece of

string pushed through and knotted, so the brush could be hung up by the fireplace.

THE ROWAN TREE (MOUNTAIN ASH) is believed to hold great magical powers. In the story 'The Sunday Visit and the Ghost Story' it will be noted that Old Saiforella threw herself under the rowan tree where she slept in safety. Amongst her people was a practice of tying a little bag of rowan berries round a new-born baby's neck to ward off evil spirits.

PATTERAN (OR PATRIN) SIGNS. These were the signs left at crossroads and junctions to show which way a party had gone. The signs were varied; a few handfuls of grass placed at a junction, a few stones, a piece of stick with the bark partly pulled off, or a clod of earth with grass attached, which was used by Old John's people. By the 1960s there was practically no need to use these signs. The few remaining Gypsy families that still travelled with horse-drawn vehicles that had wooden wheels and iron tyres were easy to follow, the iron tyres on the tarmacked road leaving snail-like white trails.

A STALE LOAF OF BREAD could be made fresh again by putting it in water for a short time then placing it in a hot Dutch oven.

EAR PIERCING was done by severely pinching the lobe of the ear then holding a cork or potato at the back of it. A needle was then inserted into the lobe and the gold 'snaps' put in. An index finger and thumb full of butter and salt was rubbed into the ear lobe each day after and the snap turned; the healing was very quick.

SONGS. Many of the songs sung by the old people were folk ballads of a sentimental nature. The songs of the American country singer Jimmie Rodgers in the 1920s and 1930s found a listening ear with Gypsy people, for a lot of his songs were sentimental. Songs by another country artist, Hank Williams (who died in 1953), were pounced on with relish. Perhaps the best singer of Hank Williams' songs (and he knew every one) was Richard Jones of Pembrokeshire, who sadly passed away in 2011.

Kitty Wells, and the great favourite Patsy Cline (who died in a plane crash in 1963) are still imitated by Gypsy girls and women today. When Old John and Genty's daughter Addy sang Patsy Cline songs it was difficult to distinguish them. She really did have the most beautiful singing voice.

OLD JOHN'S BLACK FELT HAT. Removing his black Trilby hat from his head, he would feel the brim with his finger and thumb and say to the children, 'I wish this new felt hat felt like my old felt hat felt.'

WEAK TEA. Old John hated weak tea. If he was handed a cup he would say, 'Who looks arter this tea?' When asked what he meant he would reply, 'When I was as weak as this I 'ad my Genty a-lookin' arter me night 'n' day, day 'n' night fur four days!'

ROMANY/ROMANI. When referring to the Gypsy people or their lifestyle, the word 'Romany' is used. When referring to the language of the Romanies, the word 'Romani' is used. This is similar to the distinction between Hindi (language) and Hindu (people).

The sun is now setting in the West,
I have come to the end of the trail
And to the end of 'Wagtail Tale'.

Thank you for reading this book. I started to write it six years ago, and slowly, bit by bit, over these years it has come together. Today, January 18th (my birthday) I have finished writing it.

For 'Jim', 'Katie' and myself it has brought back so many memories – memories of over half a century ago – when Gypsy life was so much different to what it is today.

My memories have been crystal clear of that period in time – but now I have difficulty remembering what I did yesterday!

Peter Ingram
Selborne – Hampshire – 18 January 2012

No longer is the wagtail to be seen by the brook that crosses the
narrow Shropshire lane, where once the sweet smell of
woodsmoke drifted lazily in the air.